MW00843833

MARINE ENGINE ROOM BLUE BOOK

MEYERHOLTZ

Marine Engine Room Blue Book

FOURTH EDITION

BASED ON THE ORIGINAL EDITION BY WILLIAM B. PATERSON

BY

WILLIAM D. EGLINTON

CORNELL MARITIME PRESS

CENTREVILLE, MARYLAND

Copyright © 1961, 1965, 1984, 1993 by Cornell Maritime Press, Inc.

All rights reserved. No part of this book may be used or reproduced in any manner whatsoever without written permission except in the case of brief quotations embodied in critical articles and reviews. For information, address Cornell Maritime Press, Inc., Centreville, Maryland 21617.

Library of Congress Cataloging in Publication Data
Main entry under title:

Marine engine room blue book.

Bibliography: p.
1. Marine engineering—Examinations, questions, etc.
I. Paterson, William B. (William Brown) 1912-
Marine engine room blue book. II. Eglinton, William D.,
1951-
VM726.M37   1984   623.8'7'076   83-46035
ISBN 0-87033-315-1

Manufactured in the United States of America
First edition, 1961; Fourth edition, 1993; second printing, 1994

To my son,
Colby Jay

Contents

Preface

This is the fourth edition of the *Marine Engine Room Blue Book*. The first edition was published in 1961. Since that time, the pace of change in the maritime industry has been very rapid. *The Marine Engine Room Blue Book* has been an excellent source of information for those persons attempting to upgrade their engine room ratings. By offering revised materials that accurately reflect current conditions, this edition will continue to serve as an indispensable aid to those seeking advanced ratings.

Since the last printing of this book (1984), the United States Coast Guard has increased the *range* of subject matter contained in the endorsement examinations leading to QMED—Any Rating. To make the *Marine Engine Room Blue Book* as up-to-date as possible with the *range* of subject matter and *degree* of difficulty the questions will present to the mariner, over 700 new questions and answers are contained in this revision.

It is anticipated that the U.S. Coast Guard will propose major changes to Part 12 of CFR 46, Certification of Seaman. They will undoubtedly seek changes to the seatime, training, and testing requirements leading to the endorsement for QMED—Any Rating. However, any changes should not materialize for some time, due to the complicated bureaucratic process involved.

The U.S. Coast Guard has a test bank of between 20,000-25,000 engine room questions. Books are available through the Government Printing Office and elsewhere, in which these questions and answers are contained verbatim. However, most people want to learn marine engineering and not just the answers to several thousand questions.

This book should be used as a tool in preparing for those examinations leading to endorsement as QMED. To utilize this book to its fullest intended purpose, you, the prospective examinee, should acquire as much knowledge concerning the subject matter as possible. Included at the end of this text is a list of references which I recommend for further reading. After you take the sample rating examinations, you can use those books to strengthen your weak areas of engine room knowledge, or you can read them before you approach your QMED sample examination questions. With the confidence of knowing as much as you possibly can about the subject matter, you will succeed. Keep in mind that, as you take the enclosed sample QMED examinations, it is not only important that you know which answer is the correct one, but that you understand why it is correct, and why the other choices are incorrect. Then you are using the sample questions as a learning tool.

Much of the credit for the updated QMED study material contained in this book belongs to past and present members of the vocational and academic teaching staff at the Harry Lundeberg School of Seamanship. It is hoped that this edition of the *Blue Book* will continue to justify its place as the principal guide to the student endeavoring to acquire the U.S. Coast Guard endorsement as QMED—Any Rating.

William D. Eglinton

MARINE ENGINE ROOM BLUE BOOK

Introduction

The United States Coast Guard has established sixteen regional centers for examining seamen for ratings and for issuing certificates, in place of the fifty offices previously available.

The regional examination centers are located in Boston, New York City, Baltimore, Charleston, Miami, New Orleans, Houston, Memphis, St. Louis, Toledo, Long Beach, San Francisco, Seattle, Anchorage, Juneau, and Honolulu.

In addition, seamen can take examinations at monitoring stations in Norfolk and San Diego because of the large volume of applications received at these two ports. Applications to take the exams in Norfolk must be filed through the Baltimore regional center and in San Diego through the Long Beach office.

The following information, applicable to the qualified member of the engine department, is from the *Code of Federal Regulations: Title 46—Shipping* (Washington, D. C.: U. S. Government Printing Office, 1982).

U. S. Coast Guard Requirements and Examinatior for Certificate of Service as QMED

Certification required

(a) Every person employed in a rating as qualified member of the engine department on any United States vessel requiring certificated qualified members of the engine department shall produce a certificate as qualified member of the engine department before signing articles of agreement.

(b) No certificate as qualified member of the engine department is required of any person employed on any unrigged vessel, except seagoing barges.

General requirements

(a) A qualified member of the engine department is any person below the rating of licensed officer and above the rating of coal passer or wiper, who holds a certificate of service as such qualified member of the engine department issued by the Coast Guard or predecessor authority.

(b) For purposes of administering the regulation, the rating of "assistant electrician" is considered a rating not above that of coal passer or wiper, but equal thereto.

(c) An applicant, to be eligible for certification as qualified member of the engine department, shall be able to speak and understand the English language as would be required in the rating of qualified member of the engine department and in an emergency aboard ship.

Service or training requirements

(a) An applicant for a certificate of service as qualified member of the engine department shall furnish the Coast Guard proof of qualification based on six months' service in a rating at least equal to that of wiper or coal passer.

(b) Training programs approved by the Commandant may be substituted for the required service at sea in accordance with the following:

(1) A graduate of a school ship may be rated as qualified member of the engine department upon satisfactory completion of the course of instruction. For this purpose, "school ship" is interpreted to mean an institution which offers a complete course of instruction, including a period of sea training, in the skills appropriate to the rating of qualified member of the engine department.

(2) Training programs other than those classified as a school ship may be substituted for up to one-half of the required service at sea.

(c) Applicants for certification as qualified member of the engine department in ratings of pumpman, shall, by written or oral examination, demonstrate sufficient general knowledge of the subjects peculiar to the rating applied for to satisfy the Officer in Charge, Marine Inspection, that they are qualified to perform the duties of the rating.

(d) Applicants for certification as qualified members of the engine department in the rating of deck engine mechanic or engineman (see below), who have proved eligibility for such endorsement will not be required to take a written or oral examination for such ratings.

Examination requirements

(a) Applicants for certification as qualified members of the engine department in the ratings of oiler, watertender, fireman, deck engineer, refrigerator engineer, junior engineer, electrician, and machinist shall be examined orally or in writing and only in the English language on the subjects listed in paragraph (b) of this section. The applicant's general knowledge of the subjects must be sufficient to satisfy the examiner that he is qualified to perform the duties of the rating for which he makes application.

(b) List of subjects required

Subjects	Machinist	Refrigerating engineer	Fireman/Watertender	Oiler	Electrician	Junior engineer	Deck engineer
1. Application, maintenance, and use of handtools and measuring instruments	x	x	x	x	x	x	x
2. Uses of babbitt, copper, brass, steel, and other metals	x	x	x	x	x	x	x
3. Methods of measuring pipe, pipe fittings, sheet metal, machine bolts and nuts, packing, etc.	x	x	x	x	x	x	x
4. Operation and maintenance of mechanical remote control equipment	x		x	x	x	x	x
5. Precautions to be taken for the prevention of fire and the proper use of firefighting equipment	x	x	x	x	x	x	x
6. Principles of mechanical refrigeration; and functions, operation, and maintenance of various machines and parts of the systems		x		x		x	
7. Knowledge of piping systems as used in ammonia, freon, and CO_2, including testing for leaks, operation of bypasses, and making up of joints		x				x	
8. Safety precautions to be observed in the operation of various refrigerating systems, including storage of refrigerants, and the use of gas masks and firefighting equipment	x	x	x	x	x	x	x
9. Combustion of fuels, proper temperature, pressures, and atomization			x	x		x	
10. Operation of the fuel oil system on oil burning boilers, including the transfer and storage of fuel oil			x	x		x	x
11. Hazards involved and the precautions taken against accumulation of oil in furnaces, bilges, floorplates, and tank tops; flarebacks, leaks in fuel oil heaters, clogged strainers and burner tips	x	x	x	x	x	x	
12. Precautions necessary when filling empty boilers, starting up the fuel oil burning system, and raising steam from a cold boiler			x	x		x	
13. The function, operation, and maintenance of the various engineroom auxiliaries	x	x	x	x	x	x	
14. Proper operation of the various types of lubricating systems	x	x	x	x	x	x	x
15. Safety precautions to be observed in connection with the operation of engine room auxiliaries, electrical machinery, and switchboard equipment	x	x	x	x	x	x	x
16. The function, operation, and maintenance of the bilge, ballast, fire, freshwater, sanitary, and lubricating systems	x	x	x	x		x	x
17. Proper care of spare machine parts and idle equipment	x	x	x	x	x	x	x

Subjects	Machinist	Refrigerating engineer	Fireman/Watertender	Oiler	Electrician	Junior engineer	Deck engineer
18. The procedure in preparing a turbine, reciprocating, or Diesel engine for standby; also the procedure in securing			x	x		x	
19. Operation and maintenance of the equipment necessary for the supply of water to boilers, the dangers of high and low water and remedial action			x	x		x	
20. Operation, location, and maintenance of the various boiler fittings and accessories	x		x	x		x	
21. The practical application and solution of basic electrical calculations (Ohm's law, power formula, etc.)					x	x	x
22. Electrical wiring circuits of the various two-wire and three-wire D.C. systems and the various single-phase and polyphase A.C. systems					x	x	x
23. Application and characteristics of parallel and series circuits					x	x	x
24. Application and maintenance of electrical meters and instruments					x	x	x
25. The maintenance and installation of lighting and power wiring involving testing for, locating, and correcting grounds, short circuits and open circuits, and making splices					x	x	x
26. The operation and maintenance of the various types of generators and motors, both A.C. and D.C.					x	x	x
27. Operation, installation, and maintenance of the various types of electrical controls and safety devices					x	x	x
28. Testing and maintenance of special electrical equipment, such as telegraphs, telephones, alarm systems, fire-detecting systems, and rudder angle indicators					x	x	
29. Rules and Regulations and requirements for installation, repair, and maintenance of electrical wiring and equipment installed aboard ships					x	x	x
29a. Pollution laws and regulations, procedures for discharge containment and cleanup, and methods for disposal of sludge and waste from cargo and fueling operations	x	x	x	x	x	x	
30. Such further examination of a nonmathematical character as the Officer in Charge, Marine Inspection, may consider necessary to establish the applicant's proficiency	x	x	x	x	x	x	x

General provisions respecting merchant mariner's documents endorsed as qualified member of the engine department

The holder of a merchant mariner's document endorsed with one or more qualified member of the engine department ratings may serve in any unqualified rating in the engine department without obtaining an additional endorsement. This does not mean that an endorsement of one qualified member of the engine department rating authorizes the holder to serve in all qualified member of the engine department ratings. Each qualified member of the engine department rating for which a holder of a merchant mariner's document is qualified must be endorsed separately. When, however, the applicant qualifies for all ratings covered by a certificate as a qualified member of the engine department, the certification may read, "QMED—any rating." The ratings are as follows:*

> (a) Refrigerating engineer
> (b) Oiler
> (c) Deck engineer
> (d) Fireman/Watertender
> (e) Junior engineer
> (f) Electrician
> (g) Machinist
> (h) Pumpman
> (i) Deck engine mechanic
> (j) Engineman

Deck engine mechanic

(a) An applicant for a certificate as "deck engine mechanic" shall be a person holding a merchant mariner's document endorsed as "junior engineer." The applicant shall be eligible for such certification upon furnishing one of the following:

(1) Presentation of a temporary letter that was issued to the holder to serve as "deck engine mechanic" by an Officer in Charge, Marine Inspection, dated prior to December 1, 1966; or

(2) Satisfactory documentary evidence of sea service of 6 months in the rating of "junior engineer" on steam vessels of 4,000 horsepower or over; or

(3) Documentary evidence from an operator of an automated vessel that he has completed satisfactorily at least 4 weeks' indoctrination and training in the engine department of an automated steam vessel of 4,000 horsepower or over; or

---

*Prior to testing for any of the ratings at a United States Coast Guard regional examination center, a General Safety examination must be taken and passed. This examination will remain valid, when passed, for one (1) year.

(4) Satisfactory completion of a course of training for "deck engine mechanic" acceptable to the Commandant.

(b) The Officer in Charge, Marine Inspection, who is satisfied that an applicant for the rating of "deck engine mechanic" meets the requirements specified in this section, will endorse this rating on the current merchant mariner's document held by the applicant.

(c) Any holder of a merchant mariner's document endorsed for "any unlicensed rating in the engine department" or "QMED—any rating" is qualified as a "deck engine mechanic" and that endorsement will not be entered on his document.

Engineman

(a) An applicant for a certificate as "engineman" shall be a person holding a merchant mariner's document endorsed as "fireman/water-tender" and "oiler," or "junior engineer." The applicant shall be eligible for such certification upon furnishing one of the following:

(1) Presentation of a temporary letter that was issued to the holder to serve as "engineman" by an Officer in Charge, Marine Inspection, dated prior to December 1, 1966; or,

(2) Satisfactory documentary evidence of sea service of 6 months in any one or combination of "junior engineer," "fireman/watertender," or "oiler" on steam vessels of 4,000 horsepower or over; or,

(3) Documentary evidence from an operator of a "partially automated" steam vessel that he has completed satisfactorily at least 2 weeks' indoctrination and training in the engine department of a "partially automated" steam vessel of 4,000 horsepower or over; or,

(4) Satisfactory completion of a course of training for "engineman" acceptable to the Commandant.

(b) The Officer in Charge, Marine Inspection, who is satisfied that an applicant for the rating of "engineman" meets the requirements specified in this section, will endorse this rating on the current merchant mariner's document held by the applicant.

(c) Any holder of a merchant mariner's document endorsed for "any unlicensed rating in the engine department," "QMED—any rating," or "deck engine mechanic" is qualified as an "engineman" and that endorsement will not be entered on his document.

Suggestions for Engine Department Personnel

Upon joining a ship as a member of the engine department, you should become acquainted with your emergency station assigned for fire and boat drills. Duties and the stations are plainly stated in the ship's station bill. You should memorize these at once.

Also, find out what your job is and learn all you can about it as soon as possible. It is not enough to learn the layout of the machinery and what you are to do when it is running. You should get a good idea of the piping and valve arrangements and learn something about the electrical circuits. Valves and switches are usually marked. Also, it is most important for you, your shipmates, and for the ship that you know what emergency equipment is available, where it is, and how to work it or use it. Find where the portable fire extinguishers are, what type they are, and how to use them. Be sure you know the location and operation of the fixed fire-extinguishing systems. Find out if there is a gas mask available and what kind it is. Be sure you know how to use it, when to use it, and when not to use it.

There are so many kinds and types, as well as different methods of operation, of machinery on ships today, that no attempt will be made in this manual to describe in detail the duties of the various engine department ratings. There are, however, certain basic duties and responsibilities that should be assumed by all engine department personnel, and some of these are set forth below.

Most automatic machinery and equipment are fitted with gauges, meters, or "tell-tale" devices. Learn what the proper reading should be and what to do if a warning light or other safety device operates.

When working on idle machinery, take every precaution to prevent accidental starting of the machine. Remove fuses from the line to electrical equipment, secure the steam valves to steam machinery to prevent accidental opening, and open any drains. Lock or otherwise block the gears on machines that might "move."

When using a steam hose for cleaning or other purposes, one person should always stand by the cut-off valve.

Handrails are put around machines for your protection. It is advisable for you to use them.

Satisfy yourself that there is no pressure on a valve before attempting to remove a valve bonnet or the valve packing. Master valve leakage or back pressure from an unexpected source may be sufficient to cause injury. If any doubt exists, slack off securing nuts about one turn and break the joint before removal of the bonnet.

Any heavy piece of equipment or spare machinery part should be secured to prevent movement in heavy seas. Your job may not be involved, but your life may be—report it.

Whenever working around winches, either repairing, oiling, or testing, take particular precaution to see that your clothing is not caught up in the gears or some other revolving part and that there is no danger of being snared by a cable or line.

CHAPTER ONE

The Wiper

The wiper works an eight-hour day and is the entry rating in the engine room, performing general cleaning there and sanitary work in the living quarters.

Duties

The duties of the wiper include the following:

1. Daily routine cleaning to maintain the engine room in a safe and hazard free condition.
2. Daily routine sanitary cleaning of the living quarters in accordance with public health regulations.
*3. Assist the day working engineer in performing engine room maintenance.
*4. Perform soot-blowing operations to the steam generators.
*5. Perform the operations for taking on potable water.
*6. Assist in the operations of taking on bunkers to insure that pollution abatement regulations are followed.

Although not a qualified member of the engine room as defined by law, the wiper is an all-round worker in the engine department. Any person may apply for this position, the only one open in that department for beginners and others not qualified for more responsible ratings. The wiper washes paintwork, chips, scrapes, paints, and performs all duties tending to maintain the machinery spaces in a clean condition.

Generally the wiper is a day worker, and is not assigned to a watch. The wiper should, as quickly as possible, become familiar with the hazards of using oil fuels and operating pressure vessels.

A seaman first, last, and always, the wiper should be familiar with nautical terms, realizing the importance of emergency drills, knowing stations in each, and being able to do what is necessary to combat fire or to abandon ship. As the engine department worker, the wiper should have an interest in mechanics and be familiar with the names and the purposes of all the units in the power plant of the vessel.

Where overhauling and repair work of boilers and machinery is carried on, the wiper helps in various ways, and it is through the

---

*Routine off watch duties.

knowledge that you gain while doing this work that you become pre-pared for advancement. The records of all successful men and women show that they were not afraid to assume additional duties. They were not hesitant about asking questions—nor did they begrudge a small portion of their leisure time for study. This applies to any line of en-deavor, and even if the job is temporary, the knowledge gained will always be useful.

Duties aboard ship, particularly in the engine room, are unique in the large number of opportunities available. The operation of a ship's engine room covers many subjects. There is much to learn that is both interesting and profitable. Therefore, learn as much as you can; make the most of your opportunities; help the fireman, the oiler, the water-tender; learn the other jobs; and don't hesitate to do a little extra work. Use at least part of your leisure time every day to read about the equipment around you. Remember, many chief engineers were former wipers who took advantage of their opportunities.

Practical Hints

Let's assume you are joining a ship as wiper, your first job at sea. The following list of work clothes will be found convenient.

1. two pairs of work pants
2. one pair of work shoes (steel-toed)
3. three pairs of white cotton socks
4. three undershirts
5. two work shirts
6. three pairs of shorts
7. one waterproof hat of the oiler's type

At sea, cleanliness is of vital importance. Start the day's work with clean clothes along with a willingness to learn and you'll rapidly gain the respect of your shipmates.

Use rags on a sequence of jobs, starting on fine machinery or other spots where only a perfectly clean rag will do, and passing on through dirtier tasks until the rag ends up as something with which to wipe up the floor plates. Think your job through.

Polishing. Use as little polish as possible. Clean up the tight corners first; then the big open spaces will be easier. Use one rag to apply the polish, another to wipe and rub it. Stow the polishing rags where they will be kept for the same job later.

Rag disposal. Be careful where you put rags down or leave them. Rags which get into pipes, bilges, strainers, or gears can keep your watch working overtime to make repairs. This will make you unpopular. Oil soaked rags, if stored in closed places, can start fires by spontaneous combustion; they should be kept in open buckets and used to wipe up floor plates.

Machinery wiping. Do not wipe any moving, hot, or electrically charged machinery until the oiler or engineer has shown you what to do and what not to do. Otherwise, you may lose one of your hands, or even your life. Never use a rag which has been used for polishing or which contains emery on any part but the outside casing of a machine, and even then, be sure that it is impossible for grit to fall on any moving part.

Floor plates. Use old rags soaked in a mixture of kerosene and oil on floor plates to prevent rust, and be careful not to leave the plates slippery.

Emery cloth. Emery cloth is used on bare steel to remove rust, and for various smoothing jobs. There are always several grades aboard; use the coarser grades only for rough work where you must dig deep, and always use a grade too fine rather than too coarse, as the coarse grade may leave scratches which later have to be polished out.

Well-worn emery cloth leaves fewer scratches and gives higher polishes than new. A little lubricating oil helps emery to polish better, and keeps the emery from flying about.

Never use emery cloth where the emery can spill into oil, on bearings, or on moving parts of machinery. Never use emery cloth on the casings of turbines or cylinders, on chromium plate or stainless steel, or on glass. In the hands of an expert, the finest grades called "crocus" can be used on brass and copper or to finish shafts which are to be used in bearings, but do not try this unless under supervision.

Paintwork wiping. Skillful cleaning of paintwork postpones paint from chipping and the arduous work of scraping and repainting; wipe paint carefully and observe safety rules while you do it.

If there are pipes, etc., with dirt on them, go over them first with a foxtail—a long, thin brush—and get this dirt out of your way.

Look around for any electrical outlet boxes near the job, and be sure they have watertight caps or you may short circuit them. Look also for any hot surfaces or other dangerous spots, so that you can avoid touching them.

Then mix a bucket of "soogee," using proportions of soap and hot, fresh water, depending upon the kind of soap in use on the ship. Some old-timer will tell you what the right mixture is. Go over the area once with the "soogee" to loosen up the dirt, go over it a second time, and get a lot more off. Do not use boiler compound—it is dangerous.

Finally, using a bucket of fresh water, wipe the paintwork with a wrung-out rag to dry it. Do this carefully—a damp surface catches dirt and has to be washed again that much sooner.

Paint chipping. When repainting has made the paint on a surface too thick, it becomes ugly, porous, hard to clean, and likely to flake off or loosen in patches. Then the paint must be removed to bare surface and new coats of paint applied.

Engine room conditions seldom permit the use of blowtorches or chemicals for removal. Instead, chipping hammers—double-bladed, thin-edged hammers which will get into the corners—are used.

Swinging a chipping hammer requires a certain skill. Swing the hammer just hard enough to get the paint off without denting or scratching the metal beneath. Don't overswing and damage pipe insulation or mar other surfaces. The edges of the chipping hammer should be slightly rounded (not knife edges). Avoid hitting electrical wiring, or banging your hands into hot or sharp objects. Do not chip paint into oil, clean water, or machinery.

Painting. Before starting to paint, be sure of what is not to be painted. Never paint nuts or bolt heads which must be removed often, valve stems, glands, or anything made of rubber or brass. Some ships have color codes to identify different pipe lines. If you paint something the wrong color, it may lead to confusion and possible accidents.

Never paint parts which must rotate at high speed, such as blades of fans or blowers, unless under special instruction to do so, since the paint is apt to put these out of balance and cause trouble.

Ship specification paints are the best because if anything goes wrong, the trouble is with the painter and not with the paints.

Brush carefully into fine cracks and crevices so as to get coats and not pools of paint in them. If possible, paint bulkheads from the bottom up and not from the top down—you avoid dripping that way. Paint from the bare surface into the freshly painted; not "brush outward," unless told to do so on some special job. By painting towards the paint, you avoid brush marks and streaks. "Cut in" along the edges of areas first, then go at the wide open spaces; you will find the job going faster and with less trouble. Keep a rag handy; watch where the paint overreaches or drips. Wipe such places clean immediately. Be specially careful to wipe the floor plates clean of drippings. Use thin coats or the paint will dry spongy, and you will have the task of taking it off and doing the job again.

Clean brushes thoroughly by wiping with rags, soaking them in paint thinner or turpentine and wiping them again until really clean. Stow brushes by suspending them; avoid stowing them so the weight of the brush rests on the bristles.

Keep paint cans covered airtight when not in use.

Bilges. Do not drop rags, matchsticks, or anything of that kind into bilges. These things may clog the bilge pumps, much to the displeasure of firemen and oilers who must have clean and dry bilges before they go off watch.

Oil gets into the bilges and forms greasy coats on the sides. In cleaning out bilges, start the bilge pump first and keep it going. Then hook up a hose to a boiling hot mixture of salt water and steam to be run through the bilges. This hose is played on the dirty spots, great care being taken to avoid getting hot salt water onto any metal. Lastly, remove the bilge pump strainers and clean them. This usually only involves lifting up a cover, taking out a basket strainer, and cleaning it.

Heavy weather. Use the handrails when the ship starts to roll and pitch badly. It doesn't help anyone if you go flying into moving machinery, and an engine has to be stopped to remove your remains. Stow or lash everything that might start sliding about. Do not start painting or other tasks which might involve spilling anything. Stand by for whatever help is needed.

Repair work. The smartest thing a wiper can do is to take on all the repair work assisting he can, and not try to get out of any. Assisting in repair work is the road to knowledge and promotion.

CHAPTER TWO

Tools and Their Uses

With the information available in this chapter the wiper will be able to identify and locate the right tools for a job and to perform mechanical duties more efficiently. In addition, this information is critical for those wishing to take QMED examinations since every exam contains questions pertaining to tools.

Except for certain special types, all hand tools commonly used by the engineering department of a ship are described. Explanations and precautions in using and caring for these tools are also given.

Good mechanics take care of their tools at all times. Valuable time and lives depend on the accomplishment of a piece of work efficiently done by the mechanic. Keep cutting tools sharp and when through with the job, store your tools to protect them against damage or from becoming dull. Handle delicate measuring instruments with care and do not keep such instruments where they may be damaged or destroyed by more powerful instruments on board ship or by careless supervision.

The way in which tools are handled and the care given to each and every tool indicate the quality of workmanship expected from the engineering department. You are what your tools are—sharp and efficient, always ready for the job needed to be done.

Scriber. A scriber is used to make clean narrow lines on metal. It is made of tool steel. Some have single ends (Fig. 1); others have double ends with one end bent about 90° as shown in Fig. 2.

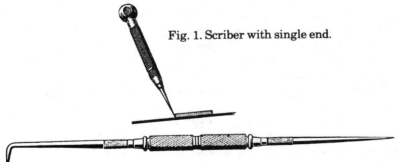

Fig. 1. Scriber with single end.

Fig. 2. Scriber with double ends.

Depth rule. As shown in Fig. 3, the depth rule has a narrow blade which slides through a slotted locking arrangement. It is used to measure the depth of holes, slots, keyways, and other recesses. Some of these rules can be used for measuring angles as well as the depth of holes drilled at an angle to the surface.

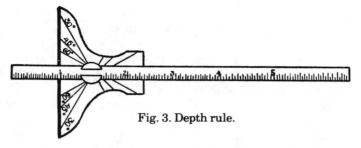

Fig. 3. Depth rule.

Combination caliper rule. As shown in Fig. 4, the combination caliper rule has jaws designed to make either inside or outside measurements. If the diameter of a hole is being measured, the graduation that lines up with the mark labeled IN is read. When measuring the diameter of a shaft, the graduation that lines up with the OUT mark is read.

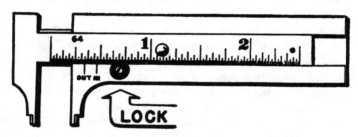

Fig. 4. Combination caliper rule.

Calipers. Calipers are used for measuring diameters and distances, or for comparing distances and sizes. The three common types are inside calipers, outside calipers, and hermaphrodite calipers, Fig. 5.

Outside calipers are used for measuring outside dimensions as, for example, the diameter of a piece of round stock, Fig. 5A.

Inside calipers have outward curving legs for measuring inside diameters, such as the diameters of holes, the distance between two surfaces, the width of slots, etc., Fig. 5B.

Hermaphrodite calipers are generally used to scribe arcs, or as a marking gauge in layout work, as shown in Fig. 5C.

Dividers are tools for measuring distances between points, for transferring distances directly from a rule, or for scribing circles or parts of circles, Fig. 5D.

Protractor. The instrument shown in Fig. 6 is known as a protractor and is used in measuring or laying out angles. It is usually made of a

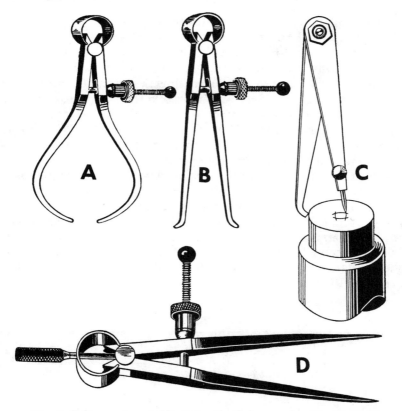

Fig. 5. Calipers: A. outside; B. inside; C. hermaphrodite; D. dividers.

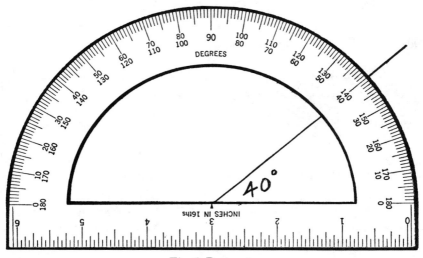

Fig. 6. Protractor.

transparent substance, such as celluloid, so that lines can be seen through it, but it can be made of metal or other materials. A protractor is made semicircular in shape so as to include 180°, and is therefore usually divided into 180 equal parts, each division representing 1°.

By placing the base of the protractor on a line, with the midpoint of the protractor where a second line intersects the first line, the angle between the two lines can be read directly from the instrument. For example, the line shown in the figure forms an angle of 40°. With the aid of a straightedge, or when used in a combination bevel protractor, lines can be drawn on sheet metal, for example, at any desired angle.

The protractor can also be used in the construction of triangles used in mathematical problems, or can be used in the graphical solution of such problems, if the work is done with great care.

Squares and combination set. In order to scribe, measure, and check angles, to construct lines at right angles to the edge of a piece of material, to establish points for lines parallel to the edge, and to serve as a guide or reference edge for other instruments, a square is essential. A steel square, 16 by 24 inches, and a smaller solid square are shown in Fig. 7.

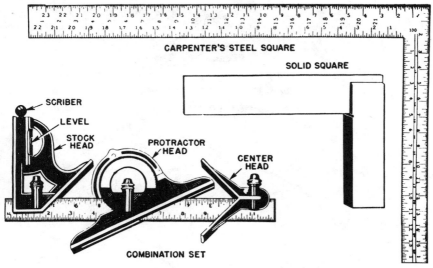

Fig. 7. Steel squares and combination set.

A combination set is shown in Fig. 7. This set can be used for various purposes, some of which are shown in Fig. 8. Note that a scriber, a spirit level, and a protractor are included.

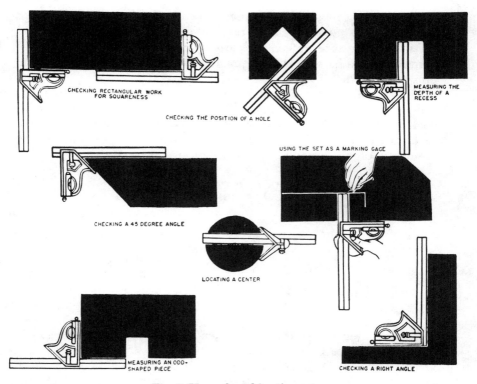

Fig. 8. Uses of combination set.

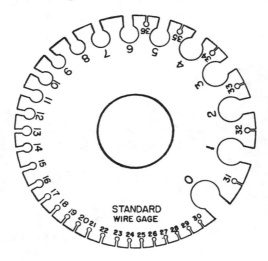

Fig. 9. Wire and sheet gauge.

Wire and sheet gauge. The gauge shown in Fig. 9 is a U. S. standard wire and sheet gauge. It can be used to measure cross sections of wire and to determine the gauge (thickness) of metal sheets. Before using one of these gauges be sure that all burrs are removed from the material being measured.

Center gauge. The gauge shown in Fig. 10 is a 60° center gauge. The notches in the edge of the gauge also have an angle of 60° and are used to check the grinding of thread-cutting tools, as American National thread has a thread angle of 60°. The center gauge can also be used for setting thread-cutting tools square with the work in a lathe.

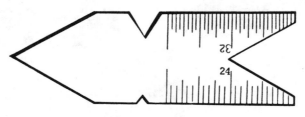

Fig. 10. Center gauge.

Center gauges are usually marked on both faces and along both edges with scales that are convenient for measuring the number of threads per inch of bolts, studs, etc. One face has 20 divisions to the inch on one edge and 14 divisions to the inch on the other edge. On the opposite face of the center gauge there are 24 divisions per inch on one edge and 32 divisions per inch on the other edge. The divisions of different sizes are used to check the pitch, or number of threads per inch,

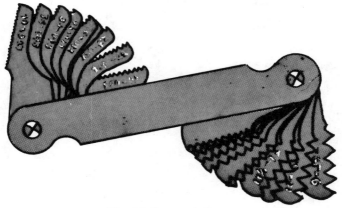

Fig. 11. Screw pitch gauge.

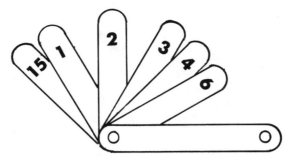

Fig. 12. Thickness gauge.

of screw threads. The different numbers of threads per inch for which each scale is suitable are those which divide into the scale number without a remainder. For example, the edge with 20 divisions is suitable for measuring 1, 2, 4, 5, 10, and 20 threads per inch, and also for any multiple of 20, such as 40, 60, 80, etc. The edge with 14 divisions may be used for measuring 1, 2, 7, or 14 threads per inch and for any multiple of 14. The scales with 24 divisions and 32 divisions are used similarly.

Screw pitch gauge. If there is any doubt as to the number of threads on a bolt, screw, nut, etc., a screw pitch gauge, Fig. 11, can be used to check. Each blade or finger is stamped with the number of threads cut on it.

Thickness gauge. The thickness gauge or feeler gauge is used for measuring distances or clearances between two surfaces, Fig. 12. The number stamped on each blade is the thickness of that particular blade in thousandths of an inch.

Hammers. An all-purpose hard hammer is the ball-peen or machinist's hammer, Fig. 13A. The ball-shaped end is called the *peen*, the flat end the *face*. This hammer is classed according to the weight of the head without the handle, i.e., 6 ounces, 8 ounces, 1 pound, etc.

When hammering or working on a finished surface, a soft hammer is used, so that the surface being struck will not be marked or marred. This hammer is usually made of rawhide, brass, lead, or plastic.

Sledgehammers are heavy hammers used for producing heavy blows. They usually weigh between 5 and 25 pounds. This type of hammer is often referred to in the trade as a *button-set*.

Scaling hammers are more often referred to as chipping hammers, Fig. 13B. They are used for removing scale, paint, etc., from metal surfaces. The edges of the chipping hammer should be slightly rounded, not ground with a sharpened edge. A sharpened or knife edge will nick the metal and leave a rough, irregular surface, thus producing air

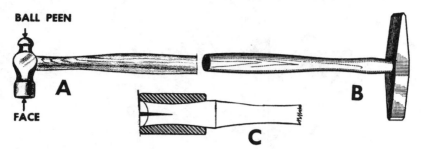

Fig. 13. A. ball-peen, or machinist's, hammer; B. chipping hammer; C. tapered
    metal edge in handle.

pockets beneath the new coat of paint and eventual blistering of the
paint.

A hammer should be held near the end of the handle. Do not hold the
handle close to the hammer head.

Most hammer accidents are caused by loose heads. The head should
fit tightly on the handle and a tapered metal wedge should be driven into
the end of the handle as shown in Fig. 13C.

Always wipe your hands dry of sweat, grease, or oil and wipe the
handle and face of the hammer before using it.

Punches. Several types of punches are shown in Fig. 14. These tools
may be used for a variety of jobs, but the correct punch for the job should
always be selected.

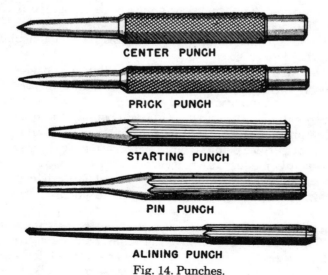

Fig. 14. Punches.

A center punch is used to make a starting mark for a drill when holes
are to be drilled in metal. If the center punch mark is not made, the drill

will wander or "walk away" from the desired center. The center punch point should be taper-ground to an angle of about 90°. Never use a center punch to remove a bolt or pin, as the sharp point will act as a wedge and tend to tighten the bolt or pin in the hole.

Prick punches are generally used for marking centers and lines in layout work.

Starting punches, sometimes called drifts, have a long taper from the tip to the body. They are made that way to withstand the shock of heavy blows. They may be used for knocking out rivets after their heads have been cut off, or for freeing pins or bolts from their holes. To start a bolt or pin that is extremely tight, use a starting punch that has a point diameter only slightly smaller than the diameter of the object that is being removed.

After a pin or bolt has been loosened or partially driven out, it may be found that the starting punch is too large to finish the job. A pin punch can then be used, as it is designed to follow through the hole without jamming. Both starting punches and pin punches must have flat ends, never pointed, edged, or rounded ones.

The aligning, or lining-up, punch is used to line up corresponding holes in adjacent parts; i.e., when working on engines that have pans and cover plates.

Bolt cutters. For heavy-duty cutting jobs, a bolt cutter, shown in Fig. 15, is used. These tools are made in several sizes, from 18 to 36 inches in length, the larger ones being used to cut mild steel bolts and rods up to ½ inch in diameter. Bolt cutters usually have special replaceable jaws of extra hard metal alloys; the jaws therefore are brittle and will break before they will bend or dent. Any twisting motion should be avoided when they are used. The cutter shown has set screws which enable the relative positions of the blades to be adjusted if they should fail to meet properly after having been sharpened.

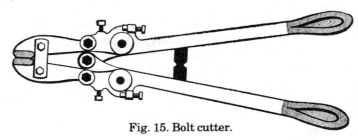

Fig. 15. Bolt cutter.

Screwdrivers. Screwdrivers are designed for one purpose, and that is to tighten or loosen screws. The tip or blade of the screwdriver is very hard so that it will hold its shape and resist the shearing action of the slot in the screw. When grinding a blade, keep the edges flat and be sure

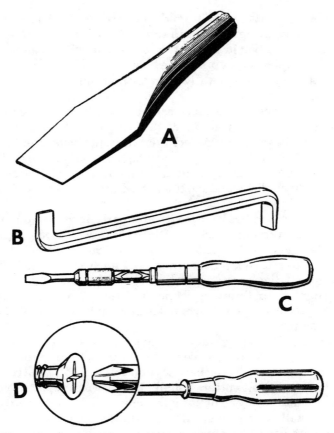

Fig. 16. Screwdrivers: A. regular driver; B. offset driver; C. ratchet driver;
D. Phillips head driver.

the edges are sharp. The end of the blade should be straight and rec-
tangular in shape, Fig. 16A. A screwdriver is ordered by the length of
the blade from tip to the handle. Heavy-duty screwdrivers are made
with heavy square shanks. This is done so that a wrench can be used
with them to obtain more leverage. Electricians' screwdrivers are made
with insulated handles. In an emergency, the handle of an ordinary
screwdriver can be insulated by wrapping it with electricians' tape.

The offset screwdriver, Fig. 16B, is used for screws located in inac-
cessible places.

The ratchet screwdriver, Fig. 16C, is a very handy tool due to the fact
that the handle can be held with a firm grasp and does not have to be
turned continually, as does the standard screwdriver.

The Phillips screwdriver, Fig. 16D, is one that fits Phillips type
screws only. These screws are cut with 4-way slots as shown.

When using a screwdriver on a small piece of work which is unattached, always hold that object in a vise and not in your other hand. Slips have all too often been the cause of severe hand injuries.

Pliers. There are many types of pliers in general use today. Fig. 17 shows some of the more common types.

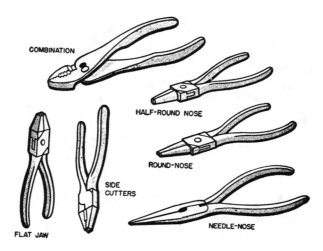

Fig. 17. Pliers.

The slip joint or combination plier has one arm of the slip joint slotted so that the hinge pin can be slipped from one position to another, thus allowing the jaws to open wider.

The side cutting plier has a sharp cutting edge on one side of each jaw. This type is used to a great extent in electrical work to strip the insulation from the wire.

The needle-nose plier is used to get into tight spaces or corners where the ordinary type of plier would not fit.

The jaws on most pliers are cut with teeth for better gripping purposes. Never use pliers to tighten nuts; they will chew off the corners of the nuts. Pliers are measured by overall length.

Wrenches. Wrenches are tools for tightening or removing bolts, nuts, studs, etc., or for gripping round material such as pipe, studs, round rods, etc. They may be classified under three general headings: adjustable, solid, and open end. Wrenches are also named for their shapes or for the particular job for which they are used, such as "S" wrench, angle wrench, pipe wrench, monkey wrench, tap wrench, etc.

Open-end wrenches are solid, nonadjustable wrenches with openings in one or both ends. The openings are set at various angles to the body of the wrench, the most common angle being 15°.

The size of a wrench is stamped on the face and denotes the size of the opening or the distance across flats, Fig. 18. This measurement is the distance across flats of a hexagon nut. A ½ inch nut measures ⅞ inch across flats, thus the wrench for a ½ inch nut would be marked ⅞ inch. Why the actual size is not used remains a mystery. This present system is most confusing.

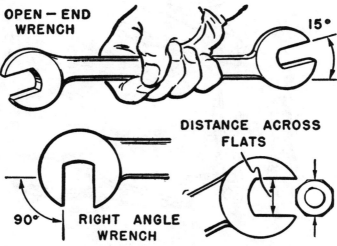

Fig. 18. Open-end wrenches.

There is a fairly simple system for converting the nut size to the wrench size, and vice versa: To determine the wrench size for a nut, divide the size of the nut by ⅔ and add ⅛. For example, the wrench size for a ¾ inch nut would be

$$¾ \div ⅔ + ⅛$$
$$¾ \times ³/₂ + ⅛$$
$$⁹/₈ + ⅛ = ¹⁰/₈ = 1²/₈ = 1¼ \text{ inches}$$

To find the nut size for the number stamped on a wrench, subtract ⅛ inch from the size of the wrench and multiply by ⅔. For example, the nut size for a wrench marked ⅞ inch would be

$$⅞ - ⅛ \times ²/₃$$
$$⁶/₈ \times ⅔ = ¹²/₂₄ = ½ \text{ inch}$$

Fig. 19 shows three other common types of open-end wrenches. The "S" wrench is used for working in close quarters. The crowfoot wrench has its head set at 90° to the axis of the handle and is used to reach nuts in out-of-the-way locations. The "spud" wrench has a long, tapered handle and is frequently used for aligning bolt holes in plates or flanges.

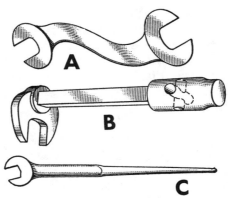

Fig. 19. Open-end wrenches: A. "S" wrench; B. crowfoot wrench; C. boiler or spud
   wrench.

In tightening or loosening large nuts (4 inches or 5 inches or larger)
which usually fit very snugly and cannot be run down the bolt threads
by hand, the regular wrench is very heavy and cumbersome. To get the
nuts down into place, or to remove them once they have been loosened
with the regular wrench, a special tool called a "skeleton" wrench is
used. As the name implies, this wrench is much lighter in weight and
easier to handle.

Never use open-end wrenches that have sprung jaws, i.e., jaws that
have been spread due to excessive pressures. Never use a wrench that is
larger than the size of the nut; a larger wrench usually slips around and
flattens out the corners of the nut. Whenever possible, pull on a wrench
and do not push on it. If it is necessary to push on a wrench due to the
location of the nut, hold the hand open and push with the base of your
palm. This will prevent bruised knuckles should the wrench slip off the
nut.

Fig. 20. Adjustable wrench.

One of the handiest of all wrenches is the adjustable or crescent
wrench, Fig. 20. This is quite similar to the open-end wrench except that

the opening is adjustable to fit any number of nuts of different sizes. Always apply the wrench to the nut so that the force of the pull comes on the solid jaw, i.e., the jaw that is part of the handle casting (note arrow in Fig. 20).

The monkey wrench, Fig. 21, is a type of adjustable wrench; however, the jaws are set at a 90° angle with the handle. The size is indicated by its overall length.

Fig. 21. Monkey wrench.

Box wrenches are very handy because they can be used in close quarters. They completely surround (box) the nut, Fig. 23. They are usually made with 12 notches (points) thereby giving them a minimum swing of 15°. There is little chance of this type of wrench slipping off the nut. Some box wrenches have their ends offset at various angles.

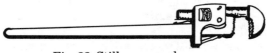

Fig. 22. Stillson wrench.

The Stillson wrench or pipe wrench, as the name implies, is used on pipes and other round objects, Fig. 22. The jaws have teeth cut in them to provide a better grip. Never use a pipe wrench on square objects or on nuts; it will chew the corners off and make the nuts useless. The size of the wrench is indicated by its overall length.

Fig. 23. Box wrench.

There are a number of different types of socket wrenches. Fig. 24 shows the offset type and the T-handle type. The most common types of socket wrenches are those that come in sets and have various handles, as shown in Fig. 25. The set usually consists of ten or twelve different size sockets, two or three types of handles, a knuckle joint and a number of extensions. The upper handle in Fig. 25 is a ratchet type and saves a great deal of time on the job. The ratchet wrench may be moved in either direction without removing it from the nut.

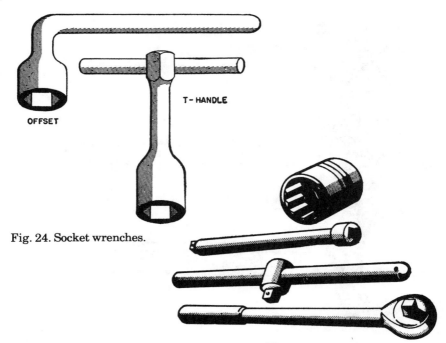

OFFSET

T - HANDLE

Fig. 24. Socket wrenches.

Fig. 25. Socket head and handles.

There are a number of types of spanner wrenches in general use, Fig. 26. Fire hoses and fire hydrant connections on board ship are usually of the spanner type construction. Some pumps are fitted with slotted packing gland nuts which require spanner wrenches.

Allen set screws and cap screws are headless and are intended to set flush with or below the surface of the part into which they are screwed. A hexagonal hole is made in the end of the screw as shown in Fig. 27. The Allen wrench is a piece of hexagon stock usually bent as shown in the diagram. The Allen set screw is the same diameter over its entire length. The Allen cap screw is made with a round head which is larger in diameter than the body of the screw. This larger head also fits into a hole in the part into which it is screwed.

Cutting tools. The hacksaw is used for cutting metal. There are two types of hacksaw frames—solid and adjustable, Fig. 28. The solid type will only hold one size of blade; the adjustable type can be fitted with different length blades.

Hacksaw blades come in two general forms—hard back and flexible back. The hard-back type is hardened all over, and the flexible back has only its teeth hardened. The hard-back blade is generally used on steel,

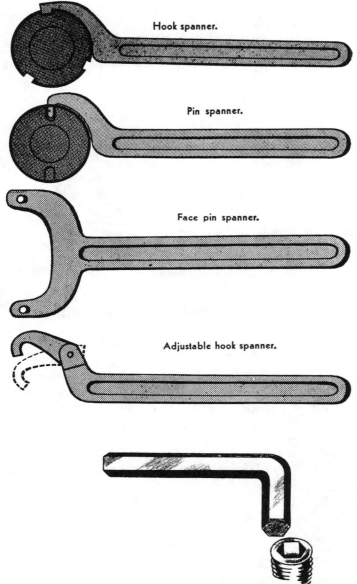

Hook spanner.

Pin spanner.

Face pin spanner.

Adjustable hook spanner.

Fig. 27. Allen wrench and set screw.

brass, cast iron, and pieces with heavy cross sections; the flexible back is used on hollow shapes and pieces having a light cross section.

Blades also come in various pitches. The pitch represents the number of teeth per inch. The standard pitches are 14, 18, 24, and 32 teeth

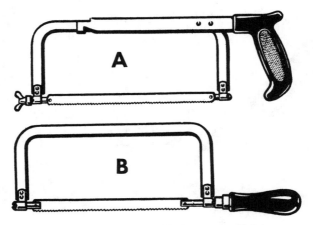

Fig. 28. Hacksaws: A. adjustable frame; B. solid frame.

per inch. For general purpose work the 18 pitch is used. The 24 pitch is used for cutting thick wall tubing, pipe, copper, brass, channel, and angle iron. The 32 pitch is used for thin wall tubing and sheet metal. The 14 pitch is used on machine steel and cold rolled steel.

Always insert the blade in the frame with the teeth pointing away from the handle. Tighten the blade with just enough tension to hold the blade rigid between the frame pins.

Take full strokes when cutting, standing with the left foot slightly forward. Inasmuch as the teeth point away from the handle, it should be remembered that the pressure should be applied on the forward stroke. No pressure should be exerted on the back stroke. Cut at about forty or fifty strokes per minute. Most trouble in hacksawing is caused by too fast a cutting speed. For cutting long narrow strips of metal the blade should be placed at right angles to the frame.

Chisels. Cold chisels are tools used for chipping or cutting cold metal. They are classified according to the shape of their point, the most common being flat, cape, diamond point, and round nose, Fig. 29.

The size of a flat cold chisel is determined by the width of the cutting edge. Chisels are usually made of octagonal tool steel bar stock, carefully hardened and tempered. Note that the cutting edge is slightly convex. This prevents the weak corners from chipping.

Cape chisels are used for cutting keyways where square corners on the slot are necessary.

Round nose chisels are usually used for cutting oil grooves in bearings.

The diamond point chisel is used for cutting "V" grooves and inside sharp angles.

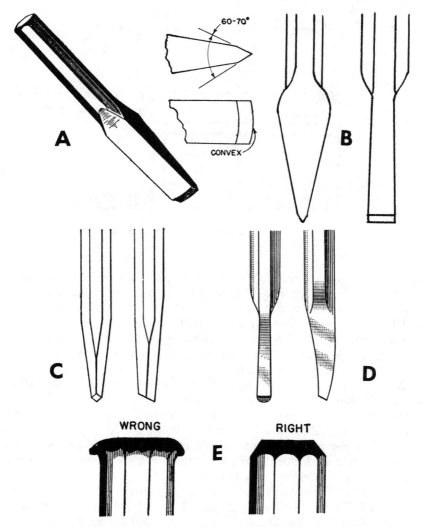

Fig. 29. Cold chisels: A. flat chisel and point angle; B. cape chisel; C. diamond
   point; D. round nose; E. right and wrong head.

When chipping steel, lubricate the chisel point with light machine
oil. This makes the chisel easier to drive. Don't use oil on cast iron.
Always use goggles when chipping. Keep the chisel handle and hammer
handle dry and clean to prevent slipping. Do not let the chisel heads
become mushroomed as this leads to flying chips and possible injury,
Fig. 29E.

Files. Files are used for cutting, smoothing, or removing small amounts of metal. They are made in various shapes, cuts of teeth, and length.

Fig. 30 shows the names of the parts of a file. Fig. 31 shows cross sections of the most commonly used files.

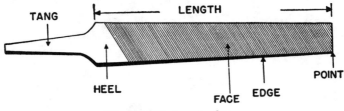

Fig. 30. File terminology.

Fig. 31. Shapes of files.

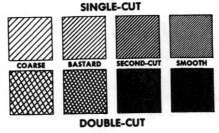

Fig. 32. Common file cuts.

Single cut files are used for sharpening tools, finish filing, and draw filing.

Double cut files are used for rough work and quick removal of metal. Fig. 32 shows some of the more common cuts of files. Small, round files are usually called rat-tails files.

Safe-edge files have no teeth on their edges and are used, for instance, in cutting alongside a shoulder where it is not desired to remove any metal from the side.

There are a number of other classifications of files but the foregoing are the most important.

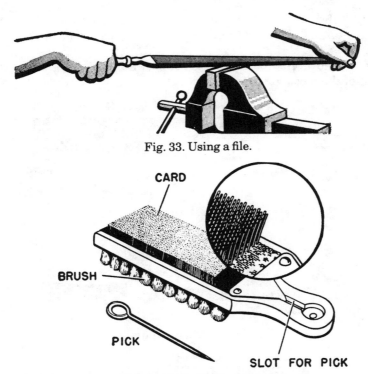

Fig. 33. Using a file.

Fig. 34. Tools for cleaning files.

Fig. 33 shows the correct position of the hands when filing. A straight stroke must be used at all times. Do not rock the file up and down like a seesaw.

When filing soft metals, small particles of the metal will remain between the file teeth. This will cause the file to scratch the metal that is being worked on. To clean the teeth a filecard is used, Fig. 34. This is a combination wire brush and bristle brush; the wire side is run across the file teeth and then cleaned off with the bristle side. If the "pins" (small pieces of metal stuck in the file teeth) are stuck too hard, a sharp pointed wire or nail will have to be used to clean them out.

Never use a file without a handle. Order a file by giving length, type, and shape, i.e., 12 inches, single-cut, smooth, flat.

Hand snips. In Fig. 35 hand snips are shown which are used for cutting sheet metal or other thin pieces of metal. The straight snips shown in the figure have straight flat blades and will cut along a straight line. Snips are also made with curved blades for cutting out circular pieces and are called circular snips.

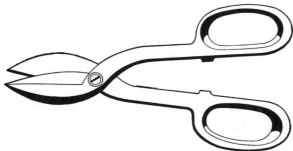

Fig. 35. Straight blade snips.

Never use snips for cutting screws, nails, etc.

Snips are ordered by their overall length and length of cutting blades.

Druls. Twist drills are made of carbon steel or high-speed alloy steel. Carbon steel drills are satisfactory for general work and are less expensive, although they may lose their hardness if heated excessively. High-speed drills are used on tough metals and at high speeds. They will keep on cutting when red hot, but should be cooled in still air; if cooled quickly, they may crack or split.

The drill shank is the end that fits into the chuck of the hand drill, electric drill, or drill press. Straight-shank drills are used to drill holes up to about ½ inch in diameter. Larger holes are usually drilled with the taper-shank drill. The square-shank drill is made to use in a brace. The various shanks are shown in Fig. 36.

Twist drills are available with either 2, 3, or 4 flutes (the spiral grooves formed along the sides), but drills having 3 or 4 flutes are used for following smaller drills or for enlarging cored holes, and are not suitable for drilling into solid stock. The spiral flutes provide several advantages:

1. They give a correct rake angle to the lips, as shown in Fig. 37.

2. They cause chips formed while drilling to curl tightly so that they occupy the minimum amount of space.

3. They form channels through which such chips escape from the hole.

4. They allow the lubricant, when one is used, to flow easily down to the cutting edge of the drill.

The twist drills used most frequently are those made in fractional sizes, from ¹/₆₄ inch up to 1 inch in diameter, although larger sizes are also found aboard ship. The size of the drill is stamped on the shank. Because the drills vary ¹/₆₄ (0.0156) inch from one size to the next, two other identification systems have been developed for special sizes:

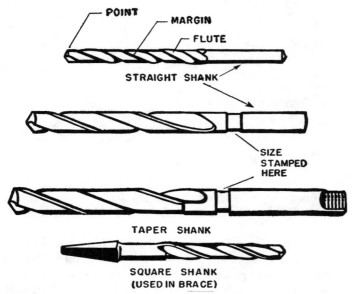

Fig. 36. Twist drill shanks.

1. Number drills, ranging from No. 80 (0.0135 inches) to No. 1 (0.228 inches).

2. Letter drills, ranging from A (0.234 inches) to Z (0.413 inches).

If the size number has worn off the drill shank, the size can be checked with a drill gauge, Fig. 38, for the number drills, with a drill stand for fractional drills, or with a micrometer for any kind of drill. When measuring a drill with a micrometer, measure from the outside of one margin to the outside of the other margin at the point of the drill. The shank diameter of a straight-shank drill is usually a few ten-thousandths of an inch smaller than the point diameter.

Use of lubricant: When drilling, some materials require no lubricant while others require a lubricant peculiar to their nature. The following tabulation may be used as a guide:

Materials To Be Drilled	*Lubricant*
Tool steel, copper	Oil
Soft steel, wrought iron	Oil or soda water
Babbitt, brass, cast iron	No lubricant (dry)
Glass	Turpentine

A drill gauge is used for determining the size of a drill in the event that the size number has been worn off. It is a flat piece of steel with a large number of holes in it. Each hole is marked with a size number, the drill is fitted to the proper hole and the size noted.

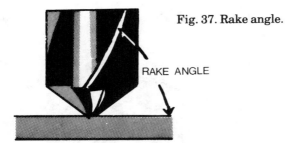

Fig. 37. Rake angle.

RAKE ANGLE

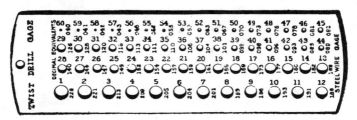

Fig. 38. Drill gauge.

To sharpen a drill properly is an art in itself. Machine shops have special jigs for holding a drill at the proper angle to the grinding wheel and these, naturally, do a perfect job. To sharpen a drill properly by hand takes much practice. The best way to learn is to sharpen some old, broken drills and test them out on a piece of metal. Fig. 39 shows the proper angle of the lips and cutting edges. Note that the cutting edges run parallel to each other.

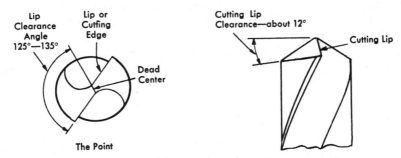

Fig. 39. Drill point showing proper angle of cutting lip.

Before drilling a large hole, it is advisable to drill a smaller or pilot hole. This helps to guide the larger drill. Always use a lubricant when drilling iron or steel.

The use of the hand drill and breast drill, Fig. 40, has been practically eliminated by the electric drill.

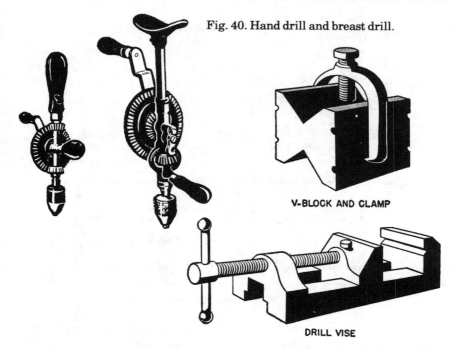

Fig. 40. Hand drill and breast drill.

V-BLOCK AND CLAMP

DRILL VISE

Fig. 41. Drill vise and V-block.

When drilling a piece of metal in a drill press, always secure the metal by some means such as a "V" block or a drill vise, Fig. 41. The "V" block is most suitable for drilling holes in round stock which can be secured by the clamps and is thus prevented from turning.

If for some reason the drill should slip and start cutting to one side, as shown in the first picture of Fig. 42, it can usually be brought back to the center by cutting a groove with a round nose chisel as shown in the second picture, the cut being made on the side toward which you want the direction of the drill moved.

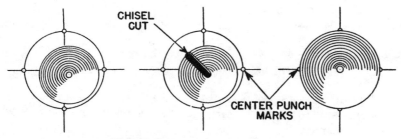

CHISEL
CUT

CENTER PUNCH
MARKS

Fig. 42. Recentering a drill cut.

Fig. 43. Countersink.

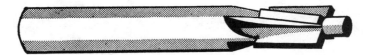

Fig. 44. Counterbore.

Countersinks are used to shape the end of drilled holes to fit screws, rivets, or bolts with countersink heads, Fig. 43.

Counterbores are used to shape the end of a drilled hole to fit fillister head bolts, screws, etc., Fig. 44.

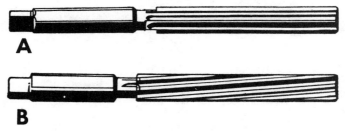

Fig. 45. Hand reamers: A. solid straight flute; B. solid spiral flute.

Fig. 46. Expansion reamer.

Reamers. Reamers are used in precision work to smooth and enlarge holes to exact size. The hole is usually drilled .003 to .007 inch undersize.

Two common types of reamer are shown in Fig. 45.

The most practical is the expansion reamer, Fig. 46. Reamers come in sets, each one increasing in diameter by $1/32$.

Taper reamers are used to smooth and true taper holes for tapered pins.

Thread forms. The four most common types of screw threads are the V-thread, the American National thread, the square thread, and the acme thread. The same rules for diameter and pitch apply to all types of threads.

The sharp V-thread, Fig. 47, has serious disadvantages and is seldom used. The sharp crests and roots are hard to cut accurately; the crests are easily dented and chipped; and the roots become clogged with dirt and bits of metal.

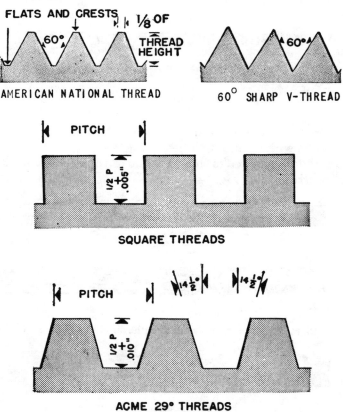

Fig. 47. Thread forms.

The American National thread, also shown in Fig. 47, resembles the sharp V-thread, except that the crests and roots are flat. The length of this flat portion, of both crest and root, is ⅛ of the pitch distance. Because of the design, American National threads are not easily damaged, and the roots are easily cleaned. This type of thread is the one generally used on the many bolts and nuts found in a ship's installation.

American National threads are standardized into two series: NC (National Coarse) and NF (National Fine). The coarse thread series is used for rough work on heavy materials, while the fine thread series is used on small bolts, machine screws, adjusting mechanisms, etc.

The square thread, shown in Fig. 47, is strong and efficient. It is used on the tightening screws of vises, clamps, and jacks.

The acme thread is a heavy-duty thread with sides forming an angle of 29° with each other. This type of thread can withstand heavy strains and loads, and is easier to machine than square threads.

Taps. The tap hole must be smaller than the diameter of the tap. The reason for this is shown in Fig. 48. Consult a tap drill table for proper size drill. Hand taps are usually provided in sets of three for each diameter and thread series. Each set contains a taper, plug, and bottom tap.

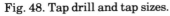
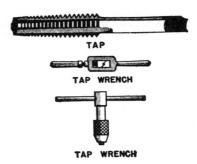

Fig. 48. Tap drill and tap sizes.   Fig. 49. Taper tap and tap wrenches.

The taper tap is used to start the tapping process because its end is tapered back a few threads. The taper tap is used when completing threads through a piece of stock when it can be run entirely through the stock. The plug tap is used when one end of the hole is closed. The bottom tap is used when it is necessary to cut a full thread to the bottom of a closed hole. Plug or bottom taps should never be used to start a thread.

It is very important to start the tap straight and keep it so throughout the work, because taps will break easily if bent or strained. The tap should not be fed into the hole with any pressure; its threads will pull it in at the proper rate. The safest procedure is to turn the tap a half turn forward (clockwise) then a quarter turn back (counterclockwise) then another half turn forward (clockwise), etc. With soft metals, such as brass or cast iron, the back turns are not necessary.

When tapping steel or bronze use a cutting oil as a lubricant. Soft metals may be tapped dry.

Fig. 49 illustrates a taper tap and two common types of tap wrenches. The first one is referred to as a straight handle and the second one as a "T" handle.

The tapping of a hole for a pipe fitting is accomplished in somewhat the same way as bolt tapping. However, the pipe tap is tapered and should never be run all the way through the hole. If the tap goes in too far, the threads will be too loose. A pipe tap should be run in approximately ¾ of its length.

Because pipe is measured by inside diameter, it can be seen that the tap drill size will be larger than the given size of pipe. Fig. 50 shows a chart of pipe tap drill sizes. For example, the tap drill for 1 inch pipe is $1^5/_{32}$.

AMERICAN STANDARD TAPER PIPE THREAD

Size of tap	Threads per inch	Size of tap drill
1/8	27	11/32
1/4	18	7/16
3/8	18	19/32
1/2	14	23/32
3/4	14	15/16
1	11 1/2	1 5/32
1 1/4	11 1/2	1 1/2
1 1/2	11 1/2	1 23/32
2	11 1/2	2 3/16
2 1/2	8	2 5/8
3	8	3 1/4

Fig. 50. American Standard taper pipe threads.

Be sure to use lubricant. Follow same instructions as for hand taps.

Even when used with care, taps will sometimes break off, and the mechanic should become familiar with the usual methods of removing the broken part of the tap from the hole. Two satisfactory ways of doing this, with a chisel or punch or with a tap extractor, are as follows:

(1) With a chisel or punch—broken taps can often be removed by using a small, blunt cold chisel or a taper punch, as shown in Fig. 51. This will frequently start the tap; the job can then be completed with a tap extractor as described below. Taps often shatter when they break; the broken pieces should be picked from the hole with a small prick punch or a magnetized scriber before any attempt is made to remove the tap.

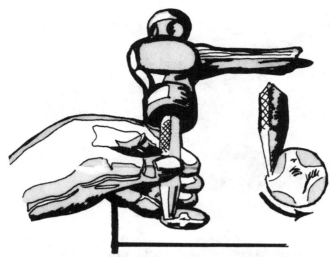

Fig. 51. Removing broken tap with punch.

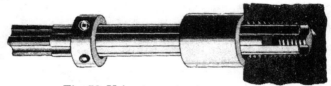

Fig. 52. Using tap extractor.

(2) With a tap extractor—Fig. 52 shows the application of a tap extractor. This tool has movable fingers which can be placed in the flutes of the broken tap, as shown, after which the collar should be brought up against the surface of the work. A tap wrench can be used on the extractor to back out the broken piece. The tap extractor will not stand much turning force without breaking the movable fingers. Removing a broken tap by any method is often a long, tedious job which requires time, skill, and patience. It is therefore wise for the mechanic to avoid breakage by being as careful as possible.

Dies. The die and stock (handle) is shown in Fig. 53. Before threading a piece of round stock its end should be tapered or chamfered slightly with a file, or by grinding, so that the die will start cutting more easily.

When using a split die such as is shown in Fig. 53, the first cut should be taken with the split in the die set opposite the set screw of the stock. As the set screw is tightened into the slot the die spreads open and therefore cuts off a relatively small amount of metal on this first cut.

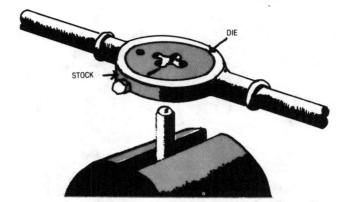

Fig. 53. Stock and die ready for use.

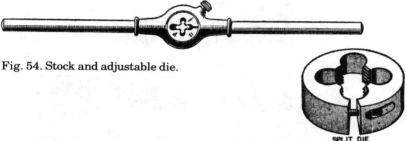

Fig. 54. Stock and adjustable die.

Fig. 55. Split or adjustable die.　SPLIT DIE (SCREW ADJUSTMENT)

You will note after this cut that there is only a rough thread. It will probably be impossible even to get a nut to fit because there is still too much metal on the rod.

Before taking the second cut, turn the die as shown in Fig. 54. Now as the set screw is tightened, the split closes in and will cut more metal, producing the final smooth thread.

Fig. 55 shows the screw adjustment type of split die. The width of the split may be adjusted by tightening or loosening the adjusting screw.

Threads and thread cutting. Threads cut on the outside of a piece of round stock are called external threads. Threads cut on the inside of a cylindrical hole are called inside threads. Dies are used for cutting the external or outside threads, and taps are used for cutting inside threads.

The two types of general threads used are the NC (National Coarse) and NF (National Fine). Pitch is the distance from the top of one thread to the top of an adjacent thread. The pitch is usually stated as the number of threads per inch, such as 8, 10, 12, etc. A tap or die marked ¼-20 indicates ¼ inch diameter and 20 threads per inch.

Fig. 56 is a table of NC and NF tap sizes and the proper size tap drill to be used in each case.

Die threads are tapered from one face only. So, be sure to start the cut with that face.

AMERICAN N.C. AND N.F. THREADS

Size of tap	Threads per inch	Size of tap drill
1/4 NC	20	7
1/4 NF	28	3
5/16 NC	18	F
5/16 NF	24	I
3/8 NC	16	5/16
3/8 NF	24	Q
7/16 NC	14	U
7/16 NF	20	25/64
1/2 NC	13	27/64
1/2 NF	20	29/64
9/16 NC	12	31/64
9/16 NF	18	33/64
5/8 NC	11	17/32
5/8 NF	18	37/64
11/16 NC	11	19/32
11/16 NF	16	5/8
3/4 NC	10	21/32
3/4 NF	16	11/16
13/16 NC	10	23/32
7/8 NC	9	49/64
7/8 NF	14	13/16
15/16 NC	9	53/64
1 NC	8	7/8
1 NF	14	15/16
1 1/8 NC	7	63/64
1 1/8 NF	12	1 3/64
1 1/4 NC	7	1 7/64
1 1/4 NF	12	1 11/64
1 3/8 NC	6	1 7/32
1 3/8 NF	12	1 19/64
1 1/2 NC	6	1 11/32
1 1/2 NF	12	1 27/64
1 5/8 NC	5 1/2	1 29/64
1 3/4 NC	5	1 9/16
1 7/8 NC	5	1 11/16
2 NC	4 1/2	1 25/32

Fig. 56. American national coarse (NC) and national fine (NF) threads.

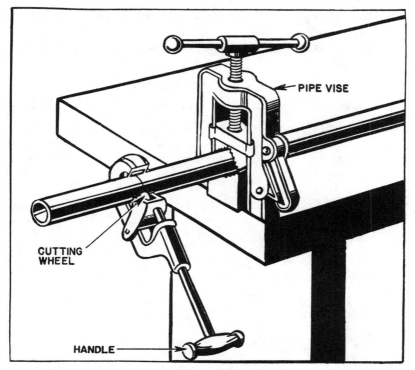

Fig. 57. Using a pipe cutter.

To start the thread, press down firmly on the stock, while turning to the right (clockwise). When the die catches, start using a cutting oil. Continue turning, following the same procedure as with tapping, half a turn clockwise and a quarter turn back, etc.

Cutting pipe. Pipe is usually cut with a hand hacksaw, a power hacksaw, or a pipe cutter. The pipe cutter is probably the most popular, inasmuch as most ships do not carry power hacksaws. The pipe cutter has special alloy steel cutting wheels. These are adjusted and tightened by turning the handle. The whole tool, Fig. 57, is revolved around the pipe.

The operation of the pipe cutter leaves a shoulder on the outside of the pipe and a burr or ragged edge on the inside. This ragged edge will catch dirt and other solid matter and must be removed. This is done with a pipe reamer as shown in Fig. 58.

Threading pipe. Pipe fittings have tapered threads, and special dies are required to cut this taper. The taper allows for tightening up the fittings to make them leakproof.

Fig. 58. Using a reamer.

There are a number of different types of pipe dies. One consists of a stock into which various sized dies may be inserted. These dies are usually in two pieces.

Another type consists of a large stock into which a set of four cutters is inserted, Fig. 59. In this type the front piece is threaded into the larger back head. It is necessary to back out this front piece before cutting a thread. As the thread is cut, this front piece turns (screws) into the back piece, which is secured rigidly to the pipe with set or thumb screws. Be particularly careful that these two sections do not come together and jam.

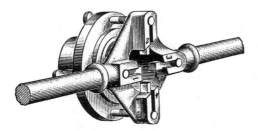

Fig. 59. Pipe threading stock and four-piece dies.

Fig. 60. Ratchet type pipe threading stock and dies.

A popular type for smaller size pipe is the ratchet stock shown in Fig. 60. A number of different dies come with the set and may be inserted and held in place by the pawl or pin, as shown. It will be noted that the part of the die stock that goes over the pipe first is recessed. This is for the insertion of a collar, which acts as a guide and holds the whole assembly in line with the pipe.

Fig. 61. Pipe reamer.

The general threading procedure should be the same as with the bolt dies, i.e., a half turn forward (clockwise), a quarter turn backward, a half turn forward, etc. This helps to break off the chip that has just been cut and prevents it from being carried ahead and possibly ruining the next thread.

Pipe shops doing a large volume of pipe threading usually cut pipe with electric motor driven dies.

Lubricate dies the same as when cutting bolt threads—this is very important.

Pipe cutter. The operation of the pipe cutter leaves a shoulder on the outside of the end of the pipe and a burr on the inside. Always remove both. If the burr on the inside is not removed, the ragged edges will catch dirt and other solid matter and will block the flow. A pipe reamer, Fig. 61, is used for the purpose.

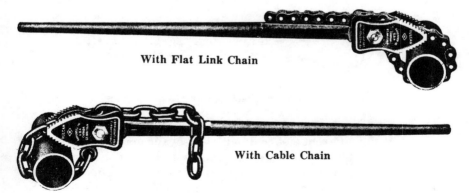

With Flat Link Chain

With Cable Chain

Fig. 62. Chain pipe wrenches.

Chain pipe wrenches. Also known as *chain tongs,* these wrenches are of the chain strap and lever type. Two examples are shown in Fig. 62. They are generally designed for use on large diameter piping, although they are also made in sizes suitable for handling small pipe.

When using this type of wrench, the best gripping position is midway on the jaw teeth. The wrench is also designed so that the handle will bend under a heavy load before the chain will break. The bending of the handle should therefore be taken as a warning that maximum load has been applied.

Fig. 63. Belt (hole) punch.

Belt (hole) punch. Fig. 63 shows a hole or belt punch. It is used for cutting the bolt holes in gasket materials or in leather belting.

Gasket cutter. There are a number of ways to cut gaskets. Two gasket cutters that can be made on board ship are shown in Fig. 64. They are not too difficult to make and are usually worth the trouble and effort because they can be used for years. Hacksaw blades sharpened on one side make good cutters.

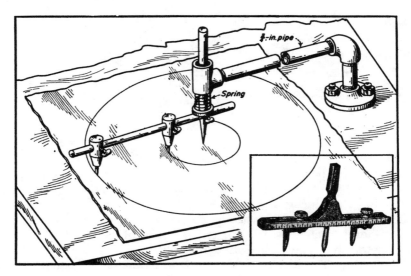

Fig. 64. Gasket cutters.

Nuts, bolts, and screws. In assembly and disassembly operation threaded parts such as nuts, bolts, and screws are handled so frequently that every mechanic should be thoroughly familiar with their various types and uses and should understand the common methods of cutting or renewing threads. The common devices used for fastening or holding metal parts together are bolts and nuts, screws, washers, and rivets. Fig. 65 shows the various types of bolts in everyday use. They are generally suitable for holding pieces or parts together that on occasion must be removed or taken apart. They are always used with a suitable nut. The types of screws the mechanic ordinarily has to work with are shown in Fig. 66. Cap screws and machine screws are generally used without nuts, so that a hole must be threaded (tapped) to receive them. Cap screws have a rounded end which pilots the thread into the tapped hole. The flat end of a machine bolt is likely to "walk" before the threads catch. All types of machine screws are available with Phillips cross-slot heads. Set screws are ordinarily used to set wheels or collars solidly on shafts. Socket-type set screws are turned by a small wrench made of a piece of hexagon rod bent and hardened. Lag screws are for holding metal to wood; sheet metal screws are hardened and cut their own threads in drilled or punched holes.

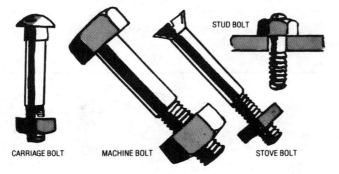

Fig. 65. Types of bolts.

At times a screw or stud will break off in a hole and must be extracted. The best method of doing this is to use a screw extractor. First drill a hole in the broken screw or stud a little smaller than its body diameter; then insert the extractor into this hole and turn it counter-clockwise. The screw extractor is tapered and has sharp ridges, similar to left-hand threads, which will grip the sides of the hole in the broken part so that it can be turned out of the hole by a wrench.

Nuts, Fig. 67, must always be used with some kind of bolt or stud, so that the two pieces, nut and bolt or nut and stud, exert holding force by

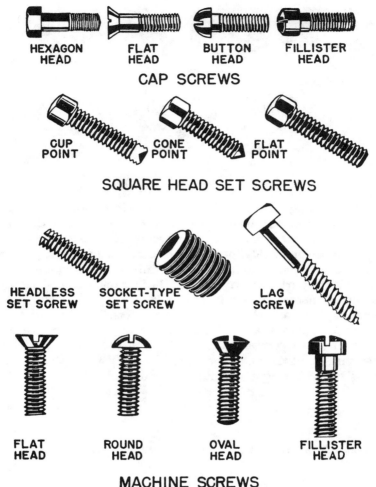

HEXAGON   FLAT   BUTTON   FILLISTER
HEAD   HEAD   HEAD   HEAD

CAP SCREWS

CUP   CONE   FLAT
POINT   POINT   POINT

SQUARE HEAD SET SCREWS

HEADLESS   SOCKET-TYPE   LAG
SET SCREW   SET SCREW   SCREW

FLAT   ROUND   OVAL   FILLISTER
HEAD   HEAD   HEAD   HEAD

MACHINE SCREWS

Fig. 66. Types of screws.

the strength of their threads. They are suited to assemblies that may have to be removed or taken apart. Wing nuts are especially useful where there is frequent occasion for hand adjustment. Castle nuts can be set immovable by a cotter pin placed through the slots provided in the nut and a hole in the bolt.

Washers, also shown in Fig. 67, are often put under nuts or bolt heads to protect the pieces being fastened or to make tightening up easier. Lock washers are made of spring steel and exert a light bite on a nut to keep it from turning and becoming loose.

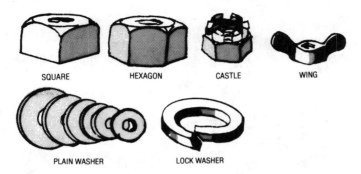

Fig. 67. Types of nuts and washers.

Rivets. Although not threaded, rivets are classified as metal fasteners, the pressure of their heads, instead of threads, exerting the holding force. Rivets are commonly used for permanent fastening and are not practical for any assembly that has to be taken apart. Rivet holes must be drilled or punched and must be carefully spaced and aligned. The thickness of the parts to be riveted and the load to be applied determine the proper diameter and length of the hole.

Tinner's rivets are used on thin metal sheets. They have flat heads, are made of soft iron or steel, and are usually coated with tin as a protection against corrosion. The weight, in pounds, of 1,000 rivets, denotes the size of rivets, as shown in Fig. 68. The length of a rivet is proportional to its weight and diameter.

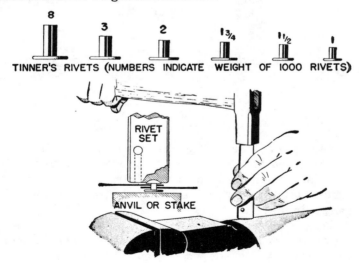

Fig. 68. Tinner's rivets and rivet set.

The use of a rivet set is necessary with tinner's rivets. After the rivet has been inserted in the holes in the pieces of material being riveted together, the set is placed over the headless end of the rivet and is used to press the sheets of metal together and against the rivet head. The recessed hole for this purpose in the set is indicated by the broken lines in Fig. 68. The set is then removed, and the rivet is upset (headed upon the headless end) with a riveting hammer. After this is done, the set is used to round the upset end. Rivet sets are available in several sizes.

Sheet metal screws. The screws shown in Fig. 69 are used to hold together sections of sheet metal, fiber, plastic, etc., and are known as sheet metal screws. They are especially useful aboard ship when applying sheet metal covering over insulation. Type A has a sharp point and resembles a wood screw, except that the threads extend to the head of the screw. Type Z screws have blunt points and may be used with heavier material. A special "self-tapping" sheet metal screw has a tap end that cuts threads as the screw is inserted.

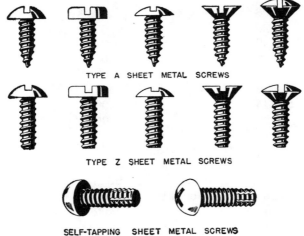

TYPE A SHEET METAL SCREWS

TYPE Z SHEET METAL SCREWS

SELF-TAPPING SHEET METAL SCREWS

Fig. 69. Sheet metal screws.

Holes for sheet metal screws should be drilled or punched to about the same diameter as the core of the screw used. The screws are available in a variety of head shapes, as shown in the illustration.

Sheet metal. Sheet metal and wire come in various thicknesses measured by number according to the American Wire Gage system. Sheet metal usually comes in sheets 4 feet by 6 feet. Some of the more common sizes are listed with their corresponding thicknesses in thousandths of an inch. See following table.

Gauge Number	American Wire Gage or Brown and Sharpe—Diameter or Thickness in Decimal Parts of Inch
0	.325
2	.258
4	.204
6	.162
8	.128
10	.102
12	.081
14	.064
16	.051
18	.040
20	.032
22	.025
24	.020
26	.0159
28	.0126
30	.010
32	.008
34	.0063
36	.005
38	.004
40	.003

Coupling and gear puller. A 3-jaw puller suitable for removing couplings, gears, etc., from shafts is shown in Fig. 70. This tool is designed to exert a strong, uniform pull, and is arranged for convenient use. Spring tension helps to hold the jaws on the work, and when the locking nut is screwed down against the yoke, the jaws are locked in position, causing the puller to maintain its grip until the locking nut is backed off. This arrangement permits both hands to be used for the actual pulling of the gear or coupling.

In order to use the puller, the jaws are hooked over the coupling or gear, and the centering tip of the stud is centered in the countersink in the end of the shaft. For shafts without countersinks, a special screw-point protector is used to prevent damage to the centering tip. By applying a wrench to the hexagon head of the stud and turning the stud clockwise, a strong pull is exerted on the part being removed. Always use a wrench that is a good fit on the hexagon end of the stud, otherwise the corners of the hex may be rounded off and the usefulness of the tool impaired. A socket wrench is preferable.

Fig. 70. Gear puller.

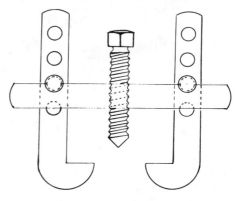

Fig. 71. Gear puller made from scrap metal.

When the stud is turned, the resulting pull tends to remove the work from the shaft, although sometimes it may be necessary to assist by tapping with a soft hammer or a hammer and a piece of wood. Be sure to tap at the hub of the coupling or gear, and not at the circumference. Tap evenly all around the hub, so that the work will not become cocked and jammed on the shaft.

Before starting to remove a coupling or gear from a shaft, it is advisable to examine for nicks and burrs on that section of shaft over which the part must slide. In some cases a film of oil or grease applied on the shaft will make for easier removal. If the part has rusted to the shaft it may be necessary to use penetrating oil to break up the corrosion.

It should be noted that the jaws of the puller are reversible permitting their use through an opening for inside pulls on sleeves, bushings, etc.

If a suitable puller is not available, one, such as shown in Fig. 71, can be made from scrap metal.

Cutting and flaring tubing. The small tubing generally used for refrigeration lines and similar purposes can be cut with the tubing cutter, shown in Fig. 72. The use of the cutter is similar to the use of the pipe cutter on a much smaller scale. A reamer for removing the burr left inside the tubing is attached to the tool. It is important that the tubing be cut off at right angles to its length, especially if it is to be flared.

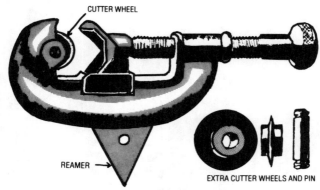

Fig. 72. Tubing cutter.

If a flare fitting is to be used, the flaring tool shown in Fig. 73 is used. The purpose of this flaring tool is to expand the end of the tubing so that it will fit into the expansion fittings frequently used as tubing connections. Always be sure the fitting is placed on the tubing before using the flaring tool. The tool clamps on the end of the tubing, and a tapered plug turned into the end of the tubing forms the flare.

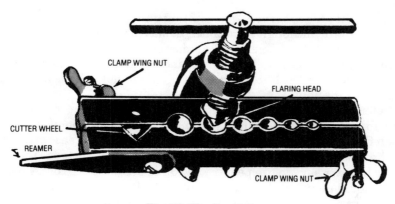

Fig. 73. Flaring tool.

Clamps. When a vise is not available, a clamp can be used to hold pieces of material together while they are being worked on. Clamps of this type are shown in Fig. 74. A different kind of clamp is often used to make a temporary fastening in the engine room when it is desired to lift or take a strain on some object. To do so, the clamp is securely fastened to a convenient beam, as shown in Fig. 75, and a line or small hoist is then suspended from the clamp.

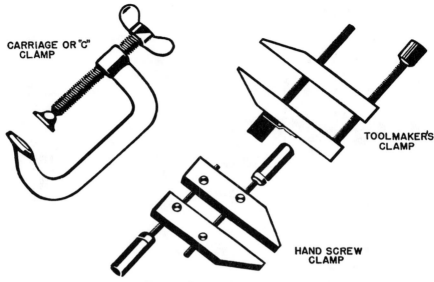

CARRIAGE OR "C" CLAMP

TOOLMAKER'S CLAMP

HAND SCREW CLAMP

Fig. 74. Screw clamps.

Grinding wheels. The term "emery wheel" is often incorrectly used in referring to grinding wheels, for emery wheels have been largely replaced by aluminum oxide and silicon carbide wheels. Aluminum oxide wheels are best for grinding materials of high tensile strength, such as carbon steels, alloy steels, malleable iron, wrought iron, tough bronze, and tungsten. Silicon carbide wheels are used to grind materials of low tensile strength, such as aluminum, bakelite, brass, common bronze, cast iron, copper, leather, and rubber.

Grinding wheels are graded according to softness and hardness. Soft wheels should be operated at slower speeds, as the grains wear away rapidly and the wheel is easily broken. Medium hard and hard wheels are operated at higher speeds.

The abrasive grains of grinding wheels are held together by special bonds, and the type of bond affects the uses of the wheel. Shellac bond wheels are used for sharpening tools and finish grinding. Silicate bond wheels are used when the heat generated in grinding must be kept at a minimum; large diameter, slow turning wheels are usually of this type. Vitrified wheels are bonded with clay or flint at high temperatures. These wheels are porous and do not clog with metal as rapidly as other wheels. Vitrified wheels of coarse grain are used where rapid removal of metal is desired. Fine grain wheels are used for precision grinding.

Vulcanite wheels are bonded with rubber by a vulcanizing process, and are strong and tough. Thin wheels used for "cutting-off" and for

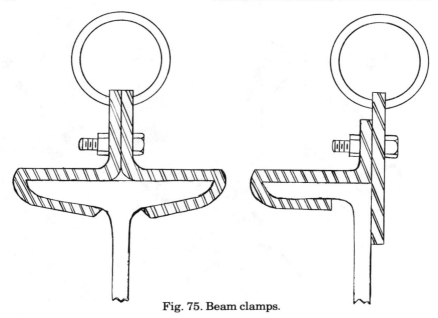

Fig. 75. Beam clamps.

high-speed grinding are rubber bonded. Resinoid wheels are bonded with synthetic resins, and may be operated at high speeds. They are especially good for fast rough grinding.

A 14- or 16-grain wheel should be used for coarse, rough grinding on castings, etc., while a 24-grain wheel is satisfactory for general shop work. A 46-grain wheel is recommended for most small-tool grinding, and a 60-grain wheel for grinding twist drills and lathe-cutting tools.

Slow turning oilstone wheels, which are soft and porous, are best for grinding keen edges on plane irons, knives, and other wood cutting tools. An abrasive wheel of this kind should be soaked with kerosene while it is being used.

Grinding wheels are manufactured in a great variety of shapes, sizes, and bores (diameter of arbor hole).

Bench grinder. An ordinary bench grinder mounts two wheels of the same size, shape, and bore, as shown in Fig. 76. They are from ½ to 1 inch thick, 6, 8, or 10 inches in diameter, and have an arbor hole of ½ to 1 inch in diameter. Usually one wheel is coarse for rough grinding, the other fine for tool sharpening and finish grinding.

Bench grinders should be sufficiently heavy and rigid to minimize vibration, and should be securely mounted in place. They should be provided with shields and guards for the safety of personnel. The shield should be adjustable and provided with nonshatterable glass. Tool rests

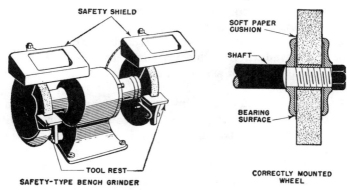

Fig. 76. Bench grinder and wheel mounting.

should be kept adjusted close to the wheel, the space between wheel and tool rest being about $^1/_{16}$ inch, never over $^1/_8$ inch. This prevents the work from being caught between the wheel and the rest. The tool rest should be securely clamped after each adjustment. The adjustment should never be made while the wheel is in motion.

Before being mounted on the shaft, grinding wheels should be closely inspected to make sure that they have not been damaged in any way, and all contacting surfaces of the wheel and grinder should be checked to see that they are free of foreign material. Some mechanics tap a new wheel lightly with a small piece of metal and check for the "ring" that indicates a sound wheel. The wheels should fit freely on the shaft; they should not be forced on, nor should they be too loose.

A thin cushion of compressible material should be fitted between the wheel and the washers, as shown in Fig. 76. If blotting paper is used for this purpose, it should not be thicker than 0.025 inch. If rubber or leather is used, it should not be thicker than $^1/_8$ inch. When tightening the nuts that hold the wheel, care should be taken to tighten them just enough to hold the wheel firmly; an excessive clamping strain may damage the wheel or its associated parts. After mounting a wheel, care should be taken that the guards and shields are properly replaced.

Precautions in the use of grinding wheels are as follows. All new wheels should be run at full operating speed for at least 1 minute, during which time the operator should stand at one side, out of the path of flying pieces, in case the wheel should be defective and break. If the wheel is chipped, or uneven in any way, it should be dressed before the grinding of fine tools is attempted.

When grinding is being done, the work should not be forced against a cold wheel, but applied gradually, giving the wheel an opportunity to warm up. This precaution minimizes the chance of breakage, and especially applies when working in a cold room, or when using new wheels that have been stored in a cool place.

Grinding on the flat sides of straight wheels is often hazardous and should not be allowed when the sides of the wheel are appreciably worn or when any considerable or sudden pressure is brought to bear against the sides of the wheels.

When a grinding wheel gets out-of-balance or out-of-round, it is necessary to dress, or true, the wheel. This can be done by means of a "star" type steel dressing tool, as shown in Fig. 77. To dress the wheel, the tool is held against the grinding wheel and moves sideways across the periphery as the wheel revolves. The work must be done carefully, however, and the operation requires considerable skill. Wheels which cannot be balanced by dressing should be removed from the machine.

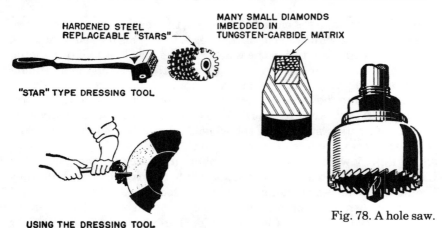

HARDENED STEEL
REPLACEABLE "STARS"

MANY SMALL DIAMONDS
IMBEDDED IN
TUNGSTEN-CARBIDE MATRIX

"STAR" TYPE DRESSING TOOL

USING THE DRESSING TOOL

Fig. 77. Grinding-wheel dressing tools.

Fig. 78. A hole saw.

After a grinding wheel has been used for some time, it will become clogged with metal, dirt, grease, etc., or the abrasive grains will become rounded or dull. The dressing tool may then be used to clean and sharpen the wheel, as it will cut away the clogged surface and break up the rounded grains so that new, sharp cutting edges are exposed.

A precision grinding wheel may be dressed by a special tool in which diamonds are mounted. The tool is mounted in a fixture designed for the purpose.

Hole saws. For making large round holes in wood or metal, a set of hole saws is useful. These tools, one of which is shown in Fig. 78, are not adjustable, but are made in all common sizes. They are also available in two types, a coarse tooth saw for cutting wood, cast iron, bakelite, and other thick, coarse material, and a fine-tooth saw for cutting sheet metal, steel, porcelain, and other fine, thin material. They can be used in a hand or electric drill.

Packing tools. Packing tools (hooks) are used to remove soft packing from the packing glands of valves and pumps, Fig. 79. The straight type is used for prying. The corkscrew type can be twisted into the packing to get a secure grip. The flexible type is probably the handiest of them all, inasmuch as the body or shank is made of a number of strands of wire which makes it very flexible. It can be maneuvered into places which would be impossible to enter with the straight or corkscrew type.

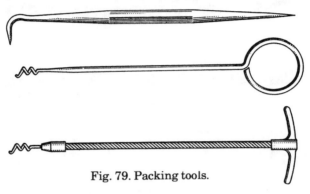

Fig. 79. Packing tools.

Scrapers. Scrapers are made in many forms, the type to be used depending on the particular job to be done. Several commonly used types are shown in Fig. 80 (top view). Flat scrapers should be used for scraping or removing high spots from flat surfaces only; bearing scrapers are used for truing up bearing surfaces; and the 3-corner scraper is commonly used for removing burrs or sharp internal edges from soft bushings, etc.

To scrape a flat surface, select a flat scraper with the length and width suitable to the work. Use a fairly light pressure to hold the scraper against the work, although the harder the material being scraped the more pressure required. The proper way to hold a flat scraper is shown in Fig. 80 (bottom view).

If there are holes in the work, avoid pushing the scraper across them; instead, work around their sides. When scraping near the edge of a piece, scrape toward the edge, or at an angle to it. Do not scrape parallel to it.

It is often necessary aboard ship to refit a bearing. This operation must be done very carefully, as the metal of the bearing must be shaped so as to fit its pin or journal with the correct clearance and without high spots.

When it is believed that a bearing needs refitting, the bearing bolts are loosened and the bearing halves removed, the exact procedure

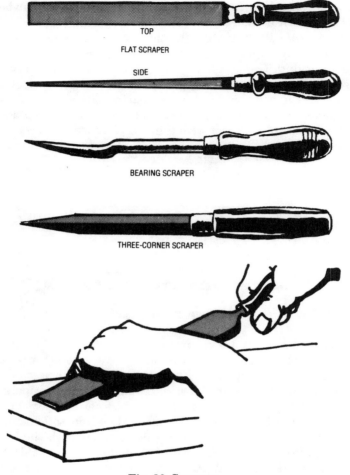

Fig. 80. Scrapers.

depending on the construction. The bearing metal is examined, and if burnished or discolored spots are present, showing contact and heating of the bearing metal, these high spots must be removed.

Each bearing half is also tested by applying a thin coating of Prussian blue to the shaft and then placing a bearing half on the shaft and rotating it back and forth several times. When the bearing is removed from the shaft, the spots of blue on the bearing metal indicate the areas of contact. These high spots are removed by the process known as "scraping in," which means that a bearing scraper is used to scrape off the contacting areas, the bearing being retested and scraped in until uniform distribution of the blue spots indicates that the bearing bears evenly over the desired surface.

Since the scraping of a bearing usually involves the removal of a comparatively small quantity of soft bearing metal, and the cutting edges of the scraper are ground to a keen edge, only a light scraping pressure is needed. If too much pressure is applied, not only will too much metal be removed, but in addition, the scraper will tend to "chatter" and leave a rough uneven surface.

When scraping a bearing, the handle of the scraper is held firmly with one hand and the blade of the scraper carefully guided with the other hand. The scraper can be pushed away or pulled toward the workman, depending on the location of the high spot, the position in which the bearing is held, or where the workman is standing in relation to the bearing. When scraping, however, always scrape in a crosswise direction, following the curve of the metal. Do not scrape lengthwise. Also be careful not to gouge or chip excess metal when scraping at the edges of oil grooves or other openings.

In general, as explained previously, it is best to remove only a small amount of metal and then recheck the location of the high spots before continuing with the scraping. Usually, the work is not considered complete until the blue spots are distributed over a combined area equivalent to about 75 percent of the total bearing surface.

Remember that scraping increases the running clearance of the bearing. If too much metal is removed, the clearance will be increased above the desired amount, and this will necessitate the removal of shims to reduce the clearance. Removal of shims might possibly create a new series of high spots and the fitting and scraping would have to be repeated.

Surface plate. A surface plate is a flat-topped steel or cast iron plate that is heavily ribbed and reinforced on the under side, as shown in Fig. 81. Its top surface is precision ground to form a true flat surface, and this surface is used as a base for making layouts with precision tools, such as the surface gauge.

The surface plate can also be used for testing machine and engine parts that are required to have flat surfaces. To do this, a thin film of Prussian blue or some other color pigment is spread evenly over the

Fig. 81. Surface plate.

surface plate. The surface of the part to be tested is then rubbed on the surface plate. The color pigment will adhere to the high spots of the part and indicate the areas to be scraped off. After scraping the high spots, the part is tested again on the surface plate and the procedure continued until the color distributes evenly over the tested surface, indicating that the job is completed.

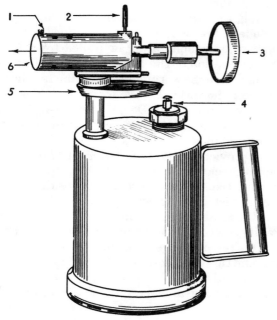

1. soldering-iron rest
2. soldering-iron hook
3. valve
4. fuel pump
5. fuel pan
6. burner tube

Fig. 82. A blowtorch.

Blowtorch. Soldering irons can be heated in various ways, but the gasoline blowtorch is one of the most convenient means aboard ship. As shown in Fig. 82, blowtorches are usually equipped with a hook and curved rest to hold the soldering iron while the point is exposed to the flame of the torch.

Before using a blowtorch, it is advisable to consider the danger of fire. Do not light or use the torch near openings where explosive gases may be present, where gasoline has been spilled, or where inflammable material may be ignited. It is good practice to have a fire extinguisher handy whenever a blowtorch is used.

In order to use a blowtorch, the tank must contain clean, white (unleaded) gasoline, and the pump on the tank must be operated to build up sufficient pressure to cause the gasoline to spray through the burner tube when the valve is opened. A piece of sheet metal or other convenient means is then used to shield the end of the burner tube and the valve is opened slightly, allowing liquid gasoline to collect in the fuel pan.

With the valve closed and the blowtorch placed so that it is clear of inflammable material and is not subjected to violent air currents, ignite the gasoline in the fuel pan and permit the flame from the burning gasoline to envelop and heat the burner tube. When the burner tube is hot, open the valve slightly, so as to permit a fine stream of gasoline to be discharged from the tank. The gasoline should vaporize immediately and burn with an almost colorless, light blue flame. Be sure to open the valve wide enough to permit satisfactory operation. When the torch is burning satisfactorily, the valve can be opened or closed slightly in order to adjust the flame to the desired intensity. A blue flame indicates good combustion conditions. While the torch is in use, it is necessary to work the pump a few strokes periodically in order to maintain pressure in the tank.

To extinguish a blowtorch, close the valve. After the torch has been extinguished, it is good practice to loosen the filling plug and relieve the pressure within the tank. When the pressure has been relieved, the filling plug is tightened again.

The valve is then opened slightly and left open. If the valve is not left open, the metal around the valve will contract, and the valve may stick so tightly that it will be damaged.

Fluxes. A flux is a chemical preparation (powder, paste, or liquid) used to keep the metal clean so that the solder will stick to it. If a flux is not used, the heat will cause oxides to form on the metal surface and prevent the solder from adhering firmly. A list of common fluxes and the metals on which they are used is given in the following:

Metals	*Fluxes*
Brass, copper, tin	Rosin
Lead	Tallow, rosin
Iron, steel	Borax, sal ammoniac
Galvanized iron, zinc	Zinc chloride

Fluxes are either corrosive or noncorrosive. The commonly used corrosive fluxes, zinc chloride and sal ammoniac, corrode the metal if allowed to remain on it after soldering. They should therefore be completely removed by a thorough washing after the work is done. It is for this reason that rosin, a noncorrosive flux, is used when soldering electrical connections. The rosin is used in powdered form, or as a liquid core in wire solder.

Paste fluxes, commercially manufactured, are available in cans of various sizes. These fluxes, which contain grease for counteracting corrosion, are substitutes for acid fluxes.

Tinning. Spreading a thin layer of solder on the surfaces of the metals that are to be soldered together, causing the solder to adhere to the metal and make a firm union with it is called tinning. The purpose of tinning is to prepare the surfaces so that they will unite readily in the process of soldering and make a firm joint. It is recommended that all metals, except lead and tin, be tinned before soldering. Lead and tin need only to be scraped clean.

Copper, brass, and ungalvanized iron may be prepared to receive solder by cleaning the surfaces and applying zinc chloride. Galvanized iron or sheet zinc should be cleaned with muriatic acid before the solder is applied. Where a metal has become tarnished, it is necessary to remove the tarnish and expose the bare, clean metal before tinning it; otherwise the solder ordinarily will not adhere to the metal.

The point of a soldering iron must be tinned before it will do a good job of soldering; tinning in this instance refers to the process of coating the point with solder to prevent oxidation when heated. The general steps in the tinning procedure are as follows:

1. File the faces of the point (or rub them with emery cloth) until they are smooth and flat.
2. Heat the point hot enough to melt the solder readily, but do not heat it red hot.
3. Rub the faces of the point on a sal ammoniac brick, applying a small amount of solder to the point as it is rubbed on the sal ammoniac. The solder will form a thin bright film on the faces of the point.
4. If a sal ammoniac brick is not available, the point can be tinned by rubbing it in pulverized rosin and solder.

When a soldering iron is overheated, the tinning is destroyed. If this happens, the point should be allowed to cool, and then should be filed and retinned.

When a soldering iron is heated, the scales that tend to form on the point can be removed by dipping the point in a dipping solution made of one part of sal ammoniac powder mixed with 40 parts of water. Only the tip of the point should be dipped in the solution and it should be withdrawn quickly. The tinned point will emerge bright and clean.

A soldering iron should never be dipped into zinc chloride or other acid solution, as the acid may spatter into the eyes or on the skin and clothing, and possible cause blindness or severe burns.

Ordinary soldering is done by heating the material to a temperature that will melt the solder, and then applying the solder to it. The procedure that will help to secure strong, neat soldering is as follows:

1. Clean the surfaces to be soldered. Solder will not stick to dirt or grease. Do not depend on the heat and flux to remove all of it.
2. Use a well-tinned soldering iron. In some cases it is advisable to have two of them, heating one while soldering with the other.
3. Use the proper flux.
4. Control the heat. Do not allow the soldering irons to overheat, but have them hot enough to melt solder readily.
5. Keep the soldered surfaces close together to ensure a strong bond.
6. Do not handle or move a soldered job until the solder has "set" and has partially cooled. Solder is weak and brittle during the process of solidification.

The ideal way to apply solder is to flow it on. To preheat the surfaces so that the solder will flow on, the point should be held as shown in Fig. 83. When the surfaces are hot enough, the point is moved slowly along the seam. Note that the solder is added to the seam, and that the point is held in such a manner that it heats the metal in advance of the flowing solder. Keep one face of the point flat against the work so that the heat will be conducted to the metal rapidly.

It is often easier to solder sheet metal if the seam is "tacked" first. This is done by applying small drops of solder at intervals along the seam, as shown in Fig. 83, one drop at a time being picked up and applied with the tip of the soldering iron.

Fig. 83. Applying solder.

Sweat soldering is used when the contacting surfaces of two pieces of metal are to be soldered together. First the surfaces are tinned and then they are placed together and a soldering iron or blowtorch used to heat them and "sweat" them together. Pipe fittings, lugs, and electrical terminals are soldered in this manner.

Electric wire splicing. The proper methods of splicing electric wires should be clearly understood, as breakdowns are often traced to faulty splicing with its resulting loose connections and opening of circuits. Loose connections also cause increased electrical resistance and may lead to a fire because of the sparking or heating that is likely to occur at such faulty joints.

The requirements of a good splice are that:

1. It be both mechanically and electrically secure without solder.
2. It be soldered well and neatly to prevent corrosion.

Wire used for lighting and power purposes has a rubber covering which is usually protected on the outside with cotton braid. The wire itself is made of copper and is often tinned to prevent corrosion. In order to make a splice with this wire, a pair of pliers and a good sharp pocketknife are necessary. The knife is used for stripping the insulation from the wire, the sharp edge of the knife blade being used for cutting the insulation and the back of the blade for scraping, so as to prevent dulling of the cutting edge.

Insulation should not be cut away as shown in Fig. 84A because this kind of cut is apt to nick the wire. A wire can be broken easily if it is nicked, and the cross section of the wire is also reduced at the nicked point, thereby increasing the resistance to flow of current.

The correct way to cut the insulation is to whittle it off in a manner similar to sharpening a pencil, as shown in Fig. 84B. When the rubber and braid have been removed for a sufficient distance, the remaining rubber is then scraped off until the metal shines. Do not scrape off the tinning, however.

To make a tap splice, strip about 4 inches of insulation off the end of the wire to be connected, and strip about 1½ inches of insulation off the running wire. Hold the wires firmly and make one turn with the connecting wire on the running wire, in the opposite direction. A tap splice, correctly made, is shown in Fig. 84D; an improper splice is shown in Fig. 84C.

The following procedure should be followed when preparing electric wires for soldering and in soldering the connection:

1. Heat the soldering iron.
2. Clean the wires to be soldered, removing insulation and scraping the surface of the wires, as explained previously, until they are bright and clean.
3. If the wires are not previously tinned, place a thin film of flux on them. (Rosin is recommended for electrical connections.) Do not use an excess of flux, however.

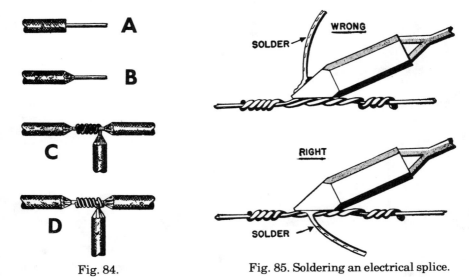

Fig. 84.   Fig. 85. Soldering an electrical splice.

4. Test the soldering iron for temperature by touching the tip to the solder. If the iron has to be held on the solder in order to melt it, the iron is not hot enough. However, if the solder melts at once, the iron is ready for use.
5. Tin the soldering iron, as previously explained.
6. With the iron hot and tinned, tin each wire by bringing the iron in contact with the wire, at the same time touching the point of contact with the solder.
7. Splice the two wires together, as explained previously. Next, apply a thin film of flux and bring the soldering iron in contact with the solder and the splice, as shown in Fig. 85. When sufficient solder is melted on the splice, remove the solder and iron. Hold the connection securely until the solder hardens.

If the temperature of the material being soldered is not brought up to the melting point of the solder, the result will be a "cold-soldered" connection. Such a joint might give the appearance of proper bonding, but the electrical continuity of the circuit would be poor, and the poorly soldered connection would offer high resistance to a flow of electric current.

After electrical splices are soldered they should be carefully taped in order to avoid short circuits. The splice should first be covered with rubber tape; then, friction tape should be wound over the rubber tape.

Screw-geared chain hoist. The screw-geared chain hoist shown in Fig. 86 is a handy portable hoist which is light and powerful. It will hold

Fig. 86. Screw-geared chain hoist.

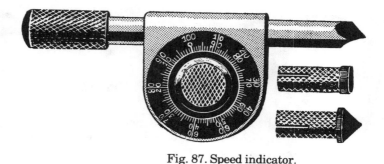

Fig. 87. Speed indicator.

its load securely and will not lower unless the chain is pulled. It has a mechanical advantage of approximately 20:1.

Speed indicator. When it is desired to know the number of revolutions per minute made by an electric motor, turbine rotor, or other revolving part, the information can be secured by using a speed indicator, such as shown in Fig. 87.

This type of speed indicator has a spindle that is free to turn in the body of the instrument, the spindle being geared to the graduated ring in such a way that 100 turns of the spindle cause the ring to make exactly one complete revolution. The ring is graduated into 100 equal parts and is numbered both right-handed and left-handed so that the indicator may be used on a shaft that is turning in either direction.

The indicator has a set of interchangeable rubber tips that fit on the spindle. Cone-shaped, flat end, and vacuum tips are usually supplied. The cuplike vacuum tip works best on the flat end of a shaft; the cone tip is best when the shaft has a countersunk end.

In order to use this type of speed indicator, a stopwatch or a watch with a sweep second hand is needed. Then place the correct tip on the

Fig. 88. Tachometer.

end of the spindle and apply the tip to the rotating shaft. When the zero is observed to pass under the starting mark, an assistant should start the stopwatch. The number of times that the zero passes the starting mark is then counted. When a minute (or any other desired period of time) has elapsed, the indicator is quickly removed from the shaft and the position of the ring noted. If, for example, the ring has made 17 revolutions during the minute and the 60 graduation stands under the starting mark, the reading is taken as 1700 + 60, or 1,760 RPM.

Tachometer. A tachometer differs from the speed indicator previously described in that it registers directly the revolutions of the rotating shaft, no timing or computation being necessary. A tachometer designed for use with either high-, medium-, or low-speed machinery is shown in Fig. 88. To use this tachometer on an alternator operating at 3,600 RPM, for example, the gear shift would be set in the HIGH position and the reading taken from the outer graduated circle. For a machine operating at 800 RPM, the tachometer gear shift would be set in the LOW position and the reading taken from the middle circle.

Fuse pullers. The fuse puller shown in Fig. 89 is designed for easy and safe removal of electric fuses. It is made of laminated fiber or plastic.

Fig. 89. Fuse puller.

Either of these materials is a nonconductor of electricity. A fuse puller should be used when pulling or replacing cartridge fuses. Removal by hand is dangerous and improper removal may bend or damage the fuse clips.

Micrometer calipers. The micrometer is the most commonly used adjustable gauge, and it is important that the mechanic understands thoroughly its mechanical principles, construction, use, and care. Fig. 90 shows a one-inch outside micrometer caliper with the various parts clearly indicated. Before making any attempt to use the tool, one should become familiar with its nomenclature, especially the frame, anvil, spindle, barrel (or sleeve), screw, and thimble. Micrometers are generally intended to measure distances to thousandths or ten-thousandths of an inch; the measurement is usually expressed or written as a decimal, so a mechanic must also know the method of writing and reading decimals.

The decimal system is a method of expressing fractions and mixed numbers. For example, written decimally, 2.000 inches indicates exactly 2 inches. All figures to the left of the decimal point are whole numbers; all figures to the right of it indicate parts of the whole numbers. Starting from the decimal point and moving to the right, the first digit indicates tenths; the second, hundredths; the third, thousandths; the fourth, ten-thousandths; and so on. Thus, 2.3 is read two and three-tenths; 1.85 is read one and eighty-five hundredths; 4.071 is read four and seventy-one thousandths; 0.2318 is read twenty-three hundred and eighteen ten-thousandths. (When there is no number to the left of the decimal point, the quantity indicated is less than 1.)

Two types of micrometers most commonly used are the outside micrometer and the inside micrometer, Fig. 91. The outside micrometer is used for measuring outside dimensions, such as the diameter of a piece of round stock. The inside micrometer is used for measuring inside dimensions, as, e.g., the inside diameter of a tube or hole, the bore of a cylinder, or the width of a recess.

The micrometer actually records the endwise travel of a screw during a whole turn or any part of a turn. The micrometer screw has a pitch of 40 threads to the inch; in other words, if the screw is turned 40 times, it will move the spindle exactly one inch either toward or away from the anvil. A clockwise turn moves the spindle toward the anvil; a counter-

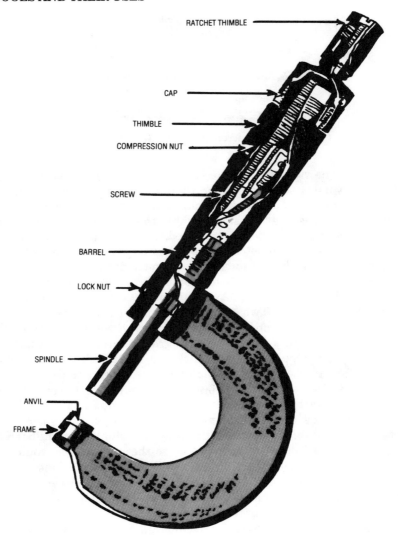

RATCHET THIMBLE

CAP

THIMBLE

COMPRESSION NUT

SCREW

BARREL

LOCK NUT

SPINDLE

ANVIL

FRAME

Fig. 90. Outside micrometer.

clockwise turn moves the spindle away from the anvil. Therefore, by simple arithmetic, it is plain that a single turn of the screw moves the spindle one-fortieth or twenty-five thousandths (0.025) of an inch. (1.000 inch ÷ 40 = 0.025 inch.)

As explained above, if the sleeve of a micrometer is turned through one complete revolution, the micrometer opens or closes 0.025 inch. Hence, to change the opening 0.001 inch, the sleeve should be turned

Fig. 91. Inside micrometer and extension rods.

through only one twenty-fifth of a revolution. To divide the inch into 1,000 parts by using the micrometer, therefore, the problem involved is to count the number of complete revolutions, plus any part of a revolution in twenty-fifths, that the sleeve makes to set the spindle and anvil exactly against the work being measured. For this purpose, the barrel and thimble of all micrometers are marked as shown in Fig. 92. The revolution line on the barrel should be understod first. It is graduated in lines 0.025 inch apart, so that each complete revolution of the sleeve moves the thimble exactly 0.025 inch along the barrel, or from one graduation to the next. Two complete revolutions move the thimble 0.050 inch, three revolutions 0.075 inch, and four revolutions 0.100 inch ($^1/_{10}$ inch). The numbers at every fourth graduation on the revolution line indicate, therefore, tenths of an inch (4 × 0.025 inch = 0.100 inch). Assuming, for example, that the micrometer is closed and the screw is turned counterclockwise through four whole revolutions, the edge of the thimble would exactly coincide with the fourth graduation on the revolution line (marked 1) and the micrometer would be opened $^1/_{10}$ inch. If the edge of the thimble coincided with the next graduation on the barrel, five revolutions would have been made, so the micrometer would be opened 0.125 inch (0.100 inch + 0.025 inch). The graduations on the barrel are numbered from 0 to 10. The mechanic should become thoroughly familiar with them before considering the graduations on the thimble.

The graduations on the barrel of the micrometer, as explained above, divide the inch into parts of twenty-five thousandths each; the graduations on the thimble further divide it into single thousandths, by indicating each twenty-fifth of a revolution of the sleeve. It has been shown in the preceding paragraph that one twenty-fifth of a revolution opens or closes the micrometer 0.001 inch. When the micrometer is closed, the edge of the thimble will coincide with zero on the barrel, and zero on the thimble will also coincide with the revolution line. As the thimble is turned, each time a graduation on the thimble passes the revolution line on the barrel, the micrometer opens 0.001 inch.

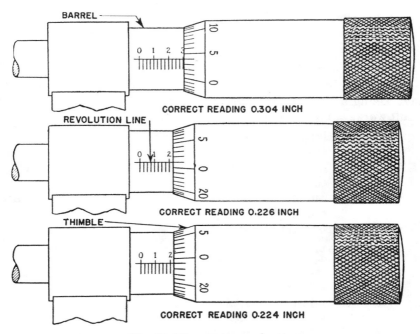

BARREL

CORRECT READING 0.304 INCH

REVOLUTION LINE

CORRECT READING 0.226 INCH

THIMBLE

CORRECT READING 0.224 INCH

Fig. 92. Micrometer graduations.

With practice the mechanic can read a micrometer correctly at a glance; however, in learning to do so the following procedure is recommended: using pencil and paper, find the largest number on the revolution line between zero and the edge of the thimble. Use the middle reading in Fig. 92 as an example; this figure is 2. Write it as 0.200 inch. Then add to it the number of unmarked graduations between this figure and the edge of the thimble, which in the example being used is 1, or 0.025 inch. Set this down under 0.200 inch, already written. At this point, if the zero graduation on the thimble coincides with the revolution line, the reading would be complete, as follows:

0.200 inch
0.025 inch
—————————
0.225 inch, final reading

However, the zero graduation on the thimble and the revolution line do not coincide, so it is necessary that the number of graduations between zero on the revolution line be added to the 0.225 inch reading. In this example, there is one such graduation. Write this as 0.001 inch, and the complete addition is as follows:

0.200 inch
0.025 inch
0.001 inch
0.226 inch, final reading

Therefore, in the example being used, the micrometer is open 0.226 inch. Using a similar procedure with the top reading in Fig. 92, the result works out as follows:

0.300 inch (largest number on revolution line between zero and
            edge of thimble)
0.000 inch (number of unmarked graduations between this and
            edge of thimble)
0.004 inch (number of graduations on the thimble between zero and
            the revolution line)
0.304 inch, correct reading

Using the same procedure again with the bottom reading in Fig. 92:

0.200 inch (largest number on revolution line between zero and
            edge of thimble)
0.000 inch (number of unmarked graduations between this and
            edge of thimble)
0.024 inch (number of graduations between zero on the thimble and
            the revolution line)
0.224 inch, correct final reading

It should be noticed particularly in this last example that the edge of the thimble appears to coincide with the 0.025 graduation on the barrel; but if this were true, the zero line on the thimble would coincide with the revolution line, which it does not do. In other words, unless the zero graduation on the thimble coincides with the revolution line, the third figure of the final reading cannot be zero.

Pressure. When dealing with the temperature of steam, we must consider pressure, for when the temperature of steam increases or decreases, so does the pressure. Pressure is a force of energy and is recorded in pounds per square inch. If a boiler is said to have a pressure of 200 pounds, it means that a force of 200 pounds is pushing outward on every square inch of the inside boiler surface. Pressure is exerted equally in all directions throughout the steam and water spaces of the boiler. The pressure of a boiler is determined by the steam pressure gauge. Steam pressures are usually measurd by an instrument known as the Bourdon pressure gauge, which consists of one or two brass tubes bent into an elliptical shape. A single tube Bourdon pressure gauge is shown, Fig. 93. This consists of a single curved brass tube, A, one end of which is secured to the base of the casing, E, the other end being free to move. When pressure is admitted into the tube through connection, F, it tends

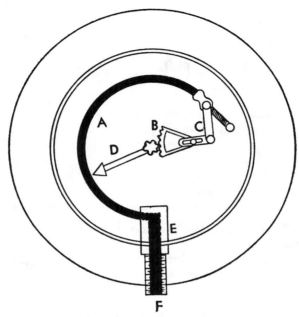

Fig. 93. Bourdon pressure gauge.

to straighten out, causing the free end to move. This movement pulls on the lever, C, which turns the geared quadrant, B, through an arc of a circle. The quadrant meshes with a pinion on the pointer shaft, and moves the pointer, D, over a graduated scale showing the pressure acting on the tube. The greater the pressure the more the tube will straighten out, causing the pointer to indicate a higher pressure reading on the graduated scale. The fireman reads the pressure in front of the pointer.

Atmospheric pressure is the pressure normally existing in the air. It is all around us pressing upon our bodies. At sea level, atmospheric pressure is 14.7 pounds per square inch, and is created by the weight of a column of air one inch square resting upon the earth. On the top of a high mountain the atmospheric pressure would be less, due to the column of air being shorter.

The pressure registered on a pressure gauge is above atmospheric pressure. For example, if the gauge pointer points to 10 pounds, the pressure in the boiler is 10 pounds greater than the atmospheric pressure, and is the kind of pressure always spoken of aboard ship.

Absolute pressure is gauge pressure plus atmospheric pressure. In the above example, if we add the gauge pressure of 10 pounds to atmospheric pressure of 14.7 pounds, we get 24.7 pounds absolute pressure in the boiler. This kind of pressure is rarely referred to aboard ship.

CHAPTER THREE

Test-taking Tactics*

The following helpful hints for *successfully* taking multiple-choice examinations should be read carefully and heeded. Besides being well prepared through study, you need to know a few "tricks of the trade" about test taking. It can can mean the difference between passing your QMED examination or failing by missing one or two questions. Furthermore, since *all* of the questions on your Coast Guard exam are multiple-choice, and multiple-choice is the most common type of test written, you should learn how to answer these kinds of questions well.

1. Read through the whole test before answering any questions.

There might be some information in some of the questions that will help you answer other questions.

2. First answer the questions you know.

You will boost your confidence and possibly jar your memory, so that you'll remember more of what you studied.

3. Work carefully but quickly.

Research proves your first choice is usually correct, if you were concentrating. Unless you have a really good reason for changing your answer, don't. You can think *too* much and confuse yourself.

4. Read the whole stem and all of the choices.

You get to know the subject well and begin to assume you know the question. Be careful . . . one small word could change the question and/or the answers.

5. Cover up the choices; Read the question; Answer it in your own words.

You will then have a pretty good idea of what the answer should be. You can eliminate some of the confusion that might occur from reading and then considering all of the choices.

Watch for . . .

6. Negatives and exceptions in the stem

The words "not" and "except" in the stem of a test item can have a big effect on the answer.

---

*Credit for this chapter is due Christina Morehouse Frazier.

7. Key words in the choices
The following words can *really* change the meaning of a statement.

all	always	only
none	never	exactly

Any choice that contains one of the "key words" must be true in every sense.

8. Common elements in stem and choices
One of the choices given may contain one or more words that are the same as words in the stem. The chances of that answer being correct are good.

9. The longest answer
Test writers want to be sure the correct answer is very clear, so that nobody can argue with them. To make it clear, writers tend to use more words.

10. Grammatical clues
Clues like "an" and "a" at the end of a stem, or plurals and singulars in both stems and answers can help you.

11. Answers that say the same thing
When two answers have the same meaning, *usually* neither one is correct. *But,* be careful to read *all* of the choices. Two answers may be correct and a third choice—the correct choice—might be, "Both b and c."

12. Two answers that are opposites
One of them is usually the correct answer.

It's a Good Idea to . . .

13. Relax!
Think of the test as a couple of sheets of paper. Can a couple of sheets of paper possibly hurt you? If you're prepared, you'll do fine!

14. Be careful with that answer sheet!
One misplaced answer could mean disaster! If you skip some questions, mark your answer sheet in some way (i.e., circle the numbers you skipped), so that you can easily locate them.

15. Check your work.
Take the time to go over your test and answer sheet after you have finished. It will give you a chance to detect and correct any errors you've made.

CHAPTER FOUR

Multiple-Choice Questions, General Safety

The following subjects are covered by the questions given in this chapter: First Aid; Classes of Fire; Fire Fighting Agents; Fire Fighting Procedures; Oil Pollution; and Safety Equipment, including OBAs (oxygen breathing apparatuses), flame safety lamps, and combustible gas indicators. You should be prepared to answer multiple-choice questions on any of these subjects.

First Aid

1. What should you put on a major burn?
   A. petroleum jelly
   B. cold water as long as possible
   C. salt water and zinc ointment
   D. wash with lukewarm water and apply a gauze dressing
2. Prior to beginning artificial respiration on a victim *not* breathing, you would:
   A. loosen clothing and necktie
   B. turn on side and slap between shoulder blades
   C. open passage for air by tilting head back
   D. clear the throat of any obstructions
3. If liquid freon should come in contact with your skin, you should:
   A. wash with salt water
   B. wash with sterile mineral oil
   C. treat it like frostbite
   D. treat it like any burn
4. When rescuing an unconscious victim from a tank, you would:
   A. not move the victim until extent of injuries is determined
   B. put a cartridge type OBA (oxygen breathing apparatus) on victim
   C. remove victim as quickly as possible
   D. test tank atmosphere with explosimeter
5. How do you treat someone suffering from electrical shock after you secure the source?
   A. check for respiration   C. treat for shock
   B. check for pulse   D. all of the above

6. Before you begin administering artificial respiration, you should be sure the victim:
   A. is comfortable
   B. is warm
   C. is not bleeding
   D. has a clear airway

7. When the victim's chest rises during mouth-to-mouth resuscitation, you should:
   A. push downward on the chest to force the air out
   B. remove your mouth from his to let him exhale naturally
   C. seal his mouth to keep the air in his lungs
   D. apply pressure on the abdomen to force the air out

8. If a person is unconscious from electric shock, you should first remove him from the electrical source and then:
   A. determine if he is breathing
   B. administer ammonia smelling salts
   C. massage vigorously to restore circulation
   D. check for serious burns on the body

9. Which is the most reliable place to take a pulse on a victim?
   A. femoral artery
   B. brachial artery
   C. carotid
   D. radial

10. When giving mouth-to-mouth resuscitation, what are the proper number of inflations per minute?
    A. 8-12 breaths per minute
    B. 12-20 breaths per minute
    C. 20-28 breaths per minute
    D. 28-32 breaths per minute

11. To remove a paint flake from the eye, you should use a:
    A. toothpick
    B. dry cotton swab
    C. pencil point
    D. moist cotton swab

12. In the case of shock, which are the fundamental factors in treatment?
    A. heat, position, and stimulants
    B. heat, position, and burns
    C. position and burns
    D. stimulants and heat

13. The best place to check for a person's pulse is the large arteries:
    A. inside the right wrist
    B. outside the left ankle
    C. in front of the ear
    D. alongside the Adam's apple

14. After removing a person suffering electrical shock from the electrical source, you discover he has stopped breathing. Your next action should be to immediately:
    A. call a doctor and treat for shock
    B. give a stimulant to restore normal breathing
    C. cover the person with blankets to restore body heat
    D. administer artificial respiration to restore normal breathing

15. If you burned your arm on a bare steam line, the most effective
    immediate treatment would be to:
    A. wrap the arm in a tight bandage
    B. soak the arm in hot salt water
    C. cover the burn with petroleum jelly
    D. put the burn in cold water
16. A person suffering from shock should be:
    A. kept warm   C. placed upright
    B. exercised vigorously   D. cooled slightly
17. Pressure points are areas of the body where the hands can be placed
    to:
    A. restore the pulse   C. determine blood pressure
    B. control bleeding   D. awaken a person
18. How many breaths per minute for an adult when giving artificial
    respiration?
    A. 1 every 5 seconds   C. 1 every 2 seconds
    B. 1 every 7 seconds   D. 1 every 10 seconds
19. The best method of artificial respiration is:
    A. arm lift method   C. chest pressure method
    B. back pressure method   D. mouth to mouth
20. If an accident occurs aboard ship, when should a badly injured
    person be moved?
    A. never
    B. after his injuries have been treated
    C. only if it will prevent further injury
    D. only if he needs to be more comfortable
21. An excellent stimulating beverage for a person suffering from shock
    is:
    A. medicinal brandy   C. warm water
    B. hot coffee   D. cold water
22. The first step you would take in helping an unconscious victim who
    is not breathing is:
    A. stop bleeding
    B. open airway
    C. mouth-to-mouth respiration
    D. call for help
23. Artificial respiration should be administered at what rate per
    minute?
    A. 6 to 12   C. 18 to 24
    B. 12 to 20   D. 22 to 30
24. The proper treatment for shock is:
    A. raise the feet
    B. raise the head

      C. keep the body cool

      D. give the victim warm liquids

25. If you are giving mouth-to-mouth respiration and the victim's chest expands but will not go down, you should:

      A. push on his chest

      B. remove your mouth and let him exhale

      C. roll him over

      D. call a doctor

Fire Fighting

1. What class of fire would probably occur in the fire room bilges?

      A. Class A   C. Class C

      B. Class B   D. Class D

2. A Class D fire is which one of the following?

      A. diesel oil   C. trash

      B. film   D. titanium

3. Which of the following would list the lifesaving equipment required for a vessel?

      A. certificate of inspection

      B. American Bureau of Shipping Classification certificate

      C. International Convention for the Safety of Life at Sea

      D. certificate of registry

4. What is a primary consideration that is important when combating a Class C fire?

      A. cooling effect   C. leaving no residue

      B. smothering effect   D. nontoxic

5. How do you set off a portable CO_2 (carbon dioxide) fire extinguisher with a squeeze grip type release valve?

      A. push upper handle down   C. open hand wheel

      B. pull lower handle up   D. none of the above

6. The alarm for the fixed CO_2 system will be sounded for at least:

      A. 5 seconds before discharging

      B. 10 seconds before discharging

      C. 15 seconds before discharging

      D. 20 seconds before discharging

7. The exact location of a vessel's fire hydrants and associated equipment is indicated on the:

      A. certificate of inspection

      B. bridge card

      C. fire fighting key plan

      D. saltwater service piping plan

8. If the threads and gasket of a fire hose coupling are in good condition, a watertight connection to another hose can be made by tightening with:

    A. your hand   C. a monkey wrench
    B. a spanner   D. a coupling wrench

9. To produce high velocity water fog with an all-purpose nozzle, you must:

    A. pull the nozzle handle halfway back
    B. push the nozzle handle completely forward
    C. insert an in-line fog nozzle
    D. change to a small nozzle tip

10. If a CO_2 extinguisher has been removed from its rack, the extinguisher should never be:

    A. laid on its side   C. shaken or agitated
    B. turned upside down   D. left standing up

11. If the fixed CO_2 fire extinguishing system for the paint locker suddenly discharges while you are in that compartment, you should immediately:

    A. drop to the deck to obtain oxygen
    B. leave the compartment for your own safety
    C. stop the ventilation and close the door
    D. look for the source of the fire

12. Why is it necessary to cool the bulkheads and decks surrounding a compartment where there is a fire?

    A. to cool the metal below its ignition temperature
    B. to form a dense coating of smothering steam
    C. to prevent oxygen from reaching the flames
    D. to prevent the fire from spreading by heat conduction

13. A portable foam fire extinguisher is placed in operation by:

    A. turning it upside down   C. squeezing the grip handle
    B. pressing the foam lever   D. opening the hose valve

14. Which types of portable extinguisher should you watch for the reflash of the fire?

    A. foam and water   C. dry chemical and water
    B. CO_2 and dry chemical   D. foam and CO_2

15. Which fire fighting device is forbidden in the engine room?

    A. any rubber lined hose
    B. semiportable CO_2 fire extinguishers
    C. all high velocity fog applicators
    D. all smooth bore fire fighting nozzles

16. What must be used with the portable in-line foam proportioner to produce foam?

    A. a common nozzle   C. a low velocity applicator
    B. an all-purpose nozzle   D. a mechanical foam nozzle

17. How many men are required to safely handle a 1½-inch fire hose at 100 PSI with the all-purpose nozzle producing a solid stream?
    A. 1   C. 3
    B. 2   D. 6

18. Why is it necessary to warn engine room personnel before activating the fixed CO_2 system?
    A. to make them aware there is a fire
    B. so they will leave the engine room for safety
    C. to prevent possible injury from frostbite
    D. because the ventilation will automatically stop

19. The figure below represents a (an):

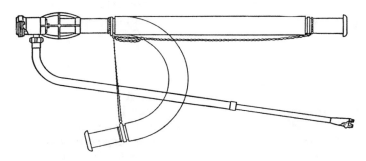

    A. all-purpose nozzle   C. high velocity fog nozzle
    B. mechanical foam nozzle   D. water spray nozzle

20. An all-purpose fire fighting nozzle is most difficult to control when changing the nozzle handle from the:
    A. closed to the solid stream position
    B. open to the closed position
    C. fog to the closed position
    D. solid stream to the fog position

21. To continuously operate a CO_2 fire extinguisher equipped with a squeeze grip handle, you remove the locking pin, depress the upper grip, and:
    A. lock the grips with the "D" ring
    B. turn the lower grip to the right
    C. depress the lower grip completely
    D. turn both grips to the left

22. In the figure shown below, "A" represents:

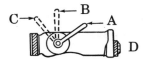

    A. solid stream   C. high velocity fog
    B. shut   D. low velocity fog

23. In the figure shown above, "B" represents:
    A. solid stream   C. high velocity fog
    B. shut   D. low velocity fog

24. The high velocity fog nozzle used with a 1½-inch, all-purpose nozzle can project a coarse water spray:
    A. 6 feet from the nozzle tip
    B. 20 feet from the nozzle tip
    C. 35 feet from the nozzle tip
    D. 100 feet from the nozzle tip

25. How many men are required to safely handle a 2½-inch fire hose at 100 PSI with the all-purpose nozzle producing a solid stream?
    A. 1   C. 3
    B. 2   D. 6

26. The high velocity fog nozzle used with the all-purpose fire fighting nozzle should always be:
    A. stored in the clip or rack at each fire station
    B. attached to the all-purpose nozzle by the chain
    C. coated with heavy grease to prevent corrosion
    D. painted red for identity as emergency equipment

27. The correct name for the device shown below is a (an):

    A. low velocity fog applicator
    B. in-line foam applicator
    C. high velocity fog applicator
    D. smooth bore water nozzle

28. What is the least amount of pressure the steam smothering system should have?
    A. 50 PSI   C. 100 PSI
    B. 75 PSI   D. 125 PSI

29. If a charged fire hose is left unattended with the nozzle shut off, the fire hose will:
    A. burst under pressure   C. remain motionless
    B. lash about violently   D. become stretched

30. The usual method of effectively appying foam on a fire is by:
    A. spraying directly on the base of the fire
    B. flowing the foam down a vertical surface
    C. sweeping the fire before you with the foam
    D. spraying directly on the surface of the fire

31. If a CO_2 fire extinguisher has been partially expended in fighting a fire, the extinguisher must be:
    A. weighed and the CO_2 loss recorded
    B. marked to identify it as used
    C. shut off and returned to the rack
    D. replaced with a fully charged extinguisher

32. The propellant in a dry chemical fire extinguisher is:
    A. compressed air   C. a chemical reaction
    B. CO_2 D. none of the above

33. Low velocity water fog is very effective in:
    A. removing toxic fumes from the air
    B. controlling the movement of burning oil
    C. removing combustible vapors from the air
    D. shielding fire fighters from the fire

34. Why should caution be exercised when you are changing an all-purpose nozzle from off to solid stream with the nozzle under pressure?
    A. to prevent injury to personnel with the water stream
    B. to prevent possible damage to the fire hose from pressure surge
    C. to prevent injury to personnel by the nozzle reaction
    D. to prevent damage to the fire pump from pressure surge

35. What danger to personnel exists when a CO_2 fire extinguisher is discharged in a small enclosed space?
    A. frostbite   C. suffocation
    B. electric shock   D. burst eardrums

36. Which fire fighting agent has the greatest capacity for absorbing heat?
    A. water   C. dry chemical
    B. foam   D. CO_2

37. A solid stream of water is produced by an all-purpose fire fighting nozzle when the handle is:
    A. pushed all the way forward
    B. pushed forward one notch
    C. pulled halfway back
    D. pulled all the way back

38. What action should be taken first to control an oil fire caused by the fireman pulling a "hot" burner from a steaming boiler?
    A. secure the fuel oil to that boiler
    B. increase the forced draft air supply to that boiler
    C. notify the engineer on watch you must secure that boiler
    D. activate the CO_2 fire extinguishers at once

39. If there is fire in a ship's service generator, you should immediately:
    A. turn on the fixed CO_2 extinguisher
    B. use a dry chemical fire extinguisher
    C. cool the generator with the ventilators
    D. secure the generator to extinguish the fire

40. Fire extinguishing foam puts out a fire by:
    A. destroying the burning material
    B. chemical reaction with the burning material
    C. absorbing the burning material
    D. smothering the burning material

41. The most important characteristic of a fire extinguishing agent to be used on electrical fires is for the agent to be:
    A. nonconducting   C. easily removable
    B. flame resistant   D. wet

42. An electrical fire is best extinguished with:
    A. soda acid   C. water fog
    B. foam   D. CO_2

43. If fire in the engine room got out of control, what should be used?
    A. foam to the bilges   C. fixed CO_2 system
    B. dry chemical to spaces D. water fog

44. Properly made up fire hose coupling connections should be untightened using:
    A. your hand   C. a monkey wrench
    B. a hose spanner   D. a coupling wrench

45. Fire hose threads must be kept clean so that they may be tightened by:
    A. spanner wrench   C. hand
    B. pipe wrench   D. strap wrench

46. Which is a true statement concerning fire hose couplings?
    A. fire hose couplings are strong and not easily damaged
    B. fire hose couplings must be lubricated with oil
    C. fire hose couplings can be easily damaged by dropping
    D. fire hose couplings should be painted red

47. A Class B fire aboard a cargo ship would probably be burning:
    A. wood   C. electrical insulation
    B. rags   D. fuel oil

48. A Class C fire would occur in:
    A. bedding   C. a generator
    B. pipe insulation   D. paint

49. Which fire extinguishing agent is incorrect for direct use on a gasoline or oil fire?
    A. high velocity water fog
    B. low velocity water fog

    C. mechanical fire fighting foam

    D. a solid stream of water

50. An oil fire on the weather deck of a ship can be fought most effectively with:

    A. dry chemical   C. foam

    B. soda acid   D. CO_2

51. Reflashing is always a danger in any fire that has been extinguished with:

    A. foam   C. water

    B. dry chemical   D. soda acid

52. A CO_2 fire extinguisher puts out a fire by:

    A. heat conduction   C. chemical reaction

    B. smothering   D. cooling

53. Why is it necessary to secure the forced ventilation to a compartment where there is a fire?

    A. to protect fire fighting personel from smoke

    B. to prevent additional oxygen from reaching the fire

    C. to allow the exhaust fans to remove smoke

    D. to extinguish the fire by carbon monoxide smothering

54. If there were a fire in the bunker tanks, you would:

    A. close the vent

    B. pump out the tank

    C. activate the fixed CO_2 system

    D. cut off the heating coils

55. All classes of fires can be safely combated using:

    A. foam   C. low velocity water fog

    B. CO_2 D. high velocity water fog

56. The longer an oil fire burns, the

    A. harder it is to extinguish

    B. easier it is to extinguish

    C. less chance there is of reignition

    D. easier it is to control

57. Spontaneous combustion could occur in:

    A. paint thinner in an open can

    B. fuel accumulation in the bilge

    C. oily rags in an unvented compartment

    D. gasoline stored in steel drums

58. If a fire occurs in the boiler room because of a leaking fuel line to a burner, you should shut off the fuel using the:

    A. burner valve   C. quick closing valve

    B. root valve   D. oil return valve

59. A straight stream of water should be used to extinguish a fire in:

    A. molten sulphur   C. fuel oil

    B. cloth materials   D. magnesium

60. To fight a running oil fire on the deck of a tanker with foam, you would:
    A. put the foam in the middle of the pool
    B. play it ahead of the burning liquid to bounce on the fire
    C. put the foam on the burning vapors
    D. aim it so it would flow over burning liquid

61. A dry chemical agent should be directed to what part of the fire?
    A. flame center   C. above the flames
    B. base of the flames   D. in the smoke

62. The heat from a fire will travel through the air in direct rays by:
    A. conduction   C. spontaneous ignition
    B. combustion   D. radiation

63. The correct name for the device shown at the right is a (an):

    A. suicide nozzle
    B. fog applicator
    C. all-purpose nozzle
    D. in-line fog nozzle

64. If you continuously discharge a stored pressure dry chemical portable fire extinguisher, how long will it discharge?
    A. 8 to 10 seconds   C. 30 to 40 seconds
    B. 12 to 20 seconds   D. 50 to 60 seconds

65. A portable 15-pound CO_2 fire extinguisher in continuous use has an effective range from the nozzle of:
    A. 2 to 3 feet   C. 8 to 10 feet
    B. 5 to 7 feet   D. 15 to 18 feet

66. Mechanical foam used for fire fighting is produced by mechanically mixing and agitating:
    A. soda acid and water
    B. dry chemical and water
    C. foam chemical with air and water
    D. bicarbonated soda with air and water

67. A fire hose should be stowed in its rack with the:
    A. hose sections disconnected
    B. foam nozzle attached
    C. all-purpose nozzle attached
    D. hose sections rolled separately

68. Fires in escaping flammable gas are quickly brought under control by:
    A. stopping the flow of gas
    B. reducing the chemical chain reaction
    C. increasing the oxygen supply
    D. cooling below the autoignition point

69. If you have to use a dry chemical extinguisher on a fire in a location where the wind is blowing, you should attack the fire from:
    A. downwind   C. across the wind
    B. upwind   D. directly above

70. A large oil fire is best extinguished with:
    A. soda acid   C. CO_2
    B. foam   D. sand

71. Water is a very effective fire extinguishing agent because it:
    A. will remove all toxic fumes from the air
    B. has the greatest cooling ability
    C. will leave no harmful residue
    D. completely removes combustible vapors from the air

72. Burning diesel oil should be combated as a Class:
    A. A fire   C. C fire
    B. B fire   D. D fire

73. Why should an oil fire after having been extinguished be kept covered with foam?
    A. to keep the oil contained
    B. to prevent spontaneous combustion
    C. to contain poisonous gases
    D. it looks good

74. If there has been a fire in a closed compartment, that compartment may be unsafe to enter because of:
    A. a lack of oxygen   C. excess nitrogen
    B. unburned carbon particles   D. excess hydrogen

75. Heat is spread through a solid by:
    A. radiation   C. conduction
    B. convection   D. combustion

Oil Pollution

1. The Federal Pollution Control Act requires the person in charge of a vessel to immediately notify the Coast Guard as soon as he knows of any oil discharge. Failure to notify the Coast Guard can lead to an individual being imprisoned for a maximum of:
    A. 30 days   C. 6 months
    B. 60 days   D. 1 year

2. The pollution prevention regulations state that anyone who causes an oil spill into United States waters and fails to report that spill to the U. S. Coast Guard may be:
    A. subject to only a fine
    B. imprisoned for up to five years

     C. fined a maximum of $5,000.00

     D. fined a maximum of $10,000.00

3. The federal pollution prevention regulations that apply to ships are enforced by the:

     A. local port authority   C. Corps of Engineers

     B. U. S. Coast Guard   D. state pollution board

4. The pollution prevention regulations state that slop oil and sludge that result as part of normal fueling operations should be disposed of by:

     A. discharging ashore into the sewer system

     B. sealing in disposable plastic barrels aboard ship

     C. discharging into a shore tank or slop barge

     D. dumping into the ship's bunker tanks

5. The pollution prevention regulations state that a ship's bilges may be pumped in port only if the:

     A. engineer on watch tells you to

     B. local port authority gives permission

     C. bilges contain no oil, grease, or other pollutants

     D. discharge is led to a slop barge or shore tank

6. The Oil Pollution Act of 1961 states that a record of oil transfers must be kept in the:

     A. deck log   C. master book

     B. engine log   D. oil record book

7. What does the term oil mean in the Oil Pollution Act of 1961?

     A. vegetable oil   C. crude oil

     B. coconut oil   D. oil of any kind

8. What type of oil is not covered in the oil pollution laws?

     A. mineral oil

     B. machinery oil being transferred for shipboard use

     C. crude oil unrefined

     D. normal bilge oil and water

9. Under the pollution prevention regulations, who is responsible for the cost of cleaning up an oil spill from a ship?

     A. the person causing the spill only

     B. the U. S. Army Corps of Engineers

     C. the owner or operator of the ship

     D. the master of the ship only

10. The pollution prevention regulations prohibit draining:

     A. waste oil into the slop tank

     B. lube oil purifiers into the bilge

     C. fuel oil heaters into buckets

     D. lube oil strainers into drip pans

11. The pollution prevention regulations state that waste which collects in drip pans, buckets, or collector troughs should be disposed of by:
    A. discharging ashore into the sewer system
    B. sealing in disposable plastic barrels aboard ship
    C. transferring to the local port authority incinerator
    D. discharging into a slop barge or shore tank

12. If you report an oil spill, you will be:
    A. fined $10,000
    B. safe from the criminal prosecution on not reporting
    C. put in jail for one year
    D. not able to ship

13. The pollution prevention regulations state that reporting an oil spill to the U. S. Coast Guard:
    A. cannot be used against you in a criminal case
    B. can be used against you, but the fine is reduced
    C. will be used against you to impose the maximum fine
    D. will only be used against the shipping company or master

14. The pollution prevention regulations require all oil spills that get into United States waters must be reported immediately to the:
    A. local port authority   C. U. S. Coast Guard
    B. Corps of Engineers   D. state pollution board

15. The pollution prevention regulations do not apply to the transfer or discharge of:
    A. bunker fuel for use aboard ship
    B. lubricating oil for use aboard ship
    C. coconut oil carried in tank vessels
    D. oily water from a ship's bilges

Safety Equipment

1. Gasoline explosive levels are 1 to 6 percent by volume in air. If a reading on a combustible vapor indicator was 30 percent of the LEL (lower explosive limit) it indicates by volume:
    A. 0.3 percent   C. 1.3 percent
    B. 0.6 percent   D. 6.3 percent

2. A flame safety lamp can be safely relit:
    A. using a torch igniter
    B. where there are no explosive gases
    C. in any type of explosive atmosphere
    D. with a safety match

3. A flame safety lamp can be used for what purposes?
   - A. testing for flammable concentrations of gases or vapors
   - B. measuring oxygen concentrations
   - C. testing for toxic concentrations of gases and vapors
   - D. determining that the oxygen concentration is above 16.5 percent

4. What is used to light a flame safety lamp?
   - A. match
   - B. spark igniter
   - C. cigarette
   - D. butane torch

5. The "safe" level for oxygen in an enclosed space is:
   - A. 19.5 percent
   - B. 20.9 percent
   - C. 16.5 percent
   - D. 10 percent

6. How should you test the seal of the mask on an OBA?
   - A. remove cannister and exhale
   - B. depress valve and inhale
   - C. blow hard
   - D. pinch hoses and inhale

7. When entering a tank or compartment in which the atmosphere is unknown the emergency equipment you must carry is:
   - A. flame safety lamp
   - B. flashlight
   - C. fresh air hose mask
   - D. cannister gas mask

8. What action should be taken by the engine room watch when the general alarm is being sounded continuously?
   - A. the fire pump should be started
   - B. the boiler fires should be secured
   - C. the fixed CO_2 system should be turned on
   - D. the engine room ventilation should be secured

9. Combustible gases or vapors can be safely detected with the:
   - A. flame safety lamp
   - B. combustible gas indicator
   - C. Halide torch
   - D. Orsat apparatus

10. What is the threshold limit value used for?
    - A. to gauge density of atmosphere
    - B. to gauge your exposure to a toxic substance
    - C. to provide a check for explosive atmospheres
    - D. to check on acute toxicity

11. When would you enter a tank alone, if it wasn't gas free?
    - A. after telling the chief engineer
    - B. after checking for proper lighting
    - C. never enter a tank alone
    - D. with an OBA, lifeline, and harness

12. Which of the following has the lowest LEL?
    - A. hydrogen
    - B. naphtha
    - C. gasoline
    - D. diesel oil

13. The fuel for a flame safety lamp is:
    A. kerosene   C. naphtha
    B. gasoline   D. diesel oil

14. What can cause oxygen to be used up in an enclosed space?
    A. rusting, organic cargo, tank coatings
    B. petroleum products, chemicals
    C. no ventilation
    D. toxic products

15. Who must inspect and certify a tank before any hot work is done?
    A. marine chemist   C. Corps of Engineers
    B. marine building inspector   D. U. S. Coast Guard

16. What type of atmospheres will cause the flame safety lamp to explode?
    A. acetylene, hydrogen   C. sulphur dioxide, phosgene
    B. phosphorus, nitrogen   D. vinyl chloride, methanol

17. An explosimeter determines explosive concentrations of vapors by:
    A. burning them   C. volume
    B. metering   D. weight

18. If the safety valve starts to whistle on an oxygen breathing apparatus, the person wearing the OBA should:
    A. go out into the fresh air
    B. open the bypass valve wide
    C. close the bypass valve until the whistling stops
    D. reset the timer for an additional ten minutes

19. The emergency signal for abandon ship is sounded with the ship's whistle and general alarm as:
    A. 1 short blast followed by 6 long blasts
    B. 2 long blasts followed by 5 long blasts
    C. 4 short blasts followed by 3 long blasts
    D. 6 short blasts followed by 1 long blast

20. The signal to lower ship's boats is sounded on the ship's whistle as:
    A. 1 short blast   C. 3 short blasts
    B. 2 long blasts   D. 1 long blast

21. What is indicated if the flame of a flame safety lamp flares up and goes out with a popping sound?
    A. there are combustible gases present
    B. the lamp is out of fuel
    C. there is not enough oxygen present
    D. the lamp wick is not trimmed correctly

22. What is used to enter a tank when the atmosphere within is unknown?
    A. gas indicator
    B. cannister gas mask

C. safety lamp

D. fresh air breathing apparatus

23. Combustible gas indicators are used to detect flammable gases or vapors in the atmosphere. This is accomplished by a (an):

    A. sensitive liquid chemical

    B. inflatable bag

    C. vapor detecting carbon absorber

    D. wheatstone bridge

24. On what principle does a combustible gas indicator work?

    A. resistance increases heat   C. cold causes resistance

    B. heat lowers resistance   D. heat increases resistance

25. A flame safety lamp will respond how when taken into a compartment containing flammable vapors?

    A. the flame will burn white and low

    B. the flame will burn blue and brighter

    C. the flame will flare up and go out

    D. the flame will die out

26. What three hazards are the most common in any enclosed space such as a cargo tank?

    A. lack of oxygen, inadequate ventilation, toxic atmosphere

    B. no lighting, pockets of gas, open holes

    C. lack of oxygen, toxic atmosphere, explosive atmosphere

    D. falling rust, pockets of gas, open holes

27. What is indicated when the flame of a flame safety lamp goes out rapidly?

    A. the air contains an explosive mixture of gases

    B. there is excess carbon monoxide in the air

    C. the flame safety lamp igniter is defective

    D. there isn't enough oxygen to support combustion

28. A precaution that should be taken when using the flame safety lamp is:

    A. do not carry the key

    B. lamp must be locked

    C. examine the lamp carefully

    D. all of the above

29. The minimum amount of oxygen required to support life is:

    A. 14 percent   C. 16 percent

    B. 15 percent   D. 17 percent

30. Why should the cannister of a Navy-type OBA not be placed in an oil/water mixture?

    A. it will boil furiously

    B. it will explode

      C. it will catch fire

      D. it will generate a poisonous gas

31. An oxygen breathing apparatus has a (an):

      A. face piece, breathing bag, and an oxygen pump

      B. oxygen cylinder, face piece, and breathing bag

      C. toggle valve, face piece, and an air hose

      D. face piece, nitrogen alarm, and an oxygen cylinder

32. Why do Coast Guard regulations require a rubber mat or wood platform in front of engine room switchboards?

      A. to protect personnel from electrical shock

      B. to prevent electrical grounds to the deck

      C. to prevent water from standing on the deck

      D. to protect the hull from electrolysis

33. What piece of equipment is used to test for oyxgen content?

      A. specific vapor tester   C. combustible gas indicator

      B. flame safety lamp   D. litmus paper

34. What is the purpose of the flame safety lamp?

      A. to test oxygen content

      B. measures combustible gases

      D. measures flammable vapors

      D. all of the above

35. The wire screens installed in fuel tank vents prevent explosions by:

      A. allowing the escape of flammable vapors

      B. dissipating heat from the fire

      C. a baffling process which turns any flames away

      D. preventing flammable vapors from entering the tank

36. What would you do if you heard the ship's alarm ring for longer than 10 seconds?

      A. abandon ship

      B. report to your lifeboat station

      C. report to your fire station

      D. warn all personnel in the area

37. What is the signal for stopping the lowering of lifeboats into the water?

      A. 1 blast on the ship's whistle

      B. 2 blasts on the ship's whistle

      C. 3 blasts on the ship's whistle

      D. none of the above

38. Breathing petroleum vapors is hazardous and may cause:

      A. temporary blindness

      B. permanent deafness

      C. severe internal bleeding

      D. unconsciousness and death

39. Your assigned emergency stations aboard ship can be found on the ship's:

    A. station bill   C. certificate of inspection

    B. clearance papers   D. permit to proceed

40. Which of the following is a potential electrostatic hazard when handling flammable liquid cargoes?

    A. spark accumulation   C. spark separation

    B. spark discharge   D. ion discharge

Answers to Multiple-Choice Questions, General Safety

First aid

1. B	8. A	15. D	22. B
2. C	9. C	16. A	23. B
3. B	10. B	17. B	24. A
4. C	11. D	18. A	25. B
5. D	12. A	19. D	
6. D	13. D	20. C	
7. B	14. D	21. B	

Fire fighting

1. B	20. A	39. D	58. C
2. D	21. A	40. D	59. B
3. A	22. B	41. A	60. B
4. C	23. C	42. D	61. B
5. A	24. B	43. C	62. D
6. D	25. C	44. B	63. A
7. C	26. B	45. C	64. B
8. A	27. A	46. C	65. C
9. A	28. C	47. D	66. C
10. D	29. C	48. C	67. C
11. B	30. B	49. D	68. A
12. D	31. D	50. C	69. B
13. A	32. B	51. B	70. B
14. B	33. D	52. B	71. B
15. D	34. C	53. B	72. B
16. B	35. C	54. A	73. B
17. B	36. A	55. B	74. A
18. B	37. D	56. A	75. C
19. B	38. A	57. C	

Oil pollution

1. D	5. D	9. C	13. B
2. D	6. D	10. B	14. C
3. B	7. D	11. D	15. B
4. C	8. B	12. B	

Safety equipment

1. A	11. C	21. A	31. B
2. B	12. B	22. D	32. A
3. C	13. C	23. D	33. B
4. B	14. A	24. D	34. A
5. B	15. A	25. C	35. B
6. D	16. A	26. C	36. C
7. C	17. A	27. D	37. B
8. A	18. A	28. D	38. D
9. B	19. D	29. C	39. A
10. B	20. A	30. B	40. B

CHAPTER FIVE

The Fireman/Watertender

The fireman/watertender works 4 hours on and 8 hours off watch duty in the fireroom monitoring and operating the steam-generating systems in accordance with the direction of the watch engineer.

Duties

The duties of the fireman/watertender include the following:

1. Monitor and control the fuel oil system for safe and efficient firing to maintain operating main steam pressure and temperature.

2. Monitor and control the forced draft air system for safe and efficient burning of the fuel and the reduction of stack emissions to within the required limits.

3. Monitor and control the feedwater system for safe and efficient steam generation to maintain operating main steam pressure.

4. Change and clean fuel oil strainers.

5. Inspect the entire steam generating system for proper safe operating condition.

6. Change and clean burners.

7. Maintain and clean burner register assembly.

8. Perform general cleaning in the fireroom.

*9. Perform engine room maintenance including pipe fitting, valve repair, and pump overhaul.

The first and most important thing that you, the fireman, must do on entering the fireroom is to look at the boiler gauge glasses, making certain that the water in the boiler is at its proper level. If you are responsible for tending the water in the boiler, blow the glasses down to ascertain the accuracy of the water level.

Allow yourself enough time to make a complete inspection before replacing the current watch. Inspect the fires and the burners. You should take note of the condition of the tile cone around the burner front to see if any carbon is building up in front of the atomizer upon which the oil will impinge. Look for oil leaks at the connections of the oil lines and burners. Inspect the fireroom and the tank tops below the floor plates for oil drippings that may cause fires. Make sure that all spots of oil are

---

*Routine off watch duties

wiped up on the floor plates and in the pans below the burners. Take note of the pressure gauge readings at various points in the oil line to ascertain the conditions of the oil strainers. Check the oil heaters by looking at the thermometer on the oil line to see if the proper temperature is being maintained. Look in the fireroom bilges to see that they are empty, check the pressure of the oil in line at the gauge nearest to the burners, and then the steam pressure of the boilers. Never be lax or late in your inspection when relieving a watch. Always remember that when you relieve the current watch, the full responsibility for the maintenance of the fireroom is yours for the next four hours. Whatever conditions may exist, regardless of who is to blame, will be your responsibility alone. After everything is apparently all right, ask the fireman who is going off watch if there has been any trouble during his watch, and if there are any special orders for you from the engineer. If all is as it should be, take over the watch, relieving the fireman on duty of all responsibilities.

After taking over the watch, your duty is to make sure that everything goes as smoothly as possible. Begin your work by changing the suction and discharge strainers and cleaning the ones that have been in use, replacing them in the body of the strainer. Leave the strainer and floor plates around the strainers clean for the next watch.

Then, change all burners. These are changed alternately from boiler to boiler and never more than one in a boiler at a time. While a burner is being changed, it is out of use for the few minutes that it takes to complete the operation. During these few minutes, there is the same amount of water entering the boiler as before but there is less steam being made. Therefore, an excess amount of water accumulates, raising the level in the boiler.

After the burners have been changed and cleaned, the strainers changed and cleaned, and the watch appears to be running smoothly, you should inspect the plant at definite intervals. Be on the alert at all times. Note that a small speck of dirt the size of a pin point can stop up a burner to the extent that the direction of the oil spray will be diverted and will strike the brickwork of the furnace where it cokes and forms carbon. This carbon continues to build up and, in the short period of a half hour, becomes large enough to completely block the burner opening. This will cause improper combustion in the furnace, forming soot on the tubes of the boiler which in turn causes considerable loss of efficiency and a lot of work to clean up.

Each fireman is responsible for keeping a part of the fireroom in a neat and tidy condition. This particular part is known as your station. It is your duty to paint, polish, etc., this station while on your watch. However, such work should never be in a part of the fireroom where it would interfere with the safe operation of the boilers. At all times, be at a point where your water gauge and steam pressure gauge are visible.

A fireman should do everything possible to maintain the boilers in a safe operating condition at all times with a maximum of efficiency. Be familiar with the pipelines and auxiliary machinery in the fireroom and know how to prevent and combat fires that may start at any time. Keep a close watch on the stack for smoke, either by looking at the top of the stack itself or through the smoke density indicator (periscope).

In the Fireroom

1. Never attempt to light a burner from a hot furnace wall. This has caused numerous serious accidents. Use a torch and stand clear.

2. Never leave a disconnected burner in place.

3. Report at once any sudden changes in water level in a boiler.

4. At the very first sign of water in the fuel, report it to the engineer on watch.

5. Keep burner tips clean and when cleaning the tips, do not use a hard implement that might enlarge or roughen the hole or the grooves.

6. Note that excess smoke from the stack indicates waste. It also may subject the vessel to penalties and fines while in port. This may be due to lack of air, dirty burners, or incorrect oil temperatures. Learn what the best conditions are for your job. Remember that all burners, except one, may be working properly.

7. Be aware that too much air is just as wasteful as too little.

8. Realize that the oil in the pipe going to the burners of the boilers that have been cut out for a while may be too cold to light off. The oil should be circulated to raise its temperature.

9. Be aware of the fact that it is possible that the water level shown in a gauge glass might not be correct. If either the top or bottom connection of a water gauge glass is closed or partly blocked, the water level indicated will be a false one. This condition can be detected by "blowing" the gauge glass. To blow the gauge glass close the top shut-off valve and open the gauge glass drain. This clears the bottom line connections. Then close the bottom shut-off valve, open the top valve, and the drain. This clears the top line connections. Next, close the drain and open the bottom shut-off valve. It will be noticed that when the lower gauge glass valve and drain are closed, the water becomes still in the glass and gradually rises as the steam above the water condenses. On the other hand, if the upper valve and drain are closed when the lower valve is open, the water in the glass will rise out of sight. This is caused by the loss of pressure in the upper end of the glass.

10. Before attempting to remove boiler manhole plates, see that the boiler drains are open even though you know the boiler is cold. No great force should be required to remove plates from a boiler in which the pressure has been equalized with the atmosphere.

11. Never depend upon the stop valve of a dead boiler being properly secured by the other watch. Determine for yourself which boiler, if any, is cut out before opening any valve. There may be a man working in one of them.

12. See that all exits from the engine room or fireroom and water-tight doors are kept free from any obstruction. The emergency may arise while you are below.

CHAPTER SIX

Multiple-Choice Questions for Fireman/Watertender

The topics covered by the questions given in this chapter are fuel oil systems and boilers. You should also be prepared to answer multiple-choice questions on any of the following subjects:*

1. Instruments and gauges
2. Hand tools
3. Measuring instruments
4. Valves and piping
5. Pumps
6. Water tube boiler construction
7. Water tube boiler operation
8. Water tube boiler casualties
9. Fuel oil transfer systems
10. Fuel oil service systems

Fuel Oil Systems

1. Using mixed sizes of sprayer plates in the same boiler will cause:
    A. pulsating fuel pressure at the atomizers
    B. pulsations in the furnace air supply
    C. improved combustion at low firing rates
    D. incomplete combustion in the furnace
2. The fuel oil service pump takes suction from the:
    A. contaminated inspection tank
    B. double-bottom tanks
    C. feed and filter tank
    D. settling tanks
3. If you have fuel oil meters to and from the burners in a return flow system, you measure the fuel oil consumption by:
    A. taking the difference between the supply and return readings
    B. taking the sum of both meters

*The fireman/watertender will find multiple-choice questions for some of these subjects in those given for the Oiler, Chapter 8, and for Fireman/Watertender and Oiler, Chapter 9.

    C. using only the supply meter

    D. using only the return meter

4. In a fuel oil service system the quick closing fuel oil shutoff valve is located between the:

    A. fuel oil heaters and the discharge strainers

    B. service pumps and the fuel oil heaters

    C. master fuel oil shutoff valve and the boiler

    D. suction strainers and the service pumps

5. The fuel oil solenoid valve may be closed by:

    A. the forced draft fan stopping

    B. the scanner failing to see a flame in furnace

    C. the fuel oil pressure dropping to 100 PSI

    D. A and B above

6. The air register on an extinguished fire should be:

    A. kept open

    B. kept closed

    C. kept half open

    D. removed and placed in rack

7. From a standpoint of efficiency, it is desirable to have all of the fuel burned in the boiler:

    A. uptakes   C. tube nests

    B. furnace   D. smoke pipe

8. If the fires in a boiler furnace begin "sputtering" or "hissing" you should suspect:

    A. excessive fuel pressure at the burners

    B. loss of fuel pump suction

    C. low fuel oil temperature

    D. water contamination of the fuel oil

9. What do you use to clean a sprayer plate orifice?

    A. a drill bit the same size as the orifice

    B. a copper wire

    C. a bent nail

    D. a scribe

10. The amount of steam a boiler will generate is controlled by the:

    A. temperature of the superheater

    B. feed pump discharge pressure

    C. size of the burner sprayer plate

    D. fuel oil temperature at the burners

11. The double-bottom tanks in a ship are used for:

    A. storing fuel oil

    B. storing fresh water

    C. ballasting when ship is light

    D. all of the above

12. The oil burners on straight mechanical fuel oil systems should be cleaned at least:
    A. once a week   C. every hour
    B. once a watch   D. once a day

13. Fuel oil when heated has an:
    A. increase in viscosity   C. increase in flash point
    B. increase in volume   D. increase in fire point

14. Which of the following gives the widest firing range:
    A. straight mechanical burners
    B. steam atomization
    C. return flow burners
    D. rotary cup burners

15. Condensate from fuel oil bunker heaters returns to:
    A. reserve feed system
    B. main feed system
    C. contaminated (observation) tank
    D. bilges

16. The burner assembly is frequently referred to as a/the:
    A. burner   C. barrel
    B. register   D. air foils

17. A fuel oil meter placed between the fuel oil service pumps and the fuel oil heaters would be a:
    A. cold type meter   C. vertical meter
    B. hot type meter   D. supermeter

18. Another name for the fuel oil discharge strainer is the:
    A. cold strainer   C. magnetic strainer
    B. hot strainer   D. coarse strainer

19. The normal fuel oil pressure will be:
    A. 50 PSI   C. 100 PSI
    B. 200 to 300 PSI   D. 125 to 175 PSI

20. In a fuel oil burner having a standard mechanical atomizer, the fuel and air are mixed as the fuel leaves the:
    A. orifice   C. tangential slots
    B. annular slots   D. oil passage

21. The fuel oil heater is located:
    A. on the discharge side of the service pump
    B. on the suction side of the service pump
    C. on the discharge side of the transfer pump
    D. between the settling tank and the service pump

22. Diesel oil is supplied to the burners:
    A. in case of heavy smoke
    B. to aid in cold starting
    C. if heavy fuel must be blended
    D. for overload capacity requirement

23. Too high a fuel oil temperature will cause:
    A. a decrease in boiler pressure
    B. fires to go out
    C. burners to go out
    D. carbon scale deposits on the fuel oil heater coils
24. All fuel oil tanks are vented through a:
    A. check vent to the settling tanks
    B. gooseneck vent located on the main deck
    C. check valve to the transfer pump
    D. gooseneck vent which discharges to the settlers
25. What would happen if you put a burner sprayer plate in backwards?
    A. fuel atomization would be poor and boiler would smoke
    B. excess fuel back pressures would cause the burner to leak
    C. the burner tip nut would overheat and probably crack
    D. the burner flame cone would swirl in the opposite direction
26. The amount of oil atomized by a straight mechanical oil burner depends on the sprayer plate size and the:
    A. oil return pressure   C. forced draft pressure
    B. fuel oil pressure   D. furnace air temperature
27. If the trap on the steam return from the fuel oil heater sticks open, the fuel temperature will:
    A. decrease   C. vary greatly
    B. increase   D. remain unchanged
28. A quick closing valve would be located as close as possible to:
    A. fuel oil pump suction   C. fuel oil settlers
    B. boiler from header   D. fuel oil service tanks
29. An oil meter registers the amount used in:
    A. pounds   C. barrels
    B. gallons   D. tons
30. Fuel oil heater leaks will be indicated by:
    A. oil in the bilges
    B. excessive use of fuel oil
    C. noting the observation tank
    D. none of the above
31. The air entering the furnace is given a swirling motion by the:
    A. diffuser   C. cone
    B. impeller   D. all of the above
32. What would cause boiler pulsations?
    A. too much air
    B. low fuel pressure and high water level
    C. high fuel pressure and low water level
    D. insufficient air
33. It is possible for water to get into the fuel oil by:

    A. leaks in the hull

    B. being pumped aboard with the oil

    C. condensation in the tanks

    D. all of the above

34. Which of the following steps would you take if you found an accumulation of oil on the furnace floor?

    A. put in smaller burner tips

    B. close all air registers

    C. open all air registers

    D. close fuel oil discharge valve

35. Why is it necessary to open the drain valve on the fuel strainer you are going to remove for cleaning?

    A. to bleed off fuel pressure before removing the strainer cover

    B. to drain off sediment and water before removing the strainer

    C. to relieve all pressure so the valve may be shifted to the other strainer

    D. to ensure there is a positive flow of oil through the strainer body

36. If a boiler starts to lose steam pressure and white smoke is coming from the stack, what could be the cause?

    A. dirty burner

    B. forced draft fan overspeeding

    C. forced draft fan running too slow

    D. fuel oil temperature too high

37. A variable capacity fuel oil system is the same as:

    A. straight mechanical   C. steam atomized

    B. return flow   D. loop injection

38. The relief valve on the fuel oil transfer pump discharges to the:

    A. settling tanks

    B. transfer pump suction line

    C. fuel oil service suction line

    D. double-bottom tanks

39. A "solenoid trip valve" on a fuel supply line:

    A. shuts off the fuel oil supply in the event of air loss

    B. shuts off the air supply in the event of air loss

    C. shuts off the fuel supply in the event of fire loss

    D. does A and C above

40. What is used to correctly set the burner barrel and tip in relation to the diffuser plate?

    A. no adjustment is needed   C. fiber rings

    B. metal washers   D. distance piece

41. What is a flame scanner used for?

    A. it adjusts fuel oil pressure and temperature for good combustion

    B. it adjusts water level in the steam drum

    C. it allows fireman to see the furnace

    D. it shuts down fuel oil if the fires fail

42. On automatic combustion control:

    A. reduce the number of burners when the oil pressure approaches the minimum specified

    B. keep the same number of burners going at all times

    C. change the size of the burner tips in all burners when the pressure drops

    D. do A and C above

43. A faulty steam trap on a fuel oil heater can cause:

    A. a lowering of the heating capacity of the heater

    B. a fuel oil leak

    C. an increase in oil temperature

    D. an increase in the heating capacity of the heater

44. If the fires in a boiler go out because of losing fuel suction, you should always:

    A. change all burners

    B. secure the fuel heater

    C. lift the safety valves by hand

    D. leave the forced draft fan running

45. If you found a burner sprayer plate nicked or damaged, you would:

    A. notify the engineer on watch

    B. replace it at once

    C. keep it for a spare

    D. do nothing, it will not cause problems

46. The purpose of fuel oil atomization is to attain thorough mixing of oil and air required for:

    A. maximum "fluff"   C. complete combustion

    B. swirling motion   D. localized heating

47. Too low a fuel oil temperature will cause:

    A. excessive steam temperature

    B. poor combustion and smokey fires

    C. the fuel oil pump to vibrate

    D. increase in super heater temperature

48. If a boiler gives off black smoke, a possible cause could be:

    A. insufficient air

    B. fuel oil temperature too low

    C. dirty burners

    D. any of the above

49. Which pump takes a suction from the double-bottom tanks and discharges to the settlers?

    A. fuel oil service pump   C. sump pump

    B. general service pump   D. fuel oil transfer pump

50. Which of the following sprayer plates has the smallest orifice?
    A. 3909   C. 3009
    B. 3509   D. 2909

51. If the fuel oil temperature going to the burners is too low, the:
    A. fuel service pump will lose suction
    B. boiler will produce heavy black smoke
    C. boiler will produce dense white smoke
    D. fuel service strainers will become clogged

52. If the fuel oil service pump was leaking upstream of the quick closing valve, you cold stop the oil leak by closing the:
    A. master oil valve   C. burner valve
    B. root valve   D. recirculation valve

53. Why is it necessary to recirculate the fuel oil before lighting off a cold boiler?
    A. to allow the fuel strainers to thoroughly clean the fuel
    B. to heat the fuel oil enough for proper atomization
    C. to insure that all water is removed from the fuel oil
    D. to allow fuel pressure to build up gradually

54. To properly remove the burner tip nut from the burner barrel, the barrel should be:
    A. clamped in a machinist's vise on the workbench
    B. fixed in the stowage rack for the burner
    C. held by the fixture on the burner bench
    D. removed from the gooseneck before removing the tip nut

55. Burning fuel contaminated with salt water will cause glassy slag formation in a furnace. This slag will:
    A. form a protective coating
    B. seal the refractory joints
    C. damage the refractory material
    D. increase furnace temperature

56. What maintenance should be used with remote control reach rods?
    A. grease occasionally   C. check universal joints
    B. test periodically   D. all of the above

57. What is a flareback?
    A. a railroad flare
    B. an explosion in the fire box
    C. a bomb
    D. detonation of fuel in the settlers

58. If you lose the fires for any reason what is the first thing you do?
    A. shut off all oil to the burners
    B. check water level
    C. check the fuel temperature
    D. do none of the above

59. Which valve is used to shut down all oil to the boiler in an emergency?
    - A. root valve
    - B. burner valve
    - C. king valve
    - D. quick closing valve

60. Both high and low suction valves are provided on fuel oil settling tanks to:
    - A. pump fuel overboard
    - B. remove water from the oil
    - C. keep the oil warm
    - D. provide full suction to the service pumps

61. On a tip marked 32Y40, the numerals 40 signify:
    - A. orifice size
    - B. drill tip size
    - C. cross-sectional area
    - D. ratio of slots to orifice

62. To safely lower the firing rate of a boiler you should *always* decrease the fuel oil pressure:
    - A. by opening the oil recirculating valve
    - B. by opening the fuel pump bypass
    - C. before decreasing the forced draft pressure
    - D. after decreasing the forced draft pressure

63. What does 29 indicate on a 2909 sprayer plate?
    - A. tangential slot area
    - B. tangential slot ratio
    - C. cross section ratio
    - D. drill size

64. When securing a steam atomization fuel oil burner:
    - A. close steam valve first
    - B. close oil valve first
    - C. close valves at the same time
    - D. close either first

65. The most important use of the remote mechanical control valve is:
    - A. to secure the fuel oil service pump
    - B. to secure the main steam valve
    - C. to pump the bilges
    - D. both A and B above

66. The normal fuel oil temperature at the burners of a steaming boiler will range between:
    - A. 130 to 140 degrees F
    - B. 180 to 220 degrees F
    - C. 230 to 240 degrees F
    - D. 250 to 300 degrees F

67. When operating with automatic combustion control always use:
    - A. at least two different sized tips in the burners
    - B. only one size tip in the system
    - C. larger tips on the boiler with lower pressure
    - D. smaller tips on the boiler with higher pressure

68. All fuel oil service pump steam valves are fitted with:
    - A. safety locks
    - B. automatic controls

    C. reach rods leading to a location outside the fireroom

    D. reach rods leading to the engine room

69. Dense white smoke or a burned out bulb will give what indication?

    A. overheated periscope   C. dark periscope

    B. light periscope   D. none of the above

70. What color stack gas indicates good combustion?

    A. black   C. light brown haze

    B. white   D. blue

71. Which of the following sprayer plates has the largest orifice?

    A. 2909   C. 3509

    B. 3009   D. 3909

72. A fuel oil burner may be lit off by: I. hot brickwork; II. torch.

    A. I only   C. both I and II

    B. II only   D. neither I nor II

73. In a straight mechanical burner system you would find all of the following except:

    A. solenoid valve   C. root valve

    B. recirculating valve   D. back pressure valve

74. Fuel oil is preheated before delivery to the atomizers (burners) to:

    A. increase its viscosity   C. increase its specific heat

    B. decrease its viscosity   D. decrease its calorific value

75. Which of the following indicates the condition of flue gases from proper combustion?

    A. high percent of CO_2, low percent O_2

    B. high percent of CO_2, low percent CO

    C. high percent of O_2, low percent CO_2

    D. high percent of CO_2, high percent CO

Boilers

1. When a boiler is brough up to pressure and put on the line what should be closed?

    A. air cock   C. recirculating valve

    B. superheater vent   D. air heater vent

2. Cooling of high temperature steam with relatively cold water is called: I. attemporating; II. desuperheating.

    A. I   C. either I or II

    B. II   D. neither I nor II

3. Sectional (sinuous) headers are found on which type boiler?

    A. bent tube   C. "D" type

    B. straight tube   D. "A" type

4. Which of the following is true?

A. boilers must have two means of indicating water level

B. boilers may have two gauge glasses

C. boilers may have one gauge glass and another means of indicating water level

D. boilers not over 250 PSI, one gauge glass and three try-cocks

5. On a tip marked 32Y40, the numerals 32 signify:

    A. orifice size   C. drill tip size

    B. cross-sectional area   D. ratio of slots to orifice

6. The function of a marine boiler dry pipe is to:

    A. provide upper surface perforations

    B. reduce moisture carry-over

    C. distribute steam evenly in the drum

    D. provide for an even withdrawal of steam from the water

7. When a boiler is cooling down, the steam drum vent is opened to:

    A. relieve any residual air pressure in the drum

    B. prevent a vacuum from forming inside the drum

    C. reduce the pressure in the drum more rapidly

    D. protect the superheater

8. A "flame scanner" is used to:

    A. check the color of the oil flame

    B. shut off the oil flow to the burner if the flame goes out

    C. control the amount of air to the burner

    D. do none of the above

9. The Bailey feedwater regulator works on the principle of:

    A. hydroelectricity   C. thermoelectricity

    B. thermohydraulics   D. pressure temperature

10. A function of the desuperheater installed in a boiler steam drum is to:

    A. add moisture to superheated steam

    B. provide steam for auxiliary machinery

    C. distribute feedwater within the boiler

    D. raise the temperature of the steam in the dry pipe

11. Why should you not blow down the waterwalls while steaming?

    A. salinity would increase

    B. circulation would be interrupted

    C. water level would rise

    D. boiler chemicals would be lost

12. Which is the most important valve on any boiler?

    A. the main steam stop valve   C. the surface blow valve

    B. the bottom blow valve   D. the boiler safety valve

13. The boiler feed stop valves are located on the:

    A. boiler water drum feed line connections

    B. DC heater water outlet connection

    C. inlet side of the boiler feed heater

    D. outlet side of the boiler economizer

14. What action should be taken first if a boiler gauge glass suddenly breaks?

    A. open the drain valve

    B. close top cut-out valve

    C. place a protective covering over the glass

    D. close bottom cut-out valve

15. On automatic combustion control at low firing rates, you should:

    A. reduce the number of burners in service

    B. keep the same number of burners in service

    C. change the size of all the burner tips

    D. change the size of half of all the burner tips

16. When operating with automatic combustion control, always use:

    A. at least two different sized tips in the system

    B. only one size tip throughout the system

    C. larger tips on the boiler with lower pressure

    D. smaller tips on the boiler with higher pressure

17. If a large section of the roof tile in a three pass boiler fell out, an immediate indication would be:

    A. a decrease in stack temperature

    B. an increase in stack pressure

    C. an increase in stack temperature

    D. an increase in boiler pressure

18. In the event of a stack fire, the fire may be arrested by the use of:

    A. steam smothering system   C. CO_2

    B. soot blowers   D. sand

19. Where is the main steam stop valve located on a "D" type boiler?

    A. superheater outlet header   C. desuperheater inlet

    B. superheater inlet header   D. desuperheater outlet

20. Downcomers are placed outside of the inner casing rather than inside to obtain:

    A. preheating of the air supply

    B. minimum boiler rating

    C. desired circulation characteristics

    D. increased generating area

21. If the fires in a boiler furnace begin sputtering or hissing, you should suspect:

    A. excessive fuel pressure at the burners

    B. fuel oil pump is losing suction

    C. the fuel oil is very cold

    D. water contamination of the fuel oil

22. The proper way to quickly reduce high water level in a steaming boiler is to use the:

A. bottom blow valve   C. water column valve
B. safety valve   D. surface blow valve

23. Before lighting any burner in a cold boiler, you should always:
  A. close the burner register completely
  B. open the furnace peephole cover
  C. purge the furnace with air
  D. reduce the forced draft pressure

24. Which of the following could cause a "flareback"?
  A. oil pressure too high
  B. trying to relight a burner from brickwork
  C. oil temperature too high
  D. opening air registers too quickly

25. In a manually controlled feedwater system, proper water level is maintained by:
  A. operating the auxiliary feed check valve
  B. opening the feedwater heater bypass
  C. the changes in the water level
  D. operating the feed check valve

26. The following valve on a steaming boiler is *never* completely closed:
  A. feed check valve   C. upper gauge glass valve
  B. feed stop valve   D. air cock

27. Pulsating fires in a boiler furnace can be caused by:
  A. low fuel pressure   C. too much air
  B. low fuel temperature   D. too little air

28. Oil or scale in boiler tubes will cause:
  A. those tubes to overheat
  B. decrease of boiler steam pressure
  C. increase of boiler steam pressure
  D. an explosion in the boiler

29. If the fires in a steaming boiler have been extinguished accidentally, you should not relight any burner until:
  A. the boiler furnace has been thoroughly purged
  B. the furnace refractory has cooled below ignition temperature
  C. all burning embers in the furnace are extinguished
  D. all the fuel has been recirculated from the burners

30. Steam escaping from the boiler casing is a good indication of:
  A. leaking screen tubes   C. broken soot blower
  B. leaking down comer tubes   D. poor refractory

31. Before using the soot blowers to blow tubes, you should:
  A. lower the water level
  B. reduce the boiler pressure
  C. increase the forced draft fan speed
  D. raise the auxiliary steam pressure

32. An integral superheater is protected from high temperature by the:
    A. screen tubes   C. control desuperheater
    B. generating tubes   D. water walls

33. If the water level remains the same in the gauge glass of a steaming boiler while maneuvering, the probable cause is the:
    A. feedwater regulator is broken
    B. gauge glass is stopped up
    C. feed pump is operating properly
    D. water level is to high

34. Which is a safety procedure concerning warm boiler operation?
    A. superheater drain should not be open with steam on the boiler
    B. registers on idle burners are always left cracked open
    C. idle burners must be left in place for later use
    D. feed valves should never be shut off on a boiler that is being fired

35. Which should be done after a boiler is on the line and supplying steam?
    A. close the air cock
    B. close the superheater vent
    C. open the main steam stop bypass
    D. open the auxiliary feed stop and check

36. Panting or rumbling in a boiler is caused by:
    A. not enough air
    B. too much steam pressure
    C. low feedwater temperature
    D. defective sprayer plates or nozzles

37. The first sign of boiler carry-over may be:
    A. lifting of the superheater relief valve
    B. sudden drop in superheater temperature
    C. water hammer in the main steam line
    D. water spraying out of the turbine glands

38. The purpose of water drum baffles are to:
    A. give added strength to the drum
    B. prevent steam from mixing with water
    C. direct the path of the feedwater through the drum
    D. prevent sloshing of the water in rough seas

39. The soot blowers in a boiler are operated in specified order to:
    A. sweep the soot up the stack
    B. prevent blowing out the fires
    C. blow the soot onto the furnace floor
    D. avoid blacking out the periscope

40. What action should you take immediately after a major flareback occurs?

    A. secure forced draft

    B. secure fuel to burners

    C. secure fireroom ventilation

    D. purge fuel oil system

41. The saturation pressure of steam at 212° F is:

    A. 14.7 PSI   C. 212 PSI

    B. 26.8 PSI   D. 388 PSI

42. When the temperature of steam in a boiler drum is 248° F, the temperature of the water is:

    A. 180° F   C. 228° F

    B. 212° F   D. 248°F

43. A "flame scanner" is used to:

    A. check the color of the oil flame

    B. shut off the oil when the flame fails

    C. check exhaust smoke color

    D. control the air flow to the burner

44. Which of the following combinations of flue gases indicates the best combustion?

    A. a high content of carbon monoxide and a low content of carbon dioxide

    B. A high content of carbon monoxide and a low content of oxygen

    C. a high content of oxygen and a low content of carbon dioxide

    D. a high content of carbon dioxide and a low content of carbon monoxide

45. The damper in the air duct between the fan and the boiler is usually a:

    A. butterfly type valve   C. gate valve

    B. double seat valve   D. spring loaded valve

46. If the fires in a boiler go out because of losing fuel suction, you should always:

    A. change all burners

    B. secure the fuel heater

    C. lift the safety valves by hand

    D. leave the forced draft fan running

47. A dirty sprayer plate will cause the boiler to:

    A. pant   C. pulsate

    B. smoke   D. overheat

48. The function of the water screen tubes in a boiler is to:

    A. allow the superheater tubes to absorb more radiant heat

    B. prevent the direct heat of the furnace from reaching the superheater tubes

    C. heat the feedwater on its way to the steam and water drum

    D. desuperheat the steam for auxiliaries

49. The valve that prevents water from backing out of the boiler into the feedline is the:

    A. bottom-blow valve   C. feed check valve
    B. skin valve   D. feed stop valve

50. All of the following are types of air heaters except:

    A. rotary   C. gas tubular
    B. direct contact   D. steam

51. Blisters on boiler tubes can be caused by:

    A. air in feed water   C. hot feed water
    B. cold feed water   D. oil in boiler water

52. If you cut out one burner in a steaming boiler, the register doors for that burner should be:

    A. left open wide   C. closed halfway
    B. left cracked open   D. closed tightly

53. The gauge glass may be blown down:

    A. when relieving the watch
    B. when there is sediment in the glass
    C. once an hour to get an accurate water level indication
    D. A and B above

54. In addition to the generating tubes in a boiler, which of the following also function as generating tubes?

    A. water wall tubes   C. superheater tubes
    B. water screen tubes   D. A and B above

55. The air cock on a boiler is located at the:

    A. end of the superheater
    B. highest point of the steam and water drum
    C. superheater inlet
    D. top of the return headers

56. The boiler superheater vents should always be open when you are:

    A. using the steam soot blowers
    B. blowing down the boiler
    C. lighting off or securing the boiler
    D. raising the water level above normal

57. While a boiler is cooling, the following valves must be open (cracked):

    A. air cock   C. superheater drains
    B. superheater vent   D. all of the above

58. When securing a steam atomized fuel oil burner:

    A. close the steam valve first
    B. close the oil valve first
    C. close the valves at the same time
    D. close either valve first

59. To safely increase the firing rate of a boiler, you should always increase the forced draft pressure:

A. after increasing the fuel pressure
B. by opening the burner register wider
C. by opening additional burner registers
D. before increasing the fuel pressure

60. The air register on an extinguished fire should be:
    A. kept open
    B. kept closed
    C. kept half open
    D. removed and placed in the rack

61. To properly clean a burner tip, you should use:
    A. light sand grit   C. a jack knife
    B. a soft metal tool   D. a wire brush

62. The boiler feed stop valve is located:
    A. between the feed check valve and the drum
    B. between the feed check valve and the economizer outlet
    C. close to the engine platform, by requirement
    D. between the feed check valve and the feed line

63. Which casualty is apt to occur immediately after a high water casualty?
    A. a massive tube failure
    B. water carry-over to the turbines
    C. excessive steam pressure
    D. excessive superheater temperature

64. Black smoke coming from a boiler can be caused by low fuel temperature and by:
    A. excessively high fuel pressure
    B. an improper air fuel ratio
    C. low fuel pressure
    D. high fuel temperature

65. Giving the boiler a surface blow would be the best action to take when:
    A. removing scale and sludge
    B. lowering boiler water level
    C. preparing to blow tubes
    D. releasing the watch

66. What could cause the fires in a steaming boiler to go out suddenly?
    A. a dirty sprayer plate   C. low fuel oil pressure
    B. water in the fuel   D. too much excess air

67. A light brown haze from the boiler smoke pipe is generally accepted to indicate:
    A. too much fuel pressure   C. good fuel combustion
    B. a high firing rate   D. dirty fuel atomizers

68. Which should be checked *first* when you are taking over the fireroom watch?

A. the fuel pressure to the burners

B. the condition of the furnace fires

C. the boiler water level

D. the boiler steam pressure

69. An economizer reduces the temperature of:

    A. boiler steam   C. feed water

    B. stack gases   D. furnace air

70. To minimize damage to a boiler if a large number of tubes fail, you should:

    A. secure the fires, steam stops, and relieve boiler pressure

    B. secure the fires and feed stops and leave the boiler cut-in

    C. increase the feedwater supply to keep the boiler cool

    D. speed up the forced draft fans to blow steam up the stack

71. When steam is being raised on a boiler, the water level will normally:

    A. drop as the boiler warms up

    B. rise as the boiler warms up

    C. remain unchanged until the boiler is hot

    D. rise and fall with the steam demand

72. A fire in the stack will cause the:

    A. boiler to smoke white

    B. burners to go out

    C. stack temperatures to go up

    D. stack temperatures to go down

73. When you are raising steam on a cold boiler, the air cock is left open until:

    A. the superheater vent starts blowing

    B. steam pressure is forming and all air is vented

    C. the superheater drains are closed

    D. steam pressure is up to normal and the boiler warmed

74. The water discharge from an economizer is led directly into the:

    A. dry pipe   C. feed check valve

    B. internal feed pipe   D. feed stop valve

75. According to furnace arrangement, a "D" type boiler is a:

    A. multiple furnace boiler   C. low pressure boiler

    B. divided furnace   D. single furnace boiler

76. What is used to protect the glass in a gauge glass?

    A. asbestos gasket   C. mica strip

    B. asbestos cushion   D. brass gasket

77. Oxygen is removed from the feedwater by the:

    A. main air ejectors jet action

    B. scrubbing action in the DC heater

    C. auxiliary air ejectors

    D. vent condenser fan

78. A boiler water test sample is taken from the:
    A. salinometer cock
    B. water wall blowdown valve
    C. gauge glass blowdown valve
    D. superheater drain

79. The main purpose of the dry pipe is to:
    A. allow air to be vented from the steam drum
    B. evenly distribute dry steam in the steam drum
    C. remove moisture from the steam
    D. control the flow of steam from the steam drum

80. Boiler water hardness is increased by:
    A. dissolved gases in the water
    B. zero alkalinity in the water
    C. improper operation of the DC heater
    D. scale forming salts in the water

81. The boiler may be given a bottom blow:
    A. to lower water level   C. only while making steam
    B. to remove scum   D. when fires are secured

82. When a boiler is brought up to pressure and put on the line, what should be closed?
    A. air cock   C. recirculating valve
    B. superheater vent   D. air heater vent

83. Which is an indication of a large number of tubes failing in a steaming boiler?
    A. the steam pressure will rise rapidly
    B. the fires will suddenly extinguish
    C. the fires will hiss and sputter
    D. the water level will drop rapidly

84. The purpose of maintaining a chemical reserve in feedwater treatment is to:
    A. increase the effect of impurities
    B. neutralize impurities as they enter the boiler
    C. combine with impurities to make boiler compound
    D. provide coating on interior of boiler tubes

85. The superheater drains and vents are left open when a boiler is being warmed up to:
    A. prevent overheating the superheater
    B. remove all condensate from the superheater
    C. drain saturated steam from the superheater
    D. prevent the desuperheater from overheating

86. Why are spaces left between bricks when laying a new boiler furnace floor?
    A. to allow for insertion of plastic chrome ore
    B. to allow slag to accumulate

C. to allow for expansion

D. to allow room for future repairs

87. Automatic feedwater regulators are:

    A. spring operated   C. manual operated

    B. pressure operated   D. thermo operated

88. Safety valves vent to:

    A. HP drains   C. the bilge

    B. the atmosphere   D. the auxiliary exhaust line

89. Why is it necessary to raise the water level in a boiler before using steam powered soot blowers?

    A. to increase the moisture in the soot blower steam

    B. to allow the feed stop to be closed while blowing tubes

    C. to momentarily lower the boiler

    D. to prevent low water because of steam loss through the soot blower

90. How would a sinuous header type boiler be classified?

    A. bent tube   C. straight tube

    B. curved tube   D. double furnace

91. The water level in a steaming boiler will always:

    A. vary as the steam demand changes

    B. remain constant as long as the feed pump operates

    C. fall when the steam pressure is decreased

    D. rise when the steam pressure is increased

92. The water level showing in a boiler water gauge glass is usually:

    A. higher than the actual drum water level

    B. equal to the actual drum water level

    C. increasing due to steam condensation in the glass

    D. lower than the actual drum water level

93. Sludge is most likely to be found in:

    A. desuperheater   C. downcomers

    B. floor tubes   D. generating tubes

94. Why is it necessary to purge the furnace of a cold boiler?

    A. to provide oxygen for combustions

    B. to warm the furnace before lighting off

    C. to remove explosive gases from furnace

    D. to blow soot up the stack

95. A dazzling white burner flame in the boiler furnace indicates:

    A. proper combustion   C. water in the fuel

    B. excess air   D. cold fuel oil

96. White smoke may be caused by:

    A. high fuel oil temperature   C. low fuel oil

    B. low fuel oil temperature   D. high fuel oil pressure

97. The feedwater check valves are located on the:

    A. feed pump suction line   C. hot well
    B. shell of the feed heater   D. feedlines to the boiler

98. The function of the screen tubes is to protect the:
    A. superheater   C. steam drum
    B. refractory   D. water walls

99. Steam stops on a cold boiler should be eased up before the first burner is lit to prevent the valves:
    A. leaking when steam pressure forms
    B. leaking as the boiler warms up
    C. jamming when they heat up
    D. jamming when steam pressure forms

100. If at a normal steaming condition and water goes out of sight in gauge glasses the action you should take is: I. secure oil to fires; II. increase feed pump pressure.
    A. I   C. I and II
    B. II   D. neither I nor II

Answers to Multiple-Choice Questions, Fireman/Watertender

Fuel oil systems

1. D	20. A	39. D	58. A
2. D	21. A	40. D	59. D
3. A	22. B	41. D	60. B
4. C	23. D	42. A	61. C
5. D	24. B	43. C	62. C
6. B	25. A	44. D	63. D
7. B	26. B	45. B	64. B
8. D	27. A	46. C	65. D
9. B	28. B	47. B	66. B
10. C	29. B	48. D	67. B
11. D	30. C	49. D	68. C
12. B	31. C	50. A	69. C
13. B	32. D	51. B	70. C
14. B	33. D	52. A	71. A
15. C	34. C	53. B	72. B
16. B	35. A	54. C	73. D
17. A	36. D	55. C	74. B
18. B	37. B	56. D	75. A
19. B	38. B	57. B	

Boilers

1. B	26. B	51. D	76. C
2. C	27. D	52. D	77. B
3. B	28. A	53. D	78. A
4. A	29. A	54. D	79. C
5. C	30. B	55. B	80. D
6. B	31. C	56. C	81. D
7. B	32. A	57. D	82. B
8. B	33. B	58. B	83. D
9. B	34. D	59. D	84. B
10. B	35. B	60. B	85. A
11. B	36. A	61. B	86. C
12. D	37. B	62. A	87. B
13. A	38. D	63. B	88. B
14. B	39. A	64. B	89. D
15. A	40. B	65. B	90. C
16. B	41. A	66. B	91. A
17. B	42. D	67. C	92. D
18. C	43. B	68. C	93. B
19. A	44. D	69. B	94. C
20. C	45. A	70. A	95. B
21. D	46. D	71. B	96. A
22. D	47. B	72. C	97. D
23. C	48. B	73. B	98. A
24. B	49. C	74. B	99. C
25. A	50. B	75. B	100. A

CHAPTER SEVEN

The Oiler

The oiler works a 4 hours on and 8 hours off watch in the engine room making scheduled rounds of the engineering plant monitoring and controlling temperatures, pressures, and processes in accordance with the direction of the watch engineer. The duties include the following:

1. Monitor the main propulsion system.
2. Monitor and operate the main and auxiliary condensate systems.
3. Monitor the main generators and the electrical distribution systems.
4. Assist the watch engineer in the monitoring and controlling of the main propulsion system.
5. Monitor and control the shipboard refrigeration system and the air conditioning system.
6. Monitor the steering gear system.
7. Change and clean strainers.
8. Monitor and operate the distillation system.
9. Monitor and operate the sewage treatment system.
*10. Perform engine room maintenance including pipe fitting.
*11. Perform welding repairs.
12. Perform general cleaning in the engine room.

Duties

The following are routine operations the oiler performs while on watch:

Care of engine bearings

The oiler feels all the bearings on the main engine to make sure there is no overheating, examining all lubricating devices and systems to make sure they are functioning properly. Lube oil lines on turbines are usually fitted with small metal flags, called spinners, which revolve if oil is passing through the pipeline.

Noting bearing temperatures

Oil lubricates better when hot than when cool. The lubricants, therefore, must be at correct temperatures. The oiler must avoid overheating of lubricants.

Checking thermometers

Many bearings, especially those of turbines, are fed with constant flows of oil. Thermometers are installed in these oil feed lines, usually at

*Routine off watch duties.

the points where the oil leaves the cooling devices in the circulating system. The oiler reads these thermometers and makes sure that temperatures are correct.

Some bearings are water cooled. The water runs through cores in the castings. Thermometers may be mounted in these streams of water at the points where they leave the bearings; and if so, the oiler reads these temperatures also.

Checking auxiliary machinery

The oiler checks up on the temperatures and the lubricators of feed pumps, condensate pumps, lubricating oil circulating pumps and all other auxiliary machinery.

Checking condensers

Exhaust steam is passed through condensers to cool it to the point where it condenses into water for recirculation in the boilers. These condensers are cooled by sea water; they can develop leaks and let sea water into the condensate, which will quickly ruin boilers. The oiler may have the duty of watching out for this hazard. If so, he/she must check the condensate by observing instruments, which on modern ships are always in place and functioning. The best of these instruments have automatic alarms, which warn instantly if salt gets into the condensate; nevertheless, the oiler checks up to make sure the instruments are operating. The procedure varies from ship to ship.

Checking electrical readings

In many ships, the oiler checks the dials on the instrument panel to make sure that electrical readings are correct, and also checks the generators for any unduly high temperatures or for sparking of brushes or other signs of impending trouble.

Checking on bilges

The oiler pumps all fireroom, engine room, and shaft alley bilges before going off watch and, in turn, he/she sees to it that they are pumped dry before accepting his/her watch.

Checking the feed water

Tanks, pumps, and circulating systems for boiler feed water are likely to be in the engine room, and with this room shut off from the boiler room, these devices come under the care of the oiler. The oiler checks the circulating system to make sure it is working correctly. Before accepting the watch, find out which tanks the makeup water is being taken from, check the valves, and check the levels so that you know how much is left in those tanks and how soon to change over to the others.

CHAPTER EIGHT

Multiple-Choice Questions for the Oiler

The topics covered by the questions given in this chapter are engine room procedures, feed systems, and turbines and lube oil systems. You should also be prepared to answer multiple-choice questions on any of the following subjects:*

1. Instruments
2. Hand tools
3. Measuring instruments
4. Valves and piping
5. Pumps
6. Steam and water cycles
7. Feed systems
8. Steam turbines
9. Gravity lube oil systems
10. Diesel engines
11. Evaporators
12. Refrigeration systems

Engine Room Procedures

1. If the flow of water from a centrifugal pump is stopped by closing the discharge valve with the pump running:
   A. the relief valve will open
   B. the water pressure will stabilize at shut-off head
   C. the water pressure will tend to rise continuously
   D. the driver will be overloaded
2. A compound gauge is able to measure:
   A. either pressure or vacuum
   B. the sum of two pressures
   C. the difference between two pressures
   D. two different pressures simultaneously
3. A pyrometer is normally used to measure:
   A. steam pressure   C. draft loss
   B. gas temperature   D. humidity

---

*The oiler will find multiple-choice questions for some of these subjects in those given for the Fireman/Watertender, Chapter 6, and for Fireman/Watertender and Oiler, Chapter 9.

4. What will happen to a small diesel engine that is equipped with an "auto type" thermostat if the bellows develop a hole in it?
    A. the engine will overheat
    B. the engine will remain cold
    C. the engine will not start
    D. the cooling water will "bypass" the engine

5. What does "wet silencer" mean in diesel engine terminology?
    A. the exhaust gases are mixed with salt water
    B. the exhaust gases are mixed with fresh water
    C. the silencer jacket is always water cooled
    D. the silencer baffles are water cooled

6. The purpose of the low pressure cutout switch is to:
    A. maintain liquid refrigerant at the suction of the compressor
    B. maintain a preset suction pressure to the compressor
    C. cut out the compressor at a set pressure
    D. cut compressor in and out at a preset pressure

7. The purpose of the evaporator is to:
    A. absorb latent heat of vaporization
    B. absorb latent heat of fusion
    C. transfer latent heat of vaporization
    D. transfer latent heat of fusion

8. Intake and exhaust valves on diesel engines are of what type?
    A. tappet   C. poppet
    B. disc   D. globe

9. The instrument always used in conjunction with a salinity indicator is the:
    A. pyrometer   C. hygrometer
    B. thermometer   D. hydrometer

10. A salinity indicator is calibrated in:
    A. parts per million   C. grains per pound
    B. grains per gallon   D. density

11. The purpose of a siphon tube is to:
    A. prevent steam from coming in contact with the bourdon tube
    B. minimize pulsations
    C. absorb vibrations
    D. siphon away any condensate that might rust the bourdon tube

12. The drains from both effects in a low pressure evaporator have their pressures equalized in the:
    A. equalizer tank
    B. drain tank
    C. flash chamber
    D. air ejector condenser

13. What is the system used for measuring the ignition quality of a diesel fuel?

    A. heating valve   C. flash points

    B. cetane numbers   D. 90 percent boiling points

14. When distilling salt water the cooling-water discharge from the distiller is fed back to the evaporator as feed water:

    A. to supply hot water to the evaporator for more economical operation

    B. to cut down on the amount of cooling water needed

    C. to prevent an excess amount of cooling water from being discharged

    D. in none of the above

15. The second effect on a two-pass evaporator receives it steam from:

    A. desuperheated steam   C. auxiliary back pressure

    B. vapors from first effect   D. none of the above

16. A perfect vacuum is represented by:

    A. 30 inches of silver

                    C. 30 inches of mercury

    B. 15 inches of mercury

                    D. 15 inches of silver

17. A "manometer" measures:

    A. air pressure   C. oil pressure

    B. steam pressure   D. water pressure

18. Low lubricating oil temperature at reduced loads can be avoided by regulating the:

    A. pressure relief valve

    B. cooler bypass valve

    C. lubricating oil pump governor

    D. priming pump control

19. If a diesel engine starts, then quits, the problem may be the:

    A. ignition system   C. lube oil system

    B. fuel oil system   D. air system

20. Vacuum in the main condenser is measured in:

    A. inches of water   C. grains per gallon

    B. inches of mercury   D. parts per million

21. This gauge measures both inlet and outlet pressures of a strainer:

    A. a compound gauge   C. a biogauge

    B. a duplex gauge   D. a pressure/vacuum gauge

22. Blue smoke coming from the diesel exhaust would indicate:

    A. excessive fuel consumption/unburned fuel

    B. burning of lube oil due to possible blow-by

    C. lean fuel/air mixture, too much air

    D. none of the above

23. Lubricating oil viscosity in an operating diesel engine can be reduced by:

A. overloading the engine
B. increasing lube oil flow
C. fuel oil dilution
D. combustion by-products contamination

24. The purpose of a heat exchanger is to:
    A. eliminate hot air from the condenser
    B. maintain steady pressures in a system
    C. heat or cool one fluid by means of another fluid
    D. reduce the engine room temperature in tropical climates

25. When does a 2-stroke cycle diesel engine produce a power stroke in each cylinder?
    A. once in every 2 revolutions of the crankshaft
    B. once for every 4 strokes of the piston
    C. once for every 2 strokes of the piston
    D. directly after the exhaust stroke

26. What term is used to describe the loss of combustion pressure due to worn rings and liners?
    A. blowback   C. blow-by
    B. blowdown   D. blowup

27. Why do you add cornstarch to an evaporator?
    A. to cut down on priming and scale
    B. to make the water taste better
    C. to prevent high temperatures
    D. to increase the rate of vaporization

28. In terms of pressure and temperature, what happens to the primary refrigerant in the compressor?
    A. its pressure and temperature are both lowered
    B. its pressure and temperature are both raised
    C. its pressure is lowered and its temperature is raised
    D. its pressure is raised and its temperature is lowered

29. All of the following are used for low temperature starting *except*:
    A. ether
    B. jacket water heaters
    C. cylinder compression ratio reduced
    D. air intake heaters

30. All diesel lubricating systems must:
    A. have a forced feed mechanical lubricator
    B. prevent oil fog in the crankcase to avoid crankcase explosion
    C. provide oil for cooling the piston
    D. provide a film of oil between the piston and cylinder wall

31. The T.E.V. (thermostatic expansion valve) is located between:
    A. the receiver and the king valve
    B. the king valve and solenoid

C. the solenoid valve and evaporator

D. the charging valve and solenoid

32. Another name for the liquid valve is:

    A. master valve   C. freon valve

    B. king valve   D. shut off valve

33. The oil level in the compressor should be checked:

    A. while the compressor is in operation

    B. just before starting the compressor

    C. after a long period of operation

    D. for both B and C

34. What is the high side of the refrigeration system?

    A. compressor to condenser

    B. evaporator to compressor

    C. expansion valve to evaporator

    D. compressor to expansion valve

35. The low side of a refrigeration system is from the:

    A. expansion valve to compressor

    B. compressor to expansion valve

    C. expansion valve to the evaporator

    D. condenser to the expansion valve

36. The reciprocating motion of a connecting rod is transformed into a rotary motion by the:

    A. crankshaft   C. crank cheeks

    B. crank webs   D. crankpin

37. In a diesel engine closed cooling system, the flow of fresh water through the fresh water and lube oil coolers is controlled by the:

    A. speed of the engine

    B. speed of the pump impeller

    C. automatic temperature regulator

    D. suction pressure regulator

38. The bulb for the T.E.V. is located:

    A. in the middle of the evaporator coils

    B. near the evaporator coil outlet

    C. near the evaporator coil inlet

    D. on the bottom row of the evaporator

39. The solenoid valve can be typed as a:

    A. thermal valve   C. bellows valve

    B. magnetic stop valve   D. bimetallic valve

40. What is the advantage of using a hydraulic starting system for an emergency diesel?

    A. the system is inexpensive

    B. high pressure lines are not required

    C. it is compact

    D. faster cranking speeds are obtained

41. What would cause white smoke after you just started the diesel?
    A. too weak battery power   C. water in the gas
    B. water in the fuel   D. water in the oil
42. Worn bearings, rings, and valves all contribute to:
    A. poor reversal   C. hard starting
    B. quiet operation   D. high pressure
43. Precombustion chambers in a diesel engine:
    A. require that each cylinder use two spray nozzles
    B. require the use of flat-crowned pistons to obtain turbulence
    C. permit the use of a wide range of fuel in that engine
    D. contain all of the air charge at the end of the compression
       stroke
44. What refrigerant is used with centrifugal compressors?
    A. R 5   C. R 12
    B. R 11   D. ammonia
45. The turbocharger of an auxiliary diesel engine is most affected by:
    A. air inlet manifold pressure
    B. engine speed
    C. exhaust temperature
    D. engine load
46. The coils in the evaporator are attached to the headers by:
    A. pipe nipples   C. welding
    B. union-type fittings   D. bolted flanges
47. The system used for breaking scale from the evaporator coils while
    the evaporator is in operation is called:
    A. recirculating   C. cracking-off
    B. blowing-down   D. dumping
48. A "pneumercator" measures:
    A. oil pressure   C. liquid level
    B. air level   D. air pressure
49. What type of gauge reads pressure and vacuum?
    A. duplex   C. compound
    B. simplex   D. bourdon tube
50. Cylinder liners are generally used on diesel engines because:
    A. liners may be easily replaced after the cylinder walls show
       wear
    B. liners provide a more efficient cooling system
    C. rubbing speeds are reduced through the use of liners
    D. liners provide a better lubricating surface
51. An overspeeding diesel engine could best be stopped by:
    A. disconnecting the battery cables from the starting motor
    B. blocking the air intake and securing the fuel supply
    C. araining the hydraulic fluid from the governor sump
    D. blocking the flow of cooling air to the radiator

52. A pyrometer is a:
    A. high temperature thermometer
    B. thermometer marked in centigrade
    C. pneumercator
    D. manometer
53. Gauge pressure of 200 pounds is equivalent to what absolute pressure?
    A. 215
    B. 200
    C. 185
    D. 115
54. The valve which is always partially open when the evaporator is in operation is the:
    A. vapor valve
    B. continuous blowdown valve
    C. bottom blowdown valve
    D. surface blowdown valve
55. What kind of bolts would you use on a saltwater line?
    A. cold rolled
    B. brass
    C. cast iron
    D. all of the above
56. The dehydrator on a refrigeration plant is used to:
    A. add moisture to the system
    B. remove moisture from the system
    C. remove air from the system
    D. remove oil from the system
57. A BTU is used to measure:
    A. heating ability of a system only
    B. cooling ability of an R-12 system only
    C. temperature
    D. heat energy—heating or cooling
58. As freon leaves the expansion valve:
    A. pressure decreases—volume increases
    B. volume decreases—pressure increases
    C. volume increases—pressure increases
    D. pressure increases—volume decreases
59. Minor freon leaks can be detected by the use of a device called:
    A. a freon visible leak detector
    B. a freon audible leak detector
    C. the blue oven flame detector
    D. halide torch
60. Most gauges in the fireroom are:
    A. bourdon tube-type
    B. manometers
    C. thermocouples
    D. dual purpose
61. A pyrometer is normally used to measure:
    A. steam pressure
    B. stack temperature
    C. steam temperature
    D. oil temperature

62. A cause of high head pressure in an R-12 system could be:
    A. too little R-12 in the system
    B. too much cooling water
    C. the king valve was left closed
    D. not enough cooling water

63. Where is the highest temperature in R-12 system?
    A. compressor suction
    B. compressor discharge
    C. receiver
    D. between king valve and receiver

64. The instrument always used in conjunction with the salinity indicator is the:
    A. pyrometer   C. hydrometer
    B. manometer   D. thermometer

65. When distilling salt water the evaporator should be blown down when the salinity reaches:
    A. 3/32   C. 2/32
    B. 1/32   D. 5/32

66. In a solo shell, double effect evaporator, the evaporator feed in the second effect is heated by:
    A. auxiliary steam   C. first effect distillate
    B. air ejector steam   D. flash chamber leak off

67. Evaporators will remove all contaminants in the salt water except:
    A. grease or heavy oils   C. solid impurities
    B. sulphuric acid   D. light oils and bacteria

68. What is an advantage of a flash type evaporator? I. higher feedwater heating temperature; II less chance of scale formation.
    A. I only   C. both I and II
    B. II only   D. neither I nor II

69. The second effect on a two-pass evaporator receives it steam from:
    A. auxiliary back pressure   C. vapors from first effect
    B. desuperheated steam   D. none of the above

70. How would you remove the frost on evaporator coils?
    A. with a hammer   C. with a halide torch
    B. by chipping it off   D. with a hot gas line

71. Refrigerant bottles are often identified by:
    A. color   C. weight
    B. information on the cap   D. shape

72. Sounding of a salinity cell alarm to the loop seal from the first to the second stage distilling condensers of a flash evaporator would indicate:
    A. carry-over in the first stage
    B. failure of the brine overboard pump

C. low feedwater temperature

D. excessive feed pressure

73. All of the following will cause priming in an evaporator *except*:

    A. high pressure   C. low brine density

    B. change in pressure   D. high water level

74. What is the purpose of an intercooler and an aftercooler on an air compressor? I. to condense water vapor; II. to permit economical compressor operation.

    A. I only   C. both I and II

    B. II only   D. neither I nor II

75. Which of the following would be an indication of air entrainment in a hydraulic steering system?

    A. overspeeding of the hydraulic pump

    B. sluggish responding of the rudder

    C. lifting of the cylinder relief valves

    D. overheating of the pump motor

76. Chill shocking of tubes in an evaporator is done to:

    A. prepare for a hydrostatic test

    B. crack scale

    C. increase first and and second stage vacuum

    D. wash evaporator's internals

77. Accumulation of scale on evaporator tubes causes: I. low heat transfer; II. high brine density.

    A. I only   C. both I and II

    B. II only   D. neither I nor II

78. The purpose of the receiver is to:

    A. cool the refrigerant gas

    B. separate the oil from the refrigerant

    C. store the refrigerant

    D. condense the refrigerant

79. The function of the expansion valve is to:

    A. change the high pressure liquid to a low pressure liquid

    B. regulate the amount of liquid refrigerant to the expansion coils

    C. change the gas refrigerant to a liquid

    D. shut off the flow of refrigerant to the condenser

80. How often should the emergency diesel be run under load?

    A. once a year   C. once a week

    B. once a month   D. at inspection time only

81. If black smoke is coming from the exhaust stack of a diesel engine, what could be the trouble?

    A. bad exhaust valves   C. leaky fuel injectors

    B. not enough air   D. all of the above

82. The heat required to change the physical state of a substance is called:

    A. sensible heat   C. centigrade heat

    B. latent heat   D. radiant heat

83. If the lube oil in a diesel engine is too cold, the result would be:

    A. lube oil pump would lose suction

    B. diesel would not start

    C. diesel would be hard starting

    D. overheating of the cooling system due to excess friction

84. If the relief valve on a diesel engine cylinder lifts, the cause could be:

    A. too much fuel injected into the cylinder

    B. high head pressure

    C. water in the cylinder

    D. exhaust valve stuck closed

85. How would you switch over the steering gear?

    A. start the stand-by pump, put the rudder to midships, and switch over six-way valve

    B. open suction and discharge valves to the standby pump and start pump

    C. rudder in midships position, open the relief valves, and start the pump

    D. switch over six-way valve, open pump suction and discharge valves, and start pump

86. What prevents the rudder from over travelling?

    A. six-way valve   C. relief valves

    B. rudder angle indicator   D. follow-up mechanism

87. What system is most likely to be at fault if a diesel engine runs rough?

    A. lubrication   C. fuel

    B. cooling   D. ignition

88. With the diesel running, white smoke starts coming out of the stack and then the diesel stops. What would be the cause?

    A. low lube oil pressure

    B. fuel oil filters full of water

    C. super charger running too fast

    D. leaky injector

89. Which of the following would be an indication of entrained air in a steering system? I. radial piston pump will overspeed; II. rudder will not respond properly.

    A. I   C. both I and II

    B. II   D. neither I nor II

90. Air pressure supplied to a boiler is measured in:

    A. PSI   C. inches of mercury

    B. inches of water   D. PSIA

91. In the event of a power failure to the steering gear motor systems which would be used? I. hand pump; II. trick wheel.
    A. I
    B. II
    C. I and II
    D. neither I nor II

92. Which of the following materials may *not* be used in gasket maintenance in a hydraulic system?
    A. lead
    B. copper
    C. rubber
    D. oil treated paper

93. In a low pressure evaporator, double effect, what is the steam pressure carried on the first stage?
    A. 10 to 25 PSI
    B. 15 to 30 PSI
    C. 5 to 10 PSI
    D. 1 to 5 PSI

94. Emulsification of oil will occur when mixed with:
    A. air
    B. water
    C. black oil
    D. ice cream

95. A thermostatic expansion valve in an R-12 system is controlled by:
    A. solenoid valve energizing coil
    B. regulating the king valve
    C. a thermal bulb on evaporator coil
    D. an electrically operated controller

96. A badly scored or pitted valve disk should be:
    A. ground with an abrasive
    B. discarded and replaced
    C. refaced in a lathe
    D. relapped

97. What advantage does a flash-type evaporator have as compared to a submerged tube type evaporator?
    A. less internal corrosion due to low brine density
    B. greater water purity due to higher temperatures
    C. lower feedwater temperature required in a flash-type evaporator
    D. less scale formation in a flash-type evaporator

98. What would you *not* do if you found fuel oil returning to the contaminated drain tank?
    A. check condensate returns from steam heating line in fuel oil tanks
    B. isolate leaky coils and repair
    C. drain contaminated tank so as to prevent oil from entering condensate system
    D. put pressure on fuel tank to find leak

99. Seawater feed is first heated in a distilling plant by the:
    A. distillate cooler
    B. saltwater feed heater
    C. air ejector cooler
    D. brine cooler

100. Both the temperature and the pressure of the refrigerant are increased in the:
    A. compressor
    B. evaporator
    C. condenser
    D. expansion valve

Feed Systems

1. What would *not* cause the vacuum to drop in the main condenser?
    A. sudden drop in seawater temperature
    B. air leaks
    C. leak in the vent between the condensate pump and the condenser
    D. no gland sealing steam
2. If the salinity alarm went off and no make up feed is being added, what could be the cause?
    A. leak in the lube oil cooler
    B. leak in the main condenser
    C. leak in the generating tubes
    D. leak in the fuel oil heater
3. What type of feedwater system is most commonly used?
    A. open type   C. vacuum closed
    B. semi closed   D. pressure closed
4. What would you do first when lighting off the main plant?
    A. open the throttle valve   C. start the lube oil system
    B. engage the jacking gear   D. fill up the DC heater
5. The condensate pumps discharge to the:
    A. feed and filter tank   C. air ejector condenser
    B. main condenser   D. economizer
6. An unfired steam generator supplies low pressure steam to the:
    A. fuel oil heater   C. feed heater
    B. air ejector   D. low pressure turbine
7. Why doesn't the condensate go directly from the condensate pump to the boiler instead of through the deaerating heater? I. because it would cause severe thermal stress to the boiler; II. because feed water must be deaerated.
    A. I only   C. both I and II
    B. II only   D. neither I nor II
8. Steam drains return to the condensate system via the: I. deaerating heater; II. main condenser.
    A. I only   C. both I and II
    B. II only   D. neither I nor II
9. The deaerating heater is used in:
    A. the open type feedwater system
    B. the low pressure type steam plant
    C. all steam plants
    D. the closed type feedwater system
10. The excess steam pressure in the back pressure system exhausts to the:

    A. feedwater heater

    B. main condenser

    C. atmosphere

    D. atmosphere through a relief valve

11. The deaerating heater is used to:

    A. heat the feedwater and remove air

    B. heat the feedwater

    C. remove air

    D. create a vacuum

12. Vacuum is maintained in the main condenser by the:

    A. condensate pump   C. feed pump

    B. air ejector   D. feed governor

13. Before raising vacuum on the main propulsion unit, all of the following steps are necessary *except*:

    A. starting the lubricating oil pumps

    B. starting the jacking gear

    C. warming up and draining the main steam lines

    D. admitting the gland sealing steam to the turbine glands

14. Some condenser tubes are packed on one end to:

    A. allow for expansion and contraction of the tubes

    B. allow for easier tube removal

    C. allow longer tubes to be used

    D. keep condensate from leaking through the tube sheets

15. What would *not* cause a loss of vacuum in a closed feedwater system?

    A. insufficient water flow through the condenser

    B. failure of the main condensate pump

    C. leak in the water box of the condenser

    D. leak in the vent line from the main condensate pump

16. A salinity indicator cell would be located in the:

    A. seawater side of the main condenser

    B. main condenser hot well

    C. evaporator brine suction line

    D. low pressure turbine casing drain

17. A two-pass condenser means that the:

    A. steam makes two passes through the condenser

    B. steam goes in one direction and the cooling water in the other direction

    C. cooling water makes two passes through the condenser

    D. steam flows vertically and the cooling water horizontally

18. If the salinity indicator registers high salinity in the main condenser hot well, you would suspect the cause to be:

    A. saturated steam coming from the boiler

    B. leaking tubes in the third stage heater

      C. leaking tubes in the main condenser

      D. high water pressure in the lube oil cooler

19. The deaerating tank (heater) is vented to the:

      A. reserve fuel tank   C. bilges

      B. distilled water tank   D. atmosphere

20. To regulate the amount of feedwater going to the boiler you could:

      A. regulate the speed of the feed pump

      B. use the feed check valves

      C. adjust the the automatic feedwater regulator

      D. do all of the above

21. The condensate from the fuel oil heaters is lead to the:

      A. feed and filter tank   C. condenser hotwell

      B. double-bottom tanks   D. drain observation tank

22. The auxiliary exhaust steam is used to:

      A. heat the feedwater   C. heat the fuel oil

      B. drive the bilge pump   D. drive small auxiliaries

23. The loop seal in a turbine installation condenser is needed:

      A. due to the difference in pressure which exists between the main and intercondenser

      B. to keep the exhaust steam from going directly through the condenser

      C. to keep a sufficient amount of water in the system

      D. to keep sufficient condensate in the system

24. If the water in the "loop seal" is lost:

      A. no condensate wil flow through the system

      B. air will run into the main condenser and kill the vacuum

      C. the air ejector will not operate

      D. the air ejector will become overheated

25. Air in a condenser is harmful because:

      A. it lowers the heat transfer process

      B. it is costly to remove

      C. it increases condenser pressure, thereby lowering vacuum

      D. it does all of the above

26. The feed pump discharge pressure is higher than the steam drum pressure to:

      A. ensure feedwater flow into the boiler

      B. keep the steam drum pressure high

      C. prevent water hammer in the feed line

      D. help the feedwater flash to steam

27. An air ejector is operated by:

      A. air   C. steam

      B. water   D. any of the above

28. A sudden loss of vacuum in the main condenser can be caused by:

    A. damaged carbon packing rings
    B. a flooded condensate pump suction
    C. a sudden decrease in sea temperature
    D. excessive condenser cooling water
29. When lighting off the first and second stage air ejector, the first thing to do is:
    A. start the condensate pump
    B. drain the loop seal
    C. start the main circulator
    D. put gland seal steam on the turbines
30. Which of the following methods is used to allow for expansion of condenser tubes? I. roll tubes at both ends and place expansion joint in condenser shell; II. packing tubes at one end and rolling them on the other end.
    A. I only   C. both I and II
    B. II only   D. neither I nor II
31. What condition could result if the gland sealing steam to the main turbines were secured while a vessel was underway?
    A. overspeeding of the main turbines
    B. loss of vacuum in the main condenser
    C. water carry-over to the main turbines
    D. damage to the labyrinth packing
32. A leaky condenser tube will:
    A. leak fresh water into the overboard discharge line
    B. permit salt water to leak into the condensate
    C. break the vacuum
    D. have no effect as it will drain into the bilges
33. An oil leak into the feedwater system could be detected by:
    A. examining the leak-off from the main feed pump
    B. checking the surface of the condensate in the deaerating heater
    C. examining the water in the drain inspection tank
    D. blowing down the contaminated evaporator and sampling the water
34. An economizer is used to:
    A. heat the fuel oil
    B. heat air before it enters the furnace
    C. desuperheat the steam
    D. heat the feedwater before it enters the boiler
35. The condensate pump takes suction from the:
    A. deaerating heater   C. fuel tank
    B. hot well   D. atmospheric drain tank
36. What is the "bilge injection" or emergency bilge suction connected to?

    A. the general service pump   C. the bilge pump

    B. the fire pump   D. the main circulator

37. How is distilled water added to the feed system?

    A. vacuum drag to the main condenser

    B. gravity from deaerating heater to feed pumps

    C. gravity from deaerating heater to main condenser

    D. pumped into main condenser

38. Vacuum in the main condenser is measured in:

    A. inches of water   C. grains per gallon

    B. inches of mercury   D. parts per million

39. The purpose of a heat exchanger is to:

    A. eliminate hot air from the condenser

    B. maintain steady pressures in a system

    C. heat or cool one fluid by means of another fluid

    D. reduce the engine room temperature in tropical climates

40. The purpose of inspection plates on the main condenser is to:

    A. give access to clean water boxes

    B. check the side of condenser

    C. check tubes without removing condenser heads

    D. check the steam baffle

41. The main feed pump takes suction from the:

    A. main condenser   C. distilled water tanks

    B. third stage heater   D. deaerating heater

42. The purpose of a steam baffle in a condenser is to:

    A. separate the steam from the cooling water

    B. prevent the hot steam from hitting directly on the cooler tubes

    C. support the tube sheets

    D. separate the steam from the condensate

43. A "scoop" type condenser must be a:

    A. two-pass condenser   C. counterflow condenser

    B. single-pass condenser   D. vertical condenser

44. A sudden loss in vacuum could be caused by:

    A. a clogged intake

    B. a sudden increase in seawater temperature

    C. mechanical troubles

    D. any of the above

45. What would do *first* when breaking vacuum?

    A. secure steam to the air ejector

    B. secure main condensate pump

    C. secure main circulating pump

    D. secure the gland sealing steam

46. If the deaerating heater were to run out of water, what would happen?

A. the feed pump would become air bound
B. the condensate pump would become air bound
C. water would back up into the condenser
D. the main circulating pump would not operate properly

47. When a ship is underway, how is make up feedwater added to the boilers?

A. by standby pump
B. by feed pump
C. by condensate pump
D. by vacuum drag

48. The cooling water supplied to the vent condenser in a deaerating heater is:

A. sea water
B. fresh water
C. portable water
D. condensate

49. The boiler feed water in the feedwater heater is heated by:

A. superheated steam
B. auxiliary exhaust steam
C. desuperheated steam
D. steam directly from the boiler

50. How do you reestablish the loop seal on an air ejector condenser?

A. close off the drain valve as provided
B. decrease the air ejector pressure
C. increase the flow of condensate through air ejector condensers
D. secure the second stage air ejector

Turbines and Lube Oil Systems

1. Before raising vacuum on the main propulsion unit, all of the following steps are necessary *except*:

A. starting the lubricating oil pumps
B. starting the jacking gear
C. warming up and draining the main steam lines
D. admitting gland sealing steam to the turbine glands

2. Which of the following is normally entered in the log book at the end of a watch? I. sea temperature; II boiler pressure.

A. I
B. II
C. I and II
D. neither I nor II

3. Rotation is imparted to the oil in a Sharples centrifugal purifier by use of a:

A. series of discs
B. three wing device
C. distributing ring
D. driving spindle

4. A poorly cleaned lube oil purifier will result in:

A. excessive water discharge
B. improper separation

      C. excessive lube oil consumption

      D. insufficient lube oil supply to the gravity tanks

5. Pertaining to a lube oil gravity system for a turbine plant:

      A. there is a stop check valve on the discharge side of the lube oil pump

      B. the discharge line on the gravity tank goes to the suction side of the pump

      C. the gravity tank overflow goes directly to the lube oil sump

      D. the gravity tank overflow line has an alarm

6. All of the following contaminants can be removed from lubricating oil by using the centrifuge as a separator *except*:

      A. water   C. carbon residue

      B. fuel oil   D. metal particles

7. In a water lubricated stern tube a slight amount of leakage out of the stern gland is allowed to:

      A. flush out dirt and grit from the stern gland

      B. cool the stern tube

      C. cool the gland packing

      D. flush out dirt and grit from between the bearing staves

8. On a fully automated vessel which of the following consoles have direct control of the ahead and astern steam valves? I. engine room; II. bridge.

      A. I   C. I and II

      B. II   D. neither I nor II

9. A steam pressure gauge is usually connected to a steam source by means of a "pigtail" or loop in order to:

      A. prevent steam from entering the gauge

      B. prevent water from entering the gauge

      C. provide for temperature compensation

      D. provide for pipe expansion

10. A gas pocket formed in a liquid due to decreased pressure is called:

      A. water hammer   C. cavitation

      B. agitation   D. depression

11. Removing water from lube oil with a centrifuge is called:

      A. emulsifying   C. clarifying

      B. demulsifying   D. separating

12. A centrifugal lube oil purifier can remove the following from lubricating oil:

      A. acid   C. additives

      B. kerosene   D. dissolved solid

13. The jacking gear on main propulsion turbines is used to:

      A. cool the rotor evenly

      B. provide propulsion for emergencies

    C. lift the reduction gear casing

    D. reduce turbine speed during maneuvering

14. When reassembling a lube oil purifier, make sure that:

    A. the inlet valves are closed

    B. the belt between the motor and purifier has a half inch slack in it

    C. all the purifier discs have a light coat of grease on them

    D. all the purifier discs are installed

15. What is the usual lube oil pump discharge pressure in a gravity system?

    A. 10 to 20   C. 35 to 45

    B. 20 to 30   D. 65 to 75

16. To assure that a bearing is receiving proper oil supply, you should check the:

    A. bull's eye in the gravity tank overflow

    B. lube oil temperature at the cooler outlet

    C. lube oil strainer magnets

    D. sight flow glass in the bearing oil supply line

17. What is the usual turbine gland seal steam pressure?

    A. 1 to 3   C. 25 to 45

    B. 5 to 10   D. 75 to 100

18. When a disc type centrifugal purifier is operated as a separator, priming the bowl with fresh water is necessary before any oil is admitted to the purifier. If the bowl is not primed, the:

    A. oil has a tendency to emulsify in the bowl

    B. purifier will act as a clarifier at the discharge ring

    C. oil will be lost through the water discharge ports

    D. oily solids will be deposited only at the intermediate top disc

19. Reduction gears on main propulsion units are lubricated by:

    A. grease cups and gravity feed lines

    B. oil flinger rings mounted on the shaft

    C. leak-off lines from the lube oil cooler

    D. spray nozzles at the gear meshing points

20. In a disc type lube oil purifier, heavy impurities collect most:

    A. at the bottom of the unit   C. at the water discharge

    B. along the center shaft   D. on the inside of the bowl

21. Oil is heated in a purifier before centrifuging in order to:

    A. boil off water   C. reduce friction

    B. prevent corrosion   D. improve purification

22. A grease gun is used to lubricate:

    A. the main condensate pump bearings

    B. the main turbine bearings

       C. the generator bearings
       D. line shaft bearings
23. What is a major cause of overheating of a spring bearing?
       A. engine running slow   C. oil ring stuck
       B. high RPM   D. lack of cooling water
24. How are the reduction gears lubricated?
       A. oil spray into the gear mesh
       B. rifle drilled passages
       C. tips of the gears picking oil off the bottom of the sump
       D. submerging the gears in oil
25. If the sight glass on the main thrust bearing shows milky color, the
    problem is:
       A. too much air in the oil   C. oil too cold
       B. water in the oil   D. low oil pressure
26. What would you do if you noticed the Kingsbury thrust bearing
    temperature had risen slightly?
       A. keep a close eye on the bearing
       B. nothing until the temperature rises greatly
       C. notify the engineer on watch
       D. call the chief engineer
27. Which of the following is the best method of removing water from
    fuel oil?
       A. filtering   C. centrifuging
       B. straining   D. settling
28. An increase in the acid content of an oil decreases its:
       A. viscosity
       B. demulsibility
       C. resistance to pressure
       D. surface tension
29. The viscosity of a lubricating oil is:
       A. the degree of fluidity of the oil
       B. the amount of acid contained in the oil
       C. the lowest temperature at which ignitable vapors form
       D. the lowest temperature at which it will pour
30. When lube oil pressure suddenly increases the first item to check
    should be:
       A. discharge valve   C. suction strainer
       B. lube oil flow from bearing   D. lube oil temperature
31. Babbitt metal is used in:
       A. bearings   C. propellers
       B. pump casings   D. refrigerators
32. What is used to lubricate and cool the lignum vitae bearing in the
    stern tube?

A. lube oil   C. priming water
B. sea water   D. soap and water

33. What is the best indication that a bearing is getting *proper* lubrication?
    A. thermometer located at bearing
    B. check visual flow indicator to bearing
    C. discharge pressure of lube oil pump
    D. pressure to bearings

34. After passing through the bearings and gears, the lube oil in a turbine installation goes to the:
    A. settling tank   C. day tank
    B. sump tank   D. storage tank

35. A sudden increase in lube oil pressure in a turbine installation would be caused by:
    A. a clogged oil line   C. too much oil in the system
    B. a dirty strainer   D. A and B above

36. If a coil should leak in a turbine oil cooler, water cannot mix with the oil because:
    A. the oil pressure is greater than the water pressure
    B. it is in a separate compartment
    C. the cooling pump would shut off automatically
    D. all of the above

37. When taking over the oiler watch on a turbine, check the:
    A. oil pressure gauges
    B. oil sight glasses and spinners
    C. all thermometer readings
    D. all of the above

38. Oil flowing through the sight glass in the line between the lube oil gravity tank and sump indicates that the:
    A. gravity tank is overflowing
    B. lube oil pump is stopped
    C. lube oil suction strainer is clogged
    D. lube oil sump is full

39. In a lube oil cooler, the oil pressure should always be higher than the water pressure in order to:
    A. obtain maximum cooling
    B. prevent water leakage into the oil
    C. prevent turbulence in the cooler
    D. vent all air from the cooler

40. What type of strainer is used on main turbine propulsion system lube oil system to remove metallic particles?
    A. metal edge   C. magnetic basket
    B. fuller's earth   D. basket type

41. When first starting a turbo generator with a forced feed lube oil system to ensure oil flow, what is used?
    A. oil can   C. hand pump
    B. wick feed   C. relief valve

42. When vacuum is lost on a turbo generator the trip is actuated by:
    A. sentinel valve   C. slugs of water
    B. back pressure   D. overspeed trip

43. Excessive steam leaks from high pressure turbine gland would most likely be due to:
    A. excessive gland seal steam pressure
    B. worn carbon rings
    C. loose casing bolts
    D. packing improperly seated

44. The guarding valve prevents steam from entering the:
    A. ahead turbine while maneuvering
    B. the astern turbine
    C. the ahead turbine at all times
    D. none of the above

45. The guarding valve remains open:
    A. never
    B. during maneuvering
    C. at all times
    D. only during turbine warm up

46. A spring bearing on the line shaft is lubricated by:
    A. the lube oil gravity tank
    B. water leak-off from the stern tube
    C. an oil ring and scraper
    D. the main lube oil pump

47. In case of carry-over, the best corrective action is to:
    A. blow down the boiler with the surface blow
    B. trip the turbine and open the turbine casing drains
    C. close the steam line drains and run the turbine astern
    D. put the turbine throttle full astern

48. What would be the first indication of lube oil trouble?
    A. lube oil gravity tank low level alarm goes off
    B. low lube oil sump level
    C. low outlet temperature from lube oil coolers
    D. no flow through bull's eye from gravity tank observed

49. Magnets are installed in the propulsion turbine lube oil strainers to attract metal particles from the:
    A. turbine bearings   C. turbine blading
    B. bearing journals   D. reduction gears

50. Vibration in a propulsion turbine is:

   A. normal when first starting up
   B. abnormal and should be investigated
   C. caused by high condenser vacuum
   D. prevented by flexible shaft couplings
51. Loss of lube oil pressure requires:
   A. securing the turbine   C. shifting strainers
   B. stopping the turbine   D. shifting lube oil pumps
52. The normal pressure to the bearings in a turbine lube oil system will
    range between:
   A. 3 to 4 PSI   C. 8 to 10 PSI
   B. 5 to 6 PSI   D. 18 to 20 PSI
53. When making an inspection of the steering gear, the most important
    thing to check for is:
   A. which machinery is operating
   B. saltwater leaks around rudder post
   C. hydraulic leaks
   D. electrical overloads
54. Which of the following is true about turbine bearing lube oil temp-
    erature? I. the oil outlet temperature should not exceed 180° F; II.
    the oil temperature rise across the bearing should not exceed 50°.
   A. I only   C. both I and II
   B. II only   D. neither I nor II
55. Reduction gears on main propulsion units are lubricated by:
   A. grease cups and gravity feed lines
   B. oil flinger rings mounted on the shaft
   C. leak off lines from the lube oil cooler
   D. spray nozzles at the gear meshing points
56. When oil is heated it becomes:
   A. less viscous   C. more viscous
   B. emulsified   D. vitrified
57. Turbine lubricating oil systems are fitted with:
   A. floating strainers   C. centrifugal strainers
   B. magnetic strainers   D. simplex strainers
58. In a turbine lube oil cooler which of the following is kept at the
    highest pressure?
   A. the water   C. the air
   B. the oil   D. the steam
59. If the lube oil system fails while underway, the first thing that
    should be done is to:
   A. secure the boilers
   B. open the outlet valve on the gravity tank
   C. start the standby lube oil pump
   D. stop the main engine

60. Spring or box bearings support the weight of the shaft from the reduction gears to propeller.
    A. true
    B. false

61. The presence of water in a lubricant would result in which of the following? I. decrease bearing friction; II. oil film breakdown; III. corrosion of journals and gears.
    A. I and II   C. I and III
    B. II and III   D. I, II, and III

62. Turbine main bearings are lubricated by:
    A. force feed lubrication   C. wick feed
    B. oil rings   D. grease gun

63. Spring bearings are generally lubricated by:
    A. pressure   C. oil rings
    B. wicks   D. cooled by sea water

64. Rotating flyweights acting against spring pressure make a simple type of:
    A. governor   C. safety valve
    B. reducing valve   D. feedwater regulator

65. Oil flowing through the sight glass in the line between the lube oil gravity tank and sump indicates that the:
    A. gravity tank is overflowing
    B. lube oil pump is stopped
    C. lube oil suctionstrainer is clogged
    D. lube oil sump is full

66. The oil outlet temperature from the turbine bearings of the turbine lube oil system ranges between:
    A. 130° to 160° F   C. 100° to 120° F
    B. 90° to 100° F   D. none of the above

67. The flow of lube oil through a turbine system is checked by:
    A. spinners   C. oil sight glasses
    B. gauges   D. all of the above

68. The Kingsbury thrust bearing is lubricated by:
    A. grease cups   C. a force feed lubricator
    B. running in oil   D. wick feed

69. The primary purpose of a magnetic strainer in the lube oil system is used:
    A. to pick up metal particles which may have fallen into the lube oil pump
    B. to keep the lube oil from becoming magnetized
    C. to check the wear on reduction gear teeth
    D. as a ground protector for turbines

70. Babbit is a metal alloy commonly used for lining:

A. bearings   C. bearing journals
B. shim stock   D. saltwater piping

71. If the lube oil pressure for the main turbine *suddenly* increased the cause may be:
    A. a leaking lube oil cooler   C. dirt clogging the system
    B. the oil is too cold   D. a leak in the gravity tank

72. How would you accurately check the operating speed of a turbine generator?
    A. with a hand held speedometer
    B. with the switchboard frequency meter
    C. with the switchboard RPM indicator
    D. with a hand held tachometer

73. What type of strainer is used on main turbine propulsion system lube oil system to remove metallic particles?
    A. metal edge   C. magnetic basket
    B. fuller's earth   D. basket type

74. What should the lube oil temperature be prior to entering the lube oil purifier?
    A. 110° F to 120° F   C. 160° F to 180° F
    B. 150° F to 160° F   D. 190° F to 210° F

75. In a disc type purifier the oil is thinly separated by:
    A. a three wing device   C. cone shaped disc plates
    B. oil rings   D. an injection nozzle

Answers to Multiple-Choice Questions for the Oiler

Engine room procedures

1. B	17. A	33. D	49. C
2. A	18. B	34. D	50. A
3. B	19. B	35. A	51. B
4. A	20. B	36. A	52. A
5. A	21. B	37. C	53. A
6. D	22. B	38. B	54. B
7. C	23. C	39. B	55. B
8. C	24. C	40. D	56. B
9. B	25. C	41. B	57. D
10. B	26. C	42. C	58. A
11. A	27. A	43. C	59. D
12. C	28. B	44. B	60. A
13. B	29. C	45. D	61. B
14. A	30. D	46. B	62. D
15. B	31. C	47. C	63. B
16. C	32. B	48. C	64. D

65. A	74. C	83. C	92. C
66. C	75. B	84. C	93. D
67. B	76. B	85. A	94. B
68. C	77. A	86. D	95. C
69. C	78. C	87. C	96. B
70. D	79. B	88. B	97. D
71. A	80. B	89. B	98. D
72. A	81. D	90. B	99. A
73. C	82. B	91. A	100. A

Feed systems

1. A	14. A	27. C	40. C
2. B	15. C	28. A	41. D
3. D	16. B	29. A	42. B
4. C	17. C	30. C	43. B
5. C	18. C	31. B	44. D
6. A	19. D	32. B	45. A
7. C	20. D	33. C	46. A
8. C	21. D	34. D	47. D
9. D	22. A	35. B	48. D
10. B	23. A	36. D	49. B
11. A	24. B	37. A	50. A
12. B	25. D	38. B	
13. C	26. A	39. C	

Turbines and lube oil systems

1. C	20. D	39. B	58. B
2. C	21. D	40. C	59. D
3. B	22. A	41. C	60. A
4. B	23. C	42. B	61. B
5. C	24. A	43. A	62. A
6. B	25. B	44. B	63. C
7. C	26. A	45. B	64. A
8. C	27. C	46. C	65. A
9. A	28. B	47. B	66. A
10. C	29. A	48. D	67. D
11. D	30. B	49. D	68. B
12. D	31. A	50. B	69. C
13. A	32. B	51. B	70. A
14. D	33. A	52. C	71. C
15. C	34. B	53. C	72. D
16. D	35. D	54. C	73. C
17. A	36. A	55. D	74. C
18. C	37. D	56. A	75. C
19. D	38. A	57. B	

CHAPTER NINE

Multiple-Choice Questions for Fireman/Watertender and Oiler

The fireman/watertender should also study the multiple-choice questions in Chapter 6. The oiler should also study the multiple-choice questions in Chapter 8.

Tools, Pumps, and Piping

1. If during its operation, a centrifugal pump is noisy with excessive vibration, the cause would most likely be due to:
   A. bent shaft
   B. worn wearing rings
   C. reverse rotation
   D. excessive sealing water pressure

2. What causes noises and hammering in a liquid line that has vapors in it?
   A. cavitation
   B. water hammer
   C. feathering of valve discs
   D. vapor interrupting of boundary films

3. If you close the discharge valve on a centrifugal bilge pump, what will happen?
   A. motor overloads and trips out
   B. motor overheats
   C. pump overheats
   D. relief valve opens

4. If you tap a hole by hand in a deep hole and it is not started straight, the:
   A. tap will not cut
   B. tap will break
   C. tap will cut on one side only
   D. tap will not cut to the bottom

5. Which of the following types of valves is used in the bilge manifold?
   A. swing check   C. angle
   B. nonreturn   D. globe

6. If a centrifugal pump produces a pressure less than designed discharge pressure, the cause could be:

    A. excessive pump speed   C. pump misalignment

    B. excessive suction head   D. worn wearing rings

7. Sink and shower drains are fitted with S and P traps to:

    A. reduce water velocity, minimize erosion

    B. create a strong siphon effect

    C. provide a cushion against water hammer

    D. prevent escape of sewer gases to compartments

8. An arrow cast into the valve body indicating the direction of flow is common to:

    A. gate valves only   C. check valves only

    B. globe valves only   D. globe and check valves

9. The valve located on the casing of the low pressure main propulsion turbine is properly called a:

    A. safety valve   C. turbine valve

    B. throttle valve   D. sentinel valve

10. What precautions should you take when lagging a pipeline with asbestos material?

    A. be sure there is no condensate in the lines

    B. wear a dust mask and avoid breathing the asbestos dust

    C. be aware of the flammable properties of asbestos

    D. always wear an oxygen breathing apparatus

11. After a piece of pipe has been cut, the hole is cleaned out with a:

    A. pipe reamer   C. pipe taper

    B. pipe cleaner   D. hole cleaner

12. What type hammer will *not* mar a surface?

    A. sledge hammer   C. brass hammer

    B. chipping hammer   D. rawhide hammer

13. Which of the following types of packing would be used on water flange joints?

    A. rubber   C. wire inserted rubber

    B. tux   D. A or C

14. Which of the following *cannot* be considered for use as an emergency bilge pump?

    A. general service pump   C. main bilge pump

    B. main circulation   D. fire pump

15. The pumping capacity of a reciprocating pump is determined by the:

    A. effective pressure in the liquid end during the complete cycle of operation

    B. difference between the maximum pressure developed during the discharge stroke and the minimum pressure

    C. area of the piston and its rate of travel

    D. capacity of the steam cylinder and its bore

16. When using a micrometer to measure a drill for size, you should measure across the drill:

A. margins

B. flutes

C. shank

D. web

17. The size of a drill is stamped on the:

A. point

B. shank

C. margin

D. flute

18. The tool used for cleaning files is called a:

A. file cleaner

B. file card

C. file oilstone

D. scraper

19. The advantage of a centrifugal pump as compared with a reciprocating pump is:

A. the discharge is continuous

B. it has no internal valves

C. upon accidental closing of discharge valve, excessive pressure will not build up

D. all of the above

20. Suitable clearance should be left between the ends of packing rings to allow for:

A. easy removal

B. expansion and contraction

C. air pockets

D. all of the above

21. N.C. stands for:

A. neutral cut

B. national coarse

C. national cut

D. not center

22. A Stilson wrench is used for:

A. tightening piping and pipe fittings

B. nuts and bolts

C. gaskets

D. tubing

23. The pointed end of a file is called a (an):

A. bitter end

B. point

C. tang

D. handle

24. For safety's sake all portable marine electric hand tools should be:

A. dipped in oil

B. grounded to prevent shock

C. washed after use in soap and water

D. never used

25. If a rag was stuck under a bilge valve what could it cause? I. flooding of bilges; II. bilge pump to lose suction.

A. I only

B. II only

C. both I and II

D. neither I nor II

26. The rounded ball peen of a ball peen hammer is properly used for:

A. striking chisel

B. spreading cotter pins

C. stretching metal

D. driving taper pins

27. Hand taps are provided in sets of three called:
     A. taper, plug, and end   C. taper, plug, and bottom
     B. short, taper, and bottom   D. short, medium, and long
28. Which of the following is the smallest size drill?
     A. no. 80   C. no. 1
     B. no. 60   D. no. 0
29. Insulation on deck steam lines must be installed securely because:
     A. loose insulation causes steam leaks
     B. deck steam lines are subject to vibration
     C. loose insulation prevents pipe expansion
     D. steam driven machinery cannot run with loose insulation
30. A needle valve would be used in piping systems requiring:
     A. high pressure valves
     B. little resistance to fluid flow
     C. fine adjustments in fluid flow
     D. high temperature adjustments
31. A tap or die marked ¼-20 indicates:
     A. ¼ inch radius—20 centimeters long
     B. ¼ inch radian—20 threads per inch
     C. ¼ inch diameter—20 threads per inch
     D. ¼ turn—20 times
32. The tube used to prepare copper tubing for fittings is called a tube:
     A. spreader   C. stretcher
     B. flaring tool   D. belling tool
33. If a centrifugal pump fails to deliver, the cause may be:
     A. pump speed too low   C. discharge head too high
     B. impeller passages plugged   D. any of the above
34. The volute on a centrifugal pump causes the velocity to:
     A. increase   C. remain constant
     B. decrease   D. do none of the above
35. "Groaning" in the steam end of the reciprocating pump may result
    from:
     A. cylinder misalignment   C. too tight packing
     B. broken piston rings   D. all of the above
36. The follower plate is found on which of the following parts of a
    reciprocating pump?
     A. valve chest   C. snifter valve
     B. steam chest   D. liquid plunger
37. Which of the following taps should be used to start a thread?
     A. plug   C. bottom
     B. short   D. taper
38. Pipe taps are:
     A. the same size from end to end
     B. not the same size from end to end

C. tapered

D. not hardened

39. A grinding wheel is "trued" with a:

    A. late tool

    B. dressing tool

    C. garnet stone

    D. round file

40. On cutting threads using a hand die on brass stock, what type lubrication would you use?

    A. graphite and oil

    B. white lead

    C. cutting oil

    D. threads should be cut dry

41. Which will cause a twist drill to drill oversized?

    A. a lip clearance angle greater than 20°

    B. a cutting edge angle less than 59°

    C. the cutting edges being ground at different angles

    D. the drill being used without a pilot hole

42. Which type of file will produce a fine finish when draw filing?

    A. a double-cut file

    B. a bastard file

    C. a single-cut file

    D. a second-cut file

43. What kind of tap should be used to finish the threading operation in a blind hole?

    A. a short tap

    B. a taper tap

    C. a plug tap

    D. a bottoming tap

44. Which process is used to bring a hole to finished size with high accuracy?

    A. coring

    B. boring

    C. broaching

    D. reaming

45. What would a centrifugal pump with a volute and diffuser do to the liquid pressure?

    A. increase

    B. decrease

    C. keep the same

    D. none of the above

46. What is the purpose of a relief valve?

    A. to fill 2 tanks at the same time

    B. to use pump at a higher pressure

    C. to return liquid to suction side if discharge valve is closed

    D. all of the above

47. What do you use to measure threads?

    A. bolt

    B. wire gauge

    C. screw pitch gauge

    D. center gauge

48. The twist drill gauge can be used to measure the drill:

    A. length

    B. diameter

    C. clearance angle

    D. web thickness

49. High pressure, high temperature valves usually have their discs and seats surfaced with:

    A. monel

    B. chromium

    C. carboloy

    D. stellite

50. Wire inserted packing is used on:
    A. fuel oil service pumps   C. circulating pumps
    B. main steam stops   D. lube oil pumps
51. The tool used for cutting pipe threads is called a:
    A. pipe cutter   C. pipe threader
    B. pipe stock and die   D. pipe ratchet cutter
52. Which of the following is the largest size drill?
    A. A   C. Z
    B. X   D. XX
53. How are globe and angle valves always installed in the line?
    A. with pressure acting on the bottom of the disc
    B. with pressure acting on the top of the disc
    C. makes no difference
    D. with hand wheel pointing down
54. If you completely fill the pressure tank in an automatic freshwater
    supply system, what would happen?
    A. pump would overheat
    B. pump would short cycle
    C. pump would continue running
    D. pump would stop
55. The device used on the discharge side of many reciprocating pumps
    to provide a continuous discharge is:
    A. absorbing tank   C. cushioner
    B. snifter   D. air chamber
56. A reciprocating pump:
    A. is positive displacement
    B. is intermittent displacement
    C. can be started with suction valve closed
    D. can be started with discharge closed
57. When preparing to tap a hole, the size of the drill will be:
    A. equal to the size of the tap
    B. smaller than the size of the tap
    C. larger than the size of the tap
    D. none of the above
58. N.F. stands for:
    A. national file   C. neutral file
    B. national fine   D. not found
59. The gear, screw, and lobe pumps are all classified as:
    A. variable stroke pumps
    B. multistage pumps
    C. positive displacement pumps
    D. triple-ported pumps

60. Lantern rings on a pump serve which of the following purposes:
   A. give added starting torque
   B. lubricate pump bearings
   C. lubricate and seal pump packing
   D. act as a vent
61. A pump is said to have "positive suction head" when the:
   A. pump is located above the liquid supply
   B. pump is located below the liquid supply
   C. pump is located in a separate compartment
   D. suction is lower than the discharge
62. When starting a positive displacement pump, the *first* valve to open should be the:
   A. suction valve   C. discharge valve
   B. drain valve   D. steam valve
63. A hacksaw blade is put in with the teeth:
   A. facing away from the handle
   B. facing toward the handle
   C. facing up
   D. facing to the side
64. A round nosed chisel is used to:
   A. cut keyways or slots
   B. draw back a drill that has walked away
   C. cut round stock
   D. cut sheet metal
65. The tool used in precision work to smooth or enlarge holes is called a:
   A. round cut   C. reamer
   B. drift pin   D. protractor
66. Which of the following is *not* a cut of file?
   A. smooth   C. half-round
   B. second cut   D. bastard
67. On a standard wire gauge:
   A. no. 10 is larger than no. 5
   B. no. 25 is smaller than no. 20
   C. no. 1 is smaller than no. 2
   D. no. 30 is larger than no. 25
68. The tool used when working with large sizes of pipe is called a:
   A. chain pipe wrench   C. chain holder
   B. chain tongs   D. A or B above
69. The tool used to cut threads in a hole is called a:
   A. top   C. bit
   B. tap   D. reamer
70. Which of the following chisels would be used for cutting oil grooves?
   A. diamond point chisel   C. round nose chisel
   B. cold chisel   D. hot chisel

71. Which of the following tools would be most useful when taking leads on bearings?
    A. dividers   C. micrometer
    B. outside calipers   D. center gauge

72. If the drill cutting speed is too high, the drill will:
    A. cut faster   C. cut oversized
    B. lose temper   D. not cut

73. To remove nuts which are frozen on their studs, you should use a:
    A. cape chisel   C. round nose chisel
    B. diamond point chisel   D. cold flat chisel

74. Adjustable combination pliers have a slip joint that permits the jaws to be:
    A. adjusted to easily remove electrical wire insulation
    B. opened wider for gripping large diameter objects
    C. opened wide to cut round stock
    D. adjusted to hold pump shafts

75. The relief valve will: I. relieve pressure at a set point; II. reduce pressure to a set point.
    A. I   C. both I and II
    B. II   D. neither I nor II

76. The valve which when open offers the least amount of resistance to flow is the:
    A. globe valve   C. gate valve
    B. check valve   D. relief valve

77. To measure a piece of round stock use a:
    A. wire gauge   C. dial indicator
    B. micrometer   D. circular slide rule

78. A screwdriver is made with a square shank:
    A. to prevent bending
    B. to be able to use a wrench
    C. to set in the screw slot
    D. so as to be hit with a hammer

79. The name plate on a reciprocating pump reads $7'' \times 6'' \times 4''$. What is the proper order?
    A. liquid cylinder, stroke, steam cylinder
    B. stroke, liquid cylinder, steam cylinder
    C. steam cylinder, stroke, liquid cylinder
    D. steam cylinder, liquid cylinder, stroke

80. A pump is said to have "negative suction head" when the pump is located:
    A. between the suction and discharge
    B. below the liquid supply
    C. above the liquid supply
    D. any of the above

81. The pump packing gland should be:
    A. slack enough to allow slight leakage of fluid
    B. slightly cocked
    C. brought up tight so as not to allow any leakage
    D. fitted with a relief valve

82. The volute pump is one in which the impeller:
    A. discharges into a gradually widening channel in the pump casing
    B. has stationary diffuser vanes
    C. produces no kinetic energy
    D. does all of the above

83. If you wanted to check the face of a pump slide valve or other flat-faced valve, you could check for trueness on a:
    A. flat board   C. piece of glass
    B. surface plate   D. bearing plate

84. The proper tool to use for cutting new external threads is called a thread:
    A. tap   C. broach
    B. die   D. chaser

85. If the point angle on a drill is less than 59°, the:
    A. hole will be drilled larger
    B. hole will take longer to drill
    C. drill will not center properly
    D. drill will cut undersized

86. A taper shank drill is removed from the drill press spindle with a:
    A. drill drift   C. taper punch
    B. vise grip   D. leather mallet

87. Which of the following would *not* cause a centrifugal pump to vibrate?
    A. bent shaft
    B. steam valve loose
    C. worn bearings
    D. foundation not sufficiently rigid

88. Which of the following does *not* have to be lubricated when drilling?
    A. steel   C. monel
    B. brass   D. tool steel

89. A scribe is used to:
    A. cut gaskets   C. center punch for drilling
    B. make a mark on metal   D. all of the above

90. The most accurate method to set an inside caliper is:
    A. measure with machinist rule
    B. use an outside micrometer
    C. with an inside micrometer
    D. use a telescoping gauge

91. Before drilling a hole in a piece of metal, it should be:
    A. marked with chalk   C. scribed
    B. center-punched   D. protracted
92. The flinger ring, fitted on the pump shaft, is used to:
    A. lubricate the packing
    B. seal the suction side
    C. prevent leakage of fluid into bearing housing
    D. prime the pump when first starting
93. The "discharge head" of a pumping system is:
    A. the vertical distance from the pump to the discharge level
    B. the horizontal distance from the pump to the discharge level
    C. the vertical distance from the suction to the discharge
    D. none of the above
94. With a reciprocating pump, failure to obtain proper discharge pressure may be caused by:
    A. steam pressure which is too low
    B. worn piston rings
    C. liquid plunger packing which is too tight
    D. any of the above
95. The snifter valve on reciprocating pumps does which of the following?
    A. automatically replaces the air in the air chamber
    B. relieves excess pressure on the pump
    C. lubricates the piston rods while in operation
    D. acts as a pressure regulator
96. To secure a reciprocating pump you would close in the following order:
    A. steam exhaust valve, drains, suction and discharge, steam inlet
    B. suction and discharge, steam inlet and exhaust and open drains
    C. steam inlet and exhaust, suction and discharge, and open drains
    D. suction and discharge, exhaust, drains and inlet
97. With a reciprocating pump, excessive vibration may be caused by:
    A. misalignment
    B. liquid plunger packing too tight
    C. cushion valves not set properly
    D. any of the above
98. The highest theoretical pump lift is:
    A. 15 feet   C. 34 feet
    B. 26 feet   D. 43 feet
99. To determine the size of a piece of pipe under 12 inches you should use a:

    A. ruler and inside caliper
    B. ruler and outside caliper
    C. feeler gauge and inside caliper
    D. dial indicator

100. What valve has "blowdown"?

A. relief valve	C. reducing valve
B. safety valve	D. sentinel valve

Answers to Multiple-Choice Questions, Fireman/Watertender and Oiler

Pumps, tools, and piping

1. A	26. C	51. B	76. C
2. A	27. C	52. C	77. B
3. C	28. A	53. A	78. B
4. C	29. B	54. B	79. D
5. B	30. C	55. D	80. C
6. D	31. C	56. A	81. A
7. D	32. B	57. B	82. A
8. D	33. D	58. B	83. B
9. D	34. B	59. C	84. B
10. B	35. D	60. C	85. B
11. A	36. D	61. B	86. A
12. D	37. D	62. C	87. B
13. D	38. C	63. A	88. B
14. C	39. B	64. B	89. B
15. C	40. D	65. C	90. B
16. A	41. C	66. C	91. B
17. B	42. C	67. B	92. C
18. B	43. D	68. D	93. A
19. D	44. D	69. B	94. D
20. B	45. A	70. C	95. A
21. B	46. C	71. C	96. C
22. A	47. C	72. B	97. D
23. C	48. B	73. D	98. C
24. B	49. D	74. B	99. A
25. C	50. B	75. A	100. B

Multiple-Choice Questions for the Pumpman

The pumpman works an 8-hour day and is responsible for safe and efficient cargo handling operations. Duties of the pumpman include the following:

*1. Perform all of the cargo handling operations including loading, discharging, and ballasting procedures.

2. Perform maintenance of cargo handling equipment including cargo pumps, valves, piping, reach rods, and internal cargo tank structures.

*3. Perform starting and testing operations of deck gear prior to arrival and departure.

4. Perform welding repairs.

*5. Monitor all cargo handling procedures for safe and pollution-free operations in accordance with United States Coast Guard regulations.

6. Insure compliance with vessel's certificate of inspection.

*7. Assist in tank cleaning and gas-freeing operations.

The topics covered by the multiple-choice questions in this chapter include: Pumping Procedures and Regulations; Cargo Properties; and Piping, Pumps, and Symbols. In addition you should also be prepared to answer multiple-choice questions on any of the following subjects:

1. Tanker construction
2. Valves, piping, and fittings
3. Pumps
4. Classes and properties of fuel oils
5. Loading and unloading procedures
6. Tank cleaning procedures
7. Inert gas systems
8. Pumping regulations

Pumping Procedures and Regulations

1. A recently opened cofferdam would be dangerous to enter because of lack of oxygen due to: I. rust oxidation; II. decaying matter.

    A. I   C. both I and II

    B. II   D. neither I nor II

*Routine off watch duties.

2. How should the spaces adjacent to a cargo tank be considered insofar as tank entry is concerned?
   A. same as cargo tank
   B. spot-checked for contamination
   C. as a possible oxygen deficient space
   D. as an open space

3. The maximum bunkering rate depends upon the:
   A. size of the storage tanks ashore
   B. number of tanks to be filled
   C. distance bunkers have to travel
   D. type of pumps used

4. When finished with bunkering you should:
   A. drain to a tank   C. drain to a drip pan
   B. blow to shore   D. blank the line

5. In transferring an oil cargo, what would you do if your vessel started to surge badly along the dock?
   A. slack off the mooring lines
   B. place warning signs in vicinity
   C. shut down, shorten mooring lines
   D. abandon ship

6. If scuppers were plugged and you had an oil spill, you would:
   A. remove plugs and wash overboard
   B. leave on deck until ship got to sea
   C. mop up with sawdust or other absorbent material
   D. do any of the above

7. A ship loading or unloading petroleum cargo is electric bonded to prevent sparking due to:
   A. friction   C. ship grounds in the hull
   B. static electricity   D. any of the above

8. In the event of an oil fire:
   A. get water on deck
   B. open steam or CO_2 smothering system to cargo holds
   C. close off all ventilation, blowers, doors, etc.
   D. all of the above

9. Which of the following types of matches are allowed on tank vessels?
   A. sparkless   C. safety
   B. phosphorous   D. no set requirements

10. When a one wire single flame screen is used, it should be:
   A. 30/30   C. 40/40
   B. 10/30   D. 20/20

11. When a contaminated tank is ballasted, which of the following valves should be closed before the ballast pump is stopped?
   A. sea-suction   C. tank-filling
   B. pump discharge   D. deck-line

12. What should you do when a cargo hose joint or coupling starts to leak badly?
    A. reduce pumping pressure and wrap leak securely
    B. shut down transfer and make repairs
    C. soak spill with sawdust and reduce pumping pressure
    D. wash deck immediately and close tank tops

13. Flashlights used aboard tankers must be:
    A. waterproof
    B. of the three-cell type
    C. approved by the Board of Fire Underwriters
    D. all of the above

14. What is the weight of a B II fire extinguisher?
    A. 50-pound foam
    B. 15-pound soda acid
    C. 20-pound steam smothering
    D. 15-pound CO_2

15. What principle does the combustible gas indicator work on?
    A. the temperature increases resistance
    B. the temperature decreases resistance
    C. expansion
    D. none of the above

16. When transferring petroleum cargoes:
    A. a red flag shall be displayed by day
    B. any running lights can be used
    C. a red light shall be displayed at night
    D. A and C above

17. When filling tanks, sufficient ullage must be allowed to:
    A. prevent oil spillage in rough seas
    B. allow for expansion of the liquid
    C. prevent gas pockets
    D. none of the above

18. Which of the following is the correct sequence for electrically connecting (grounding) a tank vessel to shore piping?
    A. open switch, connect ground cable, close switch, connect cargo hose
    B. connect ground cable, open switch, connect cargo hose, close switch
    C. close switch, connect cargo hose, open switch, connect ground cable
    D. connect ground cable, connect cargo hose, open switch, close switch

19. For emergency lighting purposes:
    A. any type of flashlight may be used
    B. only a 3-cell explosion-proof flashlight may be used

C. only a 2-cell vapor-proof flashlight may be used
D. any of the above may be used

20. When would you enter a tank *alone*, if it wasn't certified gas free?
    A. after telling someone   C. never
    B. any time   D. none of the above

21. How often should you check CO_2 extinguishers?
    A. when seal is broken   C. after each use
    B. once a year   D. all of the above

22. The minimum number of bolts permitted in a bolted flanged oil hose coupling is:
    A. 2   C. 4
    B. 3   D. 5

23. When loading, scuppers are plugged to:
    A. keep the sides of the ship clean in case of a spill
    B. prevent spilled oil from getting into the engine room
    C. prevent spilled oil from getting into the pump room
    D. prevent a deck spill from running overboard

24. Which of the following precautions should be taken to minimize the possibility of explosions caused by static electricity discharges?
    A. electrical grounding of vessel to shore piping
    B. insulation of electrical equipment from vessel's structure
    C. use of flashlights rather than a-c lamps in vapor-filled areas
    D. use of flame safety lamps during entry to an area that may contain explosive fumes

25. Approximately how much space should be left empty in a tank to allow for expansion due to temperature change?
    A. 3 to 5 percent   C. 1 to 3 percent
    B. none   D. 1 to 5 percent

26. Tools of nonsparking materials shall be used:
    A. when opening and closing cargo tank openings
    B. when working in pump rooms
    C. in spaces where there is a possibility of gas accumulation
    D. for all of the above

27. Cargo pump relief valves and pressure gauges shall be tested at least:
    A. once a month   C. every 2 years
    B. once every 6 months   D. once a year

28. Portable extension lights used aboard tankers must always be equipped with:
    A. an explosion-proof lamp fixture
    B. a 3-conductor grounded cable
    C. a guard
    D. all of the above

29. The decision as to when and where to allow smoking is decided by:
    A. a licensed officer   C. any member of the crew
    B. a certified tankerman   D. A or B
30. The gas free inspection required before repairs to tank vessels in-
    volving riveting, welding, or burning is *preferably* accomplished
    by a:
    A. port engineer
    B. Coast Guard inspector
    C. licensed fire inspector
    D. certified marine chemist
31. When bunkering a vessel you should have a: I. red flag during
    daytime; II. red light at night.
    A. I   C. I and II
    B. II   D. neither I nor II
32. Cargo hoses shall be designed to carry:
    A. at least 100 gallons
    B. 100 cubic inches per minute
    C. not less than 100 PSI
    D. not less than 125 PSI
33. Which of the following fire extinguishers would you use to extin-
    guish a small Class B fire?
    A. 15 pound CO_2 C. a soda and acid
    B. a solid stream of water   D. high-velocity fog
34. A person should *not* enter a tank that is not "gas-free" unless he
    has a:
    A. gas mask and flame safety lamp
    B. fresh air mask, a safety harness, and lifeline
    C. flame safety lamp and lifeline
    D. fresh air mask and a flashlight
35. Where would the required fire fighting equipment and location be
    posted on tank barges?
    A. customs house   C. certificate of inspection
    B. owner's office   D. all of the above
36. Sticking of valve stems is caused by:
    A. jamming valve shut when hot
    B. jamming valve shut when cold
    C. stuffing gland set up too tightly
    D. all of the above
37. In loading an oil cargo, what would you do if the tank valve jammed
    open?
    A. put a "cheater" on valve and proceed to close
    B. open all drains on tank
    C. order dock man to shut down
    D. slow down pumping and keep watch for an oil spill

38. The purpose of cleaning out tanks at sea is to:
    A. insure tanks being in condition to receive cargo without contamination
    B. minimize corrosion of tank structure
    C. reduce labor and expense of cleaning
    D. all of the above
39. When loading or discharging cargo at night, display:
    A. a red flag   C. a red electric lantern
    B. a red flag and red light   D. a red kerosene lamp
40. When the transferring has been finished, the oil left in the cargo hose should *not* be:
    A. drained into the vessel's tank
    B. drained overboard
    C. drained into buckets
    D. dipped out with a can
41. How much hose should be used in transferring oil in bulk?
    A. twice the distance between ship and dock
    B. one and a half times the distance between ship and dock
    C. not over 300 feet
    D. sufficient for movement of ship, including tide
42. Loose scale, rust, and sediment in tanks must be cleaned out frequently to prevent:
    A. clogging of limber holes
    B. clogging of suction lines or strainers
    C. contamination of future cargoes
    D. all of the above
43. When transferring bulk oil, what should you do *first* if the cargo hose got pinched between the vessel and the dock?
    A. examine hose for damage
    B. slack off the mooring lines
    C. hoist the hose back into place
    D. shut down the transfer of cargo
44. The "expansion factor" equals:
    A. the amount of oil in gallons times the number of degrees rise in temperature
    B. the coefficient of expansion from 1° F times the number of degrees temperature rise
    C. the amount of oil in gallons times the number of the coefficient of expansion
    D. none of the above
45. If you noticed a large quantity of oil on the water near your vessel, you should:
    A. shut down
    B. notify terminal superintendent

C. call all hands if necessary

D. do all of the above

46. Steam traps are installed in steam lines to:

    A. bypass a set amount of steam

    B. drain condensate from lines without allowing the escape of steam

    C. trap any foreign particles in the steam

    D. insure the proper steam pressure

47. Cargo tanks are vented with:

    A. a vacuum valve   C. blowers

    B. a pressure-vacuum valve   D. none of the above

48. A marine chemist's certificate stating that a tank is safe for men to enter is valid only if: I. there is no change in the status of the tank or vessel; II. the tank is steam cleaned after inspection.

    A. I   C. both I and II

    B. II   D. neither I nor II

49. How is pipe measured?

    A. by outside diameter

    B. by inside diameter

    C. by inside diameter from ⅛ inch to 12 inches, over 12 inches, by outside diameter

    D. by inside diameter from ⅛ inch to 24 inches, over 24 inches, by outside diameter

50. Which of the following should be used on a piece of metal with a very smooth finish?

    A. strapwrench   C. Stillson wrench

    B. channel locks   D. pipe wrench

51. Who can certify that a tank vessel is gas-free?

    A. a marine chemist approved by the National Fire Protection Association

    B. the owner of the vessel

    C. the shipyard superintendent

    D. a certificated tankerman

    E. the master of the vessel

52. The length of time that a tank barge is considered to be "gas-free" is:

    A. permanently (as long as no new flammable or combustible liquids are introduced)

    B. 24 hours

    C. 1 week

    D. this must be determined as necessary, by additional testing

53. The only types of portable electric equipment allowed in any space or compartment of a tank barge that is not gas-free are:

    A. approved explosion-proof, self-contained, battery-fed lamps

    B. electric chipping hammers and needle guns

    C. electric drills and grinders

    D. electric welding machines

    E. electric lights and drop cords, as long as suitable bulb guards are in place

54. The lowest temperature at which a substance will give off vapor which, when ignited, will continue to burn is called its:

    A. lower explosive limit (L.E.L.)

    B. ignition temperature

    C. flash point

    D. fire point

    E. upper explosive limit (U.E.L.)

55. The law requires keeping an oil record book on which of the following vessels making a sea voyage:

    A. all tankers under 150 gross tons

    B. all cargo and miscellaneous vessels under 500 gross tons

    C. all tankships and tank barges over 150 gross tons

    D. all of the above

56. The minimum design bursting pressure of hose used at a cargo transfer facility must be at least:

    A. 100 pounds per square inch

    B. 600 pounds per square inch

    C. 200 pounds per square inch

    D. 1,000 pounds per square inch

57. According to Coast Guard regulations, a cargo vessel's emergency bilge suction may be provided by the:

    A. main fire pump   C. main bilge pump

    B. fuel oil service pump   D. fuel oil transfer pump

58. The emergency bilge system:

    A. has no independent primary pump

    B. is independent of the main bilge system

    C. has a cross connection to the ballast system

    D. is part of the independent bilge system

59. How many remote shutdowns are required on tank barges over 1,000 tons?

    A. 2   C. 4

    B. 3   D. 1

60. Vessels over 500 tons are required to have a station bill posted:

    A. on the gangway

    B. on the bridge

    C. in the engine room

    D. in the crew quarters' area

61. The time allowed to shut down the flow of oil from the terminal is:

    A. 30 sec. after November 1, 1980

    B. 15 sec. after November 1, 1980

    C. 90 sec. before November 1, 1980

    D. 120 sec. before November 1, 1980

62. An independent bilge suction is required for:

    A. ballast tanks   C. machinery space bilges

    B. sludge tanks   D. cargo hold bilges

63. The minimum I.D. of main bilge piping allowed by Coast Guard regulations on a vessel over 150 tons is:

    A. 1½ inches   C. 3½ inches

    B. 2½ inches   D. 4½ inches

64. Accidental flooding of the engine room bilge from the bilge main is prevented by:

    A. stop check valves on the bilge suction manifolds

    B. using a positive displacement bilge pump

    C. installing eductors on all bilge rose boxes

    D. installing a swing check before each bilge valve

65. Each page of the oil record book must be signed by:

    A. the engineer on watch   C. the chief mate

    B. the chief engineer   D. the master

66. If an incorrect entry were made in the oil record book, you should:

    A. erase it

    B. notify the officer in charge

    C. completely black it out and rewrite it

    D. draw a line through it and initial it

67. The oil record book must be maintained onboard for:

    A. not less than 3 years and be available for inspection

    B. 6 months and then be submitted to the Marine Safety Officer for review

    C. an annual inspection

    D. the duration of the cruise

68. Coast Guard regulations concerning shut-off valves located in fuel oil tanks, state that the valves:

    A. shall be arranged for local control

    B. must be made of steel

    C. must be power-operated

    D. may be cast iron

69. Coast Guard regulations prohibit screwed joints from being used where severe erosion, corrosion, shock, or vibration will be encountered, and where the temperature exceeds:

    A. 450°F   C. 825°F

    B. 650°F   D. 925°F

70. Carbon steel bolts or studs may be used to make up a joint if the normal operating:

    A. temperature does not exceed 250°F

    B. temperature does not exceed 500°F

    C. pressure does not exceed 250 PSI for steam

    D. pressure does not exceed 250 PSI for water

71. According to Coast Guard pollution regulations, a 299-ton uninspected motor towing vessel without an oily water separator must have how many outlets accessible from the weather deck to discharge oily bilge slops?

    A. one

    B. two (port and starboard)

    C. three (port, starboard, and aft)

    D. two (fore and aft)

72. Sounding tubes and access openings for fuel oil tanks on cargo vessels are permitted in what space?

    A. washrooms   C. slop sinks

    B. laundries   D. corridors

73. A bulkhead that would be capable of preventing the passage of smoke and flame for one hour would be classified:

    A. A-60   C. C-60

    B. B-60   D. D-60

74. The inspection required before repairs to tank vessels involving "hot work" such as riveting, welding, and burning is preferably accomplished by a:

    A. port engineer   D. fire inspector

    B. marine chemist   E. OSHA inspector

    C. Coast Guard inspector

75. When you are making entries in the oil record book, all quantities should be:

    A. recorded as cubic meters

    B. verified by the chief engineer

    C. recorded directly from the oil discharge monitor

    D. consistently recorded in the oil record book in one specified unit

Cargo Properties

1. What is the grade classification of a petroleum liquid that when heated has a flash point of 170° F?

    A. E   C. C

    B. D   D. B

2. The volatility of a liquid is its ability to:

    A. burn   C. asphyxiate

    B. flash   D. vaporize

3. Coast Guard regulations divide petroleum products into combustible liquids and flammable liquids. Combustible liquids:

  A. give off flammable vapors at or below 150° F
  B. have a Reid vapor pressure of 14 pounds or more
  C. will self-ignite at temperatures below 150° F
  D. have a flash point above 80° F

4. If an oil is heated to 120° F the vapor will flash if it is: I. a combustible liquid; II. a flammable liquid.

  A. I   C. either I or II
  B. II   D. neither I nor II

5. Flammable liquid is defined as any liquid which gives off flammable vapors at or below:

  A. 40° F   C. 110° F
  B. 80° F   D. 150° F

6. Fuel oil vapors are heavier than air and:

  A. odorless   C. explosive
  B. non-toxic   D. visible

7. The flash point of a liquid is the:

  A. temperature at which it burns freely
  B. point at which it explodes
  C. temperature at which it changes from a liquid to a gas
  D. temperature in degrees Fahrenheit at which it gives off inflammable vapors

8. Grade D oils have a flash point below:

  A. 150° and over 80° F   C. 350° and over 200° F
  B. 100° and over 50° F   D. 200° and over 150° F

9. The tendency for a liquid to give off inflammable vapors is determined by the:

  A. setting of the pressure-vacuum valve
  B. Reid vapor pressure method
  C. Saybolt method
  D. Reid pressure-vacuum method

10. The term "barrel" means that unit of liquid measure equivalent to 42 U. S. gallons at which temperature?

  A. 50° F   C. 100° F
  B. 60° F   D. 122° F

11. A liquid that ignites at a temperature above 80° F is called:

  A. a standard liquid   C. a flammable liquid
  B. a combustible liquid   D. an inflammable liquid

12. Grade E oils have a flash point of:

  A. 100° C or over   C. 150° F or over
  B. 200° F or over   D. 80° F or over

13. Which of the following would *not* be included in a grade C oil?

  A. creosote   C. light naphtha
  B. toluene   D. benzene

14. LPG stands for:

A. low-pressure gas   C. light petroleum gas
B. liquid petroleum gas   D. none of the above

15. Upon release to the atmosphere, liquefied gases:
    A. will explode   C. will burn
    B. vaporize quickly   D. none of the above

16. Which of the following has the lowest flash point?
    A. gasoline   C. asphalt
    B. kerosene   D. heavy fuel oils

17. Kerosene is classified as a:
    A. grade A liquid   C. grade D liquid
    B. grade B liquid   D. grade E liquid

18. The danger of explosions is greatest in:
    A. full tanks
    B. half-full tanks
    C. empty compartments subject to vapor air mixtures
    D. any of the above

19. A liquid that can be ignited at a temperature below 80° F is called:
    A. an explosive liquid   C. an inflammable liquid
    B. a flammable liquid   D. all of the above

20. L.I.G. stands for:
    A. low initial gravity
    B. liquefied inflammable gases
    C. liquid internal gas
    D. any of the above

Piping, Pumps, and Symbols

1. The valve symbol ⊲⋈⊐ represents a:
    A. hose gate valve   C. reducing valve
    B. gate valve   D. hose valve

2. The symbol ⊢⊥⊣ is:
    A. screwed ell   C. union
    B. flanged tee   D. none of these

3. The valve symbol ⊲⋈⊣ represents:
    A. an angle valve   C. a spring-loaded valve
    B. a hose angle valve   D. a hose valve

4. The valve symbol ⊣⋈⊐ represents a:
    A. globe valve   C. check valve
    B. gate valve   D. plug cock

5. The valve symbol [symbol] represents a:
    A. plug cock   C. relief valve
    B. safety valve   D. pressure-reducing valve

6. The valve symbol [symbol] represents a:
    A. cross valve   C. angle valve
    B. plug cock   D. gate valve

7. Cargo hoses used for transfer of liquefied flammable gases:
    A. must be hydrostatically tested by a Coast Guard inspector
       every 2 years
    B. are not to remain in service longer than 1 year without
       testing
    C. are to be labeled by the manufacturer showing maximum
       working pressure
    D. must be designed for a bursting pressure of not less than 2
       times the safety relief valve setting

8. Which of the following would *not* cause a centrifugal pump to
   vibrate?
    A. bent shaft
    B. steam valve loose
    C. worn bearings
    D. foundation not sufficiently rigid

9. The device used on the discharge side of many reciprocating pumps
   to provide a continuous discharge is a(an):
    A. absorbing tank   C. cushioner
    B. snifter   D. air chamber

10. A reciprocating pump:
    A. is positive displacement
    B. is intermittent displacement
    C. can be started with suction valve closed
    D. can be started with discharge closed

11. To keep the liquid being pumped by the impeller from returning to
    the suction on the rotor and casing are fitted:
    A. snifting valves   C. lantern rings
    B. pressure regulators   D. wearing rings

12. You should never use what type of packing on a pump shaft?
    A. asbestos   C. wire inserted
    B. flax   D. graphite

13. If flammable liquids are being pumped with a centrifugal pump, you
    should:
    A. throttle the pump discharge valve to assure positive pumping
    B. immediately stop pump if it becomes vapor bound
    C. continuously vent pump casing to expel vapors
    D. loosen packing gland to allow leakage

14. When starting a positive displacement pump, the *first* valve to open should be the:
    A. suction valve   C. discharge valve
    B. drain valve   D. steam valve

15. "Groaning" in the steam end of the reciprocating pump may result from:
    A. cylinder misalignment
    B. broken piston rings
    C. too tight packing
    D. all of the above

16. The follower plate is found on which of the following parts of a reciprocating pump?
    A. valve chest   C. snifter valve
    B. steam chest   D. liquid plunger

17. If a centrifugal pump failed to deliver, the cause may be:
    A. pump speed too low   C. discharge head too high
    B. impeller passages plugged   D. any of the above

18. The volute on a centrifugal pump causes the velocity to:
    A. increase   C. remain constant
    B. decrease   D. do none of the above

19. How is tubing measured?
    A. by inside diameter
    B. by outside diameter
    C. by outside diameter and wall thickness
    D. by none of the above

20. Oil hoses should be supported to prevent chafing by the use of:
    A. canvas slings   C. wooden saddles
    B. tripods   D. A or C

21. The gear, screw, and lobe pumps are all classified as:
    A. variable stroke pumps
    B. multi-stage pumps
    C. positive displacement pumps
    D. triple-ported pumps

22. Lantern rings on a pump serve which of the following purposes?
    A. give added starting torque
    B. lubricate pump bearings
    C. lubricate and seal pump packing
    D. act as a vent

23. The advantage of a centrifugal pump as compared with a reciprocating pump is:
    A. that discharge is continuous
    B. that it has no internal valves
    C. upon accidental closing of discharge valve, excessive pressure will not build up
    D. all of the above

24. Suitable clearance should be left between the ends of packing rings to allow for:
    A. easy removal   C. air pockets
    B. expansion and contraction   D. all of the above

25. A relief valve for a cargo pump is generally installed:
    A. after shutoff valve   C. after suction valve
    B. before shutoff valve   D. before suction valve

26. The "discharge head" of a pumping system is:
    A. the vertical distance from the pump to the discharge level
    B. the horizontal distance from the pump to the discharge level
    C. the vertical distance from the suction to the discharge
    D. none of the above

27. The pump packing gland should be:
    A. slack enough to allow slight leakage of fluid
    B. slightly cocked
    C. brought up tight so as not to allow any leakage
    D. fitted with a relief valve

28. The volute pump is one in which the impeller:
    A. discharges into a gradually widening channel in the pump casting
    B. has stationary diffuser vanes
    C. produces no kinetic energy
    D. does all of the above

29. The device used for preventing the passage of flames into enclosed spaces is called a:
    A. flame-relief valve   C. safety valve
    B. flame stopper   D. flame arrester

30. A "wind sail" is a:
    A. canvas air duct with large side flaps to catch and direct the air for ventilating
    B. small sail used on a lifeboat
    C. flat fin built behind the stack to keep soot from falling on the deck
    D. metal scoop protruding from a porthole to catch the wind

31. When pumping ballast into a contaminated tank you should:
    A. shut discharge valve before stopping pump
    B. shut sea suction first
    C. close deck valves first
    D. shut valve to main line

32. The valve symbol ⫤▷◁⊢ represents a:
    A. globe valve   C. relief valve
    B. gate valve   D. check valve

33. The valve symbol ⊣◁▷⊢ represents a:
    A. gate valve   C. lift-check valve
    B. globe valve   D. swing-check valve
34. The transfer pump which is used to off load petroleum products must
    have two control stations. The second control station is located:
    A. in the engine room
    B. on the bridge
    C. at the officer in charge control station
    D. at the officer in charge emergency control station
35. The type of valve most commonly found on the discharge side of
    liquid cargo manifold is a:
    A. gate   C. butterfly
    B. globe   D. vacuum relief
36. Before using a centrifugal cargo pump, the first thing to do is:
    A. turn it over by hand
    B. loosen the gland
    C. switch over to high suction
    D. close the discharge valve
37. Which of the following is correct?
    A. internal threads are cut with dies
    B. internal threads are cut with reamers
    C. external threads are cut with taps
    D. external threads are cut with dies
38. Viscosity is defined as:
    A. the velocity of the fluid flowing through a pipe
    B. the difference between source of supply and point of
       discharge
    C. the internal friction of a liquid which reduces flow
    D. the temperature at which a liquid gives off inflammable vapors
39. The name plate on a reciprocating pump reads 7″ × 6″ × 4″, what is
    the proper order?
    A. liquid cylinder, stroke, steam cylinder
    B. stroke, liquid cylinder, steam cylinder
    C. steam cylinder, stroke, liquid cylinder
    D. steam cylinder, liquid cylinder, stroke
40. A pump is said to have "negative suction head" when the pump is
    located:
    A. between the suction and discharge
    B. below the liquid supply
    C. above the liquid supply
    D. any of the above

41. A cofferdam is:
    A. an empty space between tank tops and bilges
    B. a cement baffle in a freshwater tank
    C. a tank for storing chemicals
    D. an empty space separating compartments to prevent the contents of one compartment from entering another in case of leakage

42. Under each hose connection will be found:
    A. a flame arrester   C. a drip pan or bucket
    B. a scupper   D. all of the above

43. The name plate on a reciprocating pump lists the following dimensions: 7″ × 6″ × 4″. The diameter of the liquid cylinder is:
    A. 4″   C. 8″
    B. 7″   D. 6″

44. With a reciprocating pump, failure to obtain proper discharge pressure may be caused by:
    A. too low steam pressure
    B. worn piston rings
    C. liquid plunger packing too tight
    D. any of the above

45. The function of the sounding pipe on a tank is to:
    A. allow the operator to hear if any oil is entering the tank
    B. act as an overflow pipe
    C. permit the insertion of a sounding rod so that the depth of oil can be measured
    D. rid the tank of explosive fumes

46. Which of the following valves offers the least amount of resistance to flow?
    A. gate   C. globe
    B. check   D. angle

47. The flinger ring, fitted on the pump shaft, is used to:
    A. lubricate the packing
    B. seal the suction side
    C. prevent leakage of fluid into bearing housing
    D. prime the pump when first starting

48. With a reciprocating pump, failure to deliver liquid may be caused by:
    A. pump not being primed
    B. discharge head too high
    C. liquid plunger packing worn
    D. any of the above

49. All of the following steps are taken in starting a centrifugal cargo pump except:
    A. set relief valve
    B. check lubrication system
    C. vent pump casing
    D. open pump suction and discharge valves
50. The *first* thing to do in starting a rotary pump is to:
    A. check lubrication system
    B. bring prime mover up to speed
    C. open pump discharge and suction valves
    D. adjust governor to give desired pressure
51. The three basic parts of any eductor are the nozzle, the suction chamber, and the:
    A. injector   C. diffuser
    B. compressor   D. siphon
52. A close nipple is a piece of pipe that is:
    A. less than ½ inch long   C. closed at one end
    B. threaded the entire length D. made for brazing
53. To join two pipes that cannot be turned, you should use a pipe:
    A. coupling   C. union
    B. nipple   D. tee
54. A double female coupling is one that:
    A. has outside threads on one end and inside on the other
    B. has outside threads on both ends
    C. has a left-hand twist
    D. has inside threads on both ends
55. Lantern rings are provided on centrifugal pumps to:
    A. allow visual inspection of the packing
    B. provide a passage for the packing coolant
    C. adjust leakage at the shaft gland
    D. allow for distortion of the wearing rings
56. Pump shafts are usually protected from erosion, corrosion, and wear by:
    A. wearing rings
    B. renewable sleeves
    C. a hardened metal coating
    D. internally flooded lantern rings
57. Which pipes are made in standard, extra strong, and double extra strong weights?
    A. plastic pipes   C. iron pipes
    B. copper pipes   D. all of the above
58. Which statement is true regarding grades of pipe?
    A. copper pipe comes in two grades
    B. steel pipe comes in four grades

C. brass pipe comes in three grades

D. none of the above is true

59. How are nipples classified?

    A. full threaded, half threaded, long, short

    B. close, short, long, tank

    C. standard, extra strong, double extra strong

    D. cast, wrought, stainless, brass

60. A needle valve is used in a system requiring:

    A. high pressure drops   C. no pressure drops

    B. close flow regulation   D. no back flow

61. What is meant by the term load line displacement?

    A. the amount of sag in the terminal to ship line

    B. changing the product in the terminal to ship line

    C. the total length of the terminal to ship line

    D. the angle of the terminal to ship line

62. Which type of pump has no moving parts?

    A. reciprocating   C. rotary

    B. centrifugal   D. eductor

63. A swing check valve is used to:

    A. maintain a constant pressure

    B. regulate flow

    C. relieve excessive pressure

    D. allow flow in one direction only

64. If you hear a "crackling" noise in a centrifugal pump, the most probable cause would be:

    A. insufficient speed

    B. cavitation

    C. excessive speed

    D. excessive net positive suction head

65. A "crackling" noise in a centrifugal pump is often an indication of:

    A. insufficient packing   C. excessive suction lift

    B. an oversized lantern ring   D. reverse rotation

66. Reduced capacity accompanied by vibration and noise results from:

    A. cavitation   C. fluid friction

    B. water hammer   D. steam knock

67. To operate a centrifugal fire pump at reduced capacity, you should:

    A. adjust the relief valve   C. throttle the discharge line

    B. throttle the suction line   D. open the priming line

68. Which kind of lubricant is used on reciprocating pump rods?

    A. engine oil   C. graphite and oil

    B. oil mixed with kerosene   D. vegetable oil

69. Loss of efficiency in a pump might be the result of:

    A. a pinhole leak in the discharge manifold

    B. a leak in a gasket on the suction side

C. the suction valve being in the wide open position

D. the pump being installed too close to the suction tank

70. The length of the stroke in a reciprocating pump is adjusted by:
    A. changing the number of packing rings on the piston rods
    B. varying the throttle adjustment
    C. twisting the stayrod in a clockwise direction
    D. adjusting the tappet collars on the pilot valve rod

71. The first step when setting the slide valves on a duplex pump is to:
    A. open the relief valve
    B. ensure the balance piston is on the downstroke
    C. center the steam pistons in the cylinders
    D. measure the port openings so reassembly will be the same

72. After installing new impeller wearing rings, you should:
    A. dynamically balance the shaft and impeller
    B. check the shaft on centers to insure the ring surfaces are true
    C. visually inspect the rings after an hour of operation
    D. all of the above

73. The main difference between a propeller pump and a centrifugal pump is the absence of a:
    A. volute in the centrifugal pump
    B. volute in the propeller pump
    C. velocity nozzle
    D. piston

74. Operating a rotary pump at excessive speeds could cause:
    A. decreased clearances between rotating parts
    B. decreased slippage to the suction side
    C. air binding in the discharge ports
    D. erosion and excessive wear

75. Which of the following would prevent a steam reciprocating pump from delivering its rated capacity?
    A. excessive suction lift
    B. air trapped in the discharge expansion chamber
    C. a leaking snifter valve allowing air to enter the suction
    D. any of the above

76. When gland packing persists in leaking on a reciprocating pump, the cause my be:
    A. a loose tappet collar
    B. clogged suction strainers
    C. an open snifter valve
    D. misalignment of the crosshead guide

77. A pounding noise in the steam cylinder of a reciprocating pump could be caused by:
    A. lower than normal steam temperature

    B. lower than normal steam pressure

    C. loss of air charge in the plenum

    D. improper adjustment of steam cushion valves

78. Excessive lost motion in the valve mechanism of a duplex pump will cause:

    A. the pump to short stroke continuously

    B. the pistons to stop in mid-stroke

    C. the pump to operate sluggishly

    D. the cushioning valves to wear

79. If you change pump suction from one tank to another and lose suction, you should:

    A. loosen the mechanical seal

    B. vent the pump casing

    C. check the discharge strainers

    D. all of the above

80. If a centrifugal bilge pump is operated with the discharge valve closed, the:

    A. motor overload will open   C. pump will overheat

    B. relief valve will open   D. motor will overheat

81. Which of the following types of pumps depends upon a continuous gravity flow of fluid?

    A. a reciprocating pump   D. a centrifugal pump

    B. a gear pump   E. none of the above

    C. an eductor

82. Pipe from $\frac{1}{8}$ inch to 12 inches is sized by:

    A. inside diameter   C. wall thickness

    B. outside diameter   D. wall strength

83. If you were operating a centrifugal pump with worn wearing rings, the:

    A. pump would be very noisy

    B. pump would vibrate excessively

    C. pump would develop insufficient pressure

    D. stuffing box would leak excessively

84. If the capacity of a centrifugal pump decreases gradually over a long period of time, you should replace the:

    A. packing gland   C. lantern ring

    B. mechanical seals   D. wearing rings

85. Standard, extra strong, and double extra strong all have the same:

    A. inside diameter   C. wall thickness

    B. outside diameter   D. wall strength

86. Charring or glazing of the inner surface of packing rings in a centrifugal pump is caused by:

    A. undertightening the packing

    B. failure to seat the packing rings

   C. insufficient lubrication of the packing
   D. packing ring rotation
87. A centrifugal pump may fail to deliver when first started if the:
   A. water seal pipe is plugged
   B. pump is not primed
   C. seal ring is improperly located
   D. impeller is flooded
88. Tubing is sized by:
   A. allowable working pressure   C. nominal inside diameter
   B. cross-sectional area   D. nominal outside diameter
89. When a reciprocating pump is operating at maximum speed, the
   cushioning valves should be:
   A. wide open   C. ¾ opened
   B. completely closed   D. almost completely closed
90. When a centrifugal pump is operating with a positive suction head,
   the inner end of the stuffing box is:
   A. under a vacuum and air tends to leak in
   B. under pressure and fluid tends to leak out
   C. under a vacuum and will not leak
   D. sealed by the lantern ring or seal cage
91. A recirculating line or bleed line is installed on a centrifugal pump
   to:
   A. establish a back pressure to prevent leakage
   B. equalize pressure on both sides of the suction valve disc
   C. prevent the pump from overheating when operating at shut-
      off
   D. decrease the net positive suction head
92. Which type of seal is used for pumps handling toxic or flammable
   liquids?
   A. a conventional stuffing box
   B. an external mechanical seal
   C. a double mechanical seal
   D. a rubber bellows mechanical seal
93. Tank stripping is most effectively accomplished using:
   A. a centrifugal pump
   B. the load on the system
   C. the water displacement method
   D. a positive displacement pump
94. A gear pump should be operated with the discharge valves:
   A. slightly opened   C. fully opened
   B. throttled   D. halfway opened
95. The most common valve found on a tanker is:
   A. globe   C. gate
   B. butterfly   D. check

96. What is the taper of pipe threads?
    A. ¾ inch per foot   C. ¹⁄₁₆ inch per foot
    B. ⅛ inch per foot   D. threads have no taper

97. Which is *not* a standard inch pipe size?
    A. ¼   C. ½
    B. ⅜   D. ⅝

98. After repacking a pump stuffing box, the gland nut is tightened for final seating, then it is:
    A. left in that position
    B. loosened until the gland clears the stuffing box
    C. retightened after 5 minutes
    D. loosened until it is fingertight

99. Packing rings in stuffing boxes of moving rods should be cut:
    A. square   C. stepped
    B. beveled   D. diagonal

100. Total static head is the difference in elevation between the:
    A. discharge liquid level and the suction liquid level
    B. discharge liquid level and the pump centerline
    C. suction liquid level and the pump centerline
    D. suction submergence level and the pump discharge

Pumproom Maintenance Procedures

1. Why should you avoid using metallic packing on bronze or brass shafts?
    A. heat transfer is restricted
    B. scoring may result
    C. the valve seat will be damaged
    D. corrosion may result

2. A manual process used to remove small irregularities by grinding together the contact surfaces of a valve is called?
    A. spotting in   C. grinding in
    B. honing   D. refacing

3. To accurately cut the proper size gasket for a pipeline, you should use:
    A. tin snips   C. a gasket cutter
    B. a jackknife   D. a ball peen hammer

4. The best gasket material to use in cargo fuel oil lines is:
    A. sheet asbestos
    B. oil resistant sheet packing
    C. cork sheet packing
    D. unvulcanized rubber packing

5. Before breaking a joint in a pipeline you should:
    A. determine the size of the gasket

    B. hang a bucket under the joint

    C. have a first aid kit on hand

    D. be sure no pressure is on the line

6. Centrifugal pumps are superior to reciprocating pumps in all of the following ways *except:*

    A. they are smaller, more compact, and less expensive

    B. they pump more cargo in less time

    C. they produce less noise, less vibration, and less pulsation

    D. they pick up and hold their prime faster and more easily

    E. they are usually more reliable and require less maintenance

7. An inverted valve stem may be subject to wear sooner than an upright valve because:

    A. the gate's full weight is on the stem

    B. the gland stud nuts are under more pressure

    C. sediment collects in the bonnet

    D. packing won't properly adhere to the stem

8. When installing packing in a moving joint, you must be careful to prevent:

    A. excessive friction in the joint

    B. wear of the moving parts

    C. deterioration of the packing due to overtightening

    D. all of the above

9. If used for throttling service, which valve could be damaged?

    A. a plug valve   C. a gate valve

    B. a globe valve   D. a needle valve

10. Which device indicates that a tank is safe for men to enter?

    A. a combustible gas indicator   D. an explosimeter

    B. a flame safety lamp   E. none of the above

    C. an atmosphere analyzer kit

11. When a tank vessel is electrically connected to the shorepiping, you should:

    A. connect a bonding cable before connecting a cargo hose

    B. maintain the electrical connection until after the cargo is disconnected

    C. maintain the electrical connection until after any spillage is removed

    D. do all of the above

12. The purpose of a bonding wire is to:

    A. provide an alarm if a hose ruptures

    B. reduce the static noise level when the radio is transmitting and cargo pumps are working

    C. detect an oil temperature rise during transfer operations

    D. provide a safe path for static electricity to prevent sparking

13. When loading is completed the cargo hoses should be:

A. hung over the side and washed in the water to clean them

B. drained over the side and flushed out with a fire hose

C. drained in buckets or cargo tanks and then capped

D. drained in the bilges and then pumped over the side

14. Which of the following requires gas-freeing?

A. a tank vessel that will undergo repairs involving hot work

B. when a cargo is to be carried that will not tolerate residue from previous cargo

C. when a vessel must arrive in port with clean ballast

D. all of the above if it is necessary for men to enter tanks

15. On tankers with manually operated tank valves, the deck hand-wheel indicator registers the:

A. lift of the tank valve disc

B. oxygen content of the tank

C. approximate number of turns the valve has been opened

D. level of oil in the tank

16. In a compression type grease cup, the lubricant is forced into the bearing by:

A. gravity flow   C. a pressure gun

B. spring pressure   D. a Zerk fitting

17. With oil bath lubrication of ball bearings in a cargo pump, the oil level should:

A. never be higher than the center of the lowest ball in the housing

B. cover the bottom of the pump shaft

C. cover the top ball in the housing

D. be kept at the top of the reservoir

18. Before making up a flanged joint, you should:

A. be certain the flanges line up squarely

B. cut grooves in the flange faces with a chisel

C. heat the flange to expand the holes

D. have a spare gasket on hand

19. Butterworthing is a method of:

A. separating water and other impurities from petroleum products

B. cleaning cargo tanks

C. reinforcing flexible cargo hoses

D. cutting circular in the decks of barges and tank ships

20. When closing a cargo valve, to insure that it does not leak, you should:

A. close it down tightly with a wrench

B. completely open it, then close it tightly with a wrench

C. close it, reopen it slightly, then close it hard

D. use a cheater pipe on the valve handle or handwheel

E. all of the above

21. What is the primary purpose of a PV valve on a cargo tank?
>   A. it prevents the tank from blowing out or caving in as a result of any differences in atmospheric pressure
>   B. it prevents sparks from entering the tank
>   C. it prevents flames from entering the tank
>   D. it prevents insects or vermin from entering the tank
>   E. none of the above

22. On tankers with hydraulic tank valve controls, which type of valve has the highest tendency to develop leaks?
>   A. gate valve   C. globe valve
>   B. butterfly valve   D. check valve

23. The tool used to remove a ball bearing from the shaft of a motor is called:
>   A. a slugging wrench   C. a drift pin
>   B. a wheel puller   D. a come-along

24. What tool should be used to remove a tapered roller bearing from a shaft?
>   A. an arbor press
>   B. a steel drift pin and hammer
>   C. any acetylene torch and hammer
>   D. a tapered come-along

25. The Butterworth heater receives steam at approximately:
>   A. 175 PSI   C. 185 PSI
>   B. 180 PSI   D. 600 PSI

26. In order to gas-free a tank it must be pumped out and then:
>   A. washed clean, well ventilated, and its residue removed
>   B. wiped dry with rags
>   C. washed down with hot water
>   D. filled with water

27. If there is a steady flow of oil, what is the lowest pressure at which a small high-speed bearing can safely be lubricated?
>   A. 1 PSI   C. 10 PSI
>   B. 5 PSI   D. 15 PSI

28. In order to choose the proper size reducing valve, what must be known?
>   A. maximum and minimum inlet pressure
>   B. reduced pressure or pressure range
>   C. maximum and minimum flow rates (lbs/hr)
>   D. all of the above

29. Putting grease that is too soft into a roller bearing will cause:
>   A. excessive channeling of the grease
>   B. high heat through churning
>   C. emulsification
>   D. gelling of the base oil

30. As a precaution to prevent deck spills from running overboard, you should:
    A. pump cargo at reduced pressure
    B. pour sand on deck before loading the cargo
    C. wrap leaky cargo hoses with canvas
    D. plug the scuppers, and place catch pans under hose connections

31. An ullage reading is the distance from a given point at the:
    A. sounding tube to either side of the tank
    B. top of the tank to the bottom of the tank
    C. top of the liquid to the bottom of the tank
    D. top of the sounding tube to the surface of the liquid

32. Which is an example of a solid bearing?
    A. a piston pin bushing
    B. a turbine bearing
    C. a spring bearing
    D. a diesel engine main bearing

33. When using an automatic tape well for gauging tanks, the hand clutch is used to:
    A. adjust the tape weight   C. roll up the tape
    B. lower the thieving rod   D. calibrate the tape

34. With the automatic tape well, free movement of the tape is checked by:
    A. removing the side plate
    B. operating the hand clutch
    C. comparing with a hand tape
    D. using litmus paste

35. The _____ is the distance from the surface of the oil to the tank cover. When "filled," approximately 1 to 3 percent of the space in each tank should be allowed for expansion of the cargo to allow for a possible increase in temperature during the voyage.
    A. ullage   C. thiefage
    B. innage   D. dunnage

36. After a main cargo pump has lost suction during the final stages of discharging cargo, removing the remaining cargo is known as:
    A. trimming   C. stripping
    B. tramming   D. listing

37. Fabric type packing, such as flax or hemp, is best suited for:
    A. low temperature use
    B. high temperature use
    C. use where alignment is critical
    D. valves with badly grooved stems

38. What type of material is used in the mechanical seal of most centrifugal water pumps?

A. copper   C. carbon

B. copper and carbon   D. bronze

39. On most tankers, what is used to reduce pump leakage into the bilge?

    A. flinger rings   C. shaft sleeves

    B. mechanical seals   D. clipper seals

40. Which of the following is *not* generally characteristic of inhaling petroleum vapors?

    A. a slight dizziness followed by a feeling of mild elation (i.e. happiness)

    B. loss of sense of smell

    C. staggering, slurred speech, drunken behavior

    D. severe chest pains

    E. increasing sense of confusion

41. To ensure adequate lubrication and to prevent a high operating temperature, the recommended amount of grease in a ball or roller bearing is approximately:

    A. 10 to 15 percent   C. 65 to 70 percent

    B. 35 to 40 percent   D. 90 to 95 percent

42. A grease lubricated ball or roller bearing will run cooler if:

    A. the grease fills the bearing

    B. the grease is thinned with oil

    C. the grease has a low penetration number (is hard)

    D. the grease is heated prior to packing the bearing

43. To reduce pulsations in pipe lines, the discharge side of a reciprocating pump is equipped with a/an:

    A. reed valve   C. relief valve

    B. air chamber   D. feedwater regulator

44. The steam to drive a reciprocating pump is usually taken from:

    A. a desuperheated steam line via a reducing station

    B. an auxiliary exhaust line

    C. the main steam line via a reducing station

    D. a bleed line off the H.P. turbine

45. The best indication that a bearing is being properly lubricated is the:

    A. pressure at the lube oil pump discharge

    B. lube oil strainer condition during cleaning

    C. oil temperature shown by the bearing thermometer

    D. oil temperature leaving the lube oil cooler

46. An eroded disc in a globe valve could be repaired by:

    A. taking a light cut in a lathe

    B. sandblasting with light grit

    C. dressing the seat with crocus cloth

    D. filing with a bastard file

47. The ullage readings taken from a tank at 90°F when applied to the vessel's tank capacity tables:
    A. give the number of gross barrels of liquid in the tank
    B. give the number of net barrels of liquid in the tank
    C. give the API specific gravity of the product
    D. give the volume of vapor remaining above the liquid in the tank

48. A lantern ring is:
    A. the bottom ring in a set of piston rings
    B. the oil slinger on a spring bearing
    C. part of the packing used to prevent air leakage on a centrifugal pump shaft
    D. the lifting ring on each running light

49. How should oil drums be stowed on deck?
    A. on their sides with bung up
    B. on their ends with bung down
    C. on their sides with bung down
    D. on their ends with bung up and protected from contamination by a seal

50. The most effective method of transferring individual barrels of oil by crane is by using:
    A. barrel hooks   C. rope slings
    B. rolling chocks   D. nets

51. Which materials should be used for making a gasket in an oil cargo piping joint?
    A. oil resistant sheet   C. asbestos
    B. rubber   D. cork

52. How can you determine if an automatic sounding tape is working properly?
    A. check its reading against a hand held tape
    B. you can't
    C. remove the side plate
    D. use the hand clutch

53. What is the smallest graduation that can be read with a micrometer having a vernier scale?
    A. .001   C. .1000
    B. .0001   D. .01

54. How is a deflecting beam torque wrench read?
    A. on a scale on the handle C. you listen for a click
    B. on a dial on the handle   D. none of the above

55. A grease gun is used to lubricate a:
    A. condensate ball bearing   C. main turbine
    B. main shaft   D. diesel engine wrist pin

56. Which of the following uses oil fog lubrication?

    A. bearings running at minimum speed/load
    B. gearshaft bearings
    C. high speed bearings
    D. lathe lubrication

57. What should the oil level be for a one shaft roller bearing?
    A. center of bearing   C. top of bearing
    B. bottom of ball bearing   D. centerline of bottom ball

58. Pipe fittings are used on pipes with diameters:
    A. up to 4 inches   C. up to 2 inches
    B. up to 1 inch   D. up to 2½ inches

59. A tap set is used in what order?
    A. plug tap, taper tap, bottoming tap
    B. plug tap, bottoming tap, taper tap
    C. taper tap, bottoming tap, plug tap
    D. taper tap, plug tap, bottoming tap

60. Portable tank cleaning machines get their water from the:
    A. inert gas scrubber   C. mucking supply system
    B. fire main   D. pumproom sea chest

61. The purpose of a pipe tunnel is to:
    A. insulate the piping
    B. provide convenient groupings
    C. enclose all pipes leading to a single compartment
    D. segregate a pipe from the compartment through which it
       passes

62. Which type of lubrication can carry the highest unit loading?
    A. ring lubricated bearings
    B. disk lubricated bearings
    C. pressure lubricated bearings
    D. oil whip lubricated bearings

63. An acceptable means of closure for ballast and fuel oil tank vents
is by a/an:
    A. manually operated ball check valve
    B. automatically operated hinge closure
    C. permanently installed canvas cloth
    D. corrosion resistant wire screen

64. Sounding pipes terminating below the freeboard deck of a cargo
vessel must be fitted with a:
    A. globe valve   C. check valve
    B. stop-check valve   D. gate valve

65. Which of the following would cause a centrifugal pump to cavitate?
    A. leaky seals   C. foot valve stuck open
    B. suction lift too high   D. all of the above

66. A non-rising stem valve indicator on a valve would tell you:
    A. the valve is broken

B. the valve is operative

C. the valve is open or closed

D. what direction to turn the valve

67. What type of grease is used in a Zerk fitting?

    A. soft   C. hard

    B. medium   D. all of the above

68. What keeps a normally remote controlled hydraulic valve closed?

    A. air pressure   C. balance piston

    B. hydraulic pressure   D. spring pressure

69. Antifriction bearings can be removed from their shafts by using an arbor press or wheel puller and a:

    A. ring gauge

    B. split die

    C. split washer or back-up ring

    D. jack screw

70. A roller bearing should be filled to what fraction of its space cavity with lubricant?

    A. less than 1/4   C. 1/2 to 3/4

    B. 1/3 to 1/2   D. more than 3/4

71. Absolute pressure is defined as the difference in pressure between:

    A. any two pressures with a common reference

    B. atmospheric and barometric at a given point

    C. gauge pressure and ambient

    D. a perfect vacuum and the total pressure at a given point

72. Why would roller bearings have higher load capacities than ball bearings?

    A. they are installed with tighter clearances

    B. they are subjected to less pitting and metal fatigue

    C. they have high speed capabilities

    D. they have a larger contact area

73. When a small amount of a precision bearing end extends beyond the bearing housing it is called:

    A. overlap   C. lap or lead

    B. crush   D. protrusion

74. When would you disconnect the water hose from the main on a portable washing machine?

    A. after removing the machine from the tank

    B. as soon as the machine is shut down

    C. after checking the tank for cleanliness

    D. after removing the ground wire

75. What moves the inert gas from the flue to the tanks?

    A. the scrubber   C. the flue isolating valve

    B. the deck isolating valve   D. the blowers

76. You discover external leakage in an operating hydraulic unit dur-

ing a routine inspection. What may be the cause?

  A. improperly fitted gaskets   C. distorted sealing rings
  B. improperly flared tube ends   D. any of the above

77. A popping or sputtering noise in a hydraulic system indicates which of the following conditions?

  A. air leak in the pressure line
  B. air leak in the suction line
  C. air pocket in the cylinder
  D. oil leak in the pressure line

78. Which of the following conditions should you suspect if a pounding or rattling noise occurs in a hydraulic system?

  A. overtight adjustment of parts
  B. defective spring-activated valve
  C. improperly adjusted relief valve
  D. overloading of the system or high-speed operation

79. Prussian Blue is used for:

  A. grinding in   C. lapping
  B. spotting in   D. refacing

80. Which statement is true concerning anti-friction bearings installed on pumps?

  A. the inner race should be free to turn on the shaft
  B. the outer race should be free to turn in its housing
  C. alignment is not critical
  D. they are usually pressed onto their shafts

81. Which wrench is used on large diameter pipe?

  A. monkey wrench   C. stillson wrench
  B. chain pipe wrench   D. spanner wrench

82. What is the copper alloy commonly used in condensers and evaporators which resists corrosion?

  A. red brass   C. copper beryllium
  B. manganese bronze   D. cupronickle

83. The purpose of swash bulkheads is to:

  A. minimize the effect of a list
  B. restrict flooding within a tank
  C. separate cargoes in a common tank
  D. restrict liquid movement within a tank

84. A restrictor valve in a hydraulic hatch cover system does which of the following?

  A. restricts oil backflow to the actuators
  B. prevents overheating of the hydraulic pump
  C. controls the hatch cover movement speed
  D. prevents oil flow to a closed hatch cover

85. A constant pressure is maintained in the portable water system by using:

    A. constant speed supply pumps
    B. variable speed supply pumps
    C. an air cushion in the pressure tank
    D. a pressure regulator

86. Instead of air, why is nitrogen used with the oil in closed hydraulic accumulator systems?
    A. to increase the efficiency of the oil
    B. to prevent a possible explosive mixture
    C. to ensure a constant pressure within the system
    D. to eliminate contamination of the oil usually caused by air

87. Which of the following materials may not be used in gasket maintenance in a hydraulic system?
    A. lead   C. rubber
    B. copper   D. oil treated paper

88. Hydraulic chatter can be caused by:
    A. a vibrating spring-activated valve
    B. improperly secured long pipes
    C. air in the lines or binding of some part of the equipment
    D. all of the above

89. How is split sleeve bearing wear measured?
    A. steel rule   C. vernier caliper
    B. ball/anvil/ type micrometer   D. depth gauge

90. Tubes in evaporators and condensers are usually made of:
    A. copper-nickel alloy   C. manganese copper
    B. steel   D. copper-beryllium

91. What type nut should be used on machinery subject to severe vibration?
    A. acorn nut   C. castellated
    B. wing nut   D. regular

92. Which type motor could be used to actuate a valve inside the tank?
    A. steam   C. hydraulic
    B. D.C. electric   D. A.C.

93. How do you anneal a copper gasket?
    A. slowly in air with warm temperature
    B. drench in oil
    C. drench in water
    D. rapidly in cold air

94. The main advantage of a slide caliper over an ordinary caliper is:
    A. a slide caliper can be measured with any rule
    B. a slide caliper gives a direct reading
    C. a slide caliper can be used on any type of stock
    D. a slide caliper can be used in a machine shop

95. With reference to a vessel's structural integrity, the characteristic of a cryogenic liquid that is most significant is its:

    A. capability to cause brittle fractures
    B. highly corrosive action on mild steel
    C. vapor cloud which reacts violently with saltwater
    D. toxicity at atmospheric pressure

96. Babbit is a metal alloy commonly used for lining:

A. bearings	C. bearing journals
B. shim stock	D. saltwater piping

97. Which of the following thread fits cannot be turned by hand?

A. 3	C. 2
B. 1	D. 4

98. A gurgling noise coming from inside a tank would indicate:
    A. the tank is filling
    B. the pump is running too fast
    C. the pump is running too slow
    D. the pump is sucking air

99. A hand held thread chaser is used for:
    A. cleaning or repairing threads
    B. measuring thread pitch
    C. measuring thread angles
    D. threading

100. Fittings used to close the ends of pipes are called:

A. caps	C. tees
B. ells	D. plugs

Answers to Multiple-Choice Questions for the Pumpman

Pumping procedures and regulations

1. C	14. D	27. D	40. B
2. A	15. A	28. D	41. D
3. B	16. D	29. D	42. D
4. C	17. B	30. D	43. D
5. C	18. A	31. C	44. B
6. C	19. B	32. C	45. D
7. D	20. C	33. A	46. B
8. D	21. D	34. B	47. B
9. C	22. C	35. C	48. A
10. D	23. D	36. D	49. C
11. A	24. A	37. C	50. A
12. B	25. C	38. D	51. A
13. B	26. D	39. C	52. D

Pumping procedures and regulations

53. A	59. D	65. D	71. A
54. D	60. D	66. D	72. D
55. C	61. A	67. A	73. A
56. B	62. C	68. D	74. B
57. A	63. B	69. D	75. D
58. B	64. A	70. C	

Cargo properties

1. A	6. C	11. B	16. A
2. D	7. D	12. C	17. C
3. D	8. A	13. C	18. C
4. C	9. B	14. B	19. D
5. B	10. B	15. B	20. B

Piping, pumps, and symbols

1. A	26. A	51. C	76. D
2. B	27. A	52. B	77. D
3. B	28. A	53. C	78. C
4. A	29. D	54. D	79. B
5. C	30. A	55. B	80. C
6. C	31. B	56. B	81. D
7. C	32. B	57. C	82. A
8. B	33. D	58. A	83. C
9. D	34. C	59. B	84. D
10. A	35. A	60. B	85. B
11. D	36. A	61. B	86. C
12. C	37. D	62. D	87. B
13. B	38. C	63. D	88. D
14. C	39. D	64. B	89. D
15. D	40. C	65. C	90. B
16. D	41. D	66. A	91. C
17. D	42. C	67. C	92. C
18. C	43. D	68. C	93. D
19. C	44. D	69. B	94. C
20. D	45. C	70. D	95. C
21. C	46. A	71. C	96. A
22. C	47. C	72. B	97. D
23. D	48. C	73. B	98. D
24. B	49. A	74. D	99. A
25. B	50. C	75. A	100. A

Pumproom maintenance procedures

1. B	26. A	51. A	76. D
2. C	27. B	52. C	77. B
3. C	28. D	53. B	78. D
4. B	29. B	54. A	79. B
5. D	30. D	55. A	80. D
6. D	31. D	56. C	81. B
7. C	32. A	57. D	82. D
8. D	33. C	58. C	83. D
9. C	34. B	59. D	84. C
10. B	35. A	60. B	85. C
11. D	36. C	61. D	86. B
12. D	37. A	62. C	87. D
13. C	38. C	63. B	88. D
14. D	39. B	64. D	89. B
15. C	40. D	65. B	90. A
16. B	41. B	66. C	91. C
17. A	42. C	67. B	92. C
18. A	43. B	68. D	93. A
19. B	44. A	69. C	94. B
20. C	45. C	70. B	95. A
21. A	46. A	71. D	96. A
22. B	47. A	72. D	97. D
23. B	48. C	73. B	98. D
24. A	49. D	74. A	99. A
25. A	50. A	75. D	100. A

CHAPTER ELEVEN

Multiple-Choice Questions for the Machinist

The topics covered by the multiple-choice questions include: The Metal Lathe; Machine Shop Procedures; Metal-Joining Procedures; and Metal-Cutting Tools. The subjects covered in the questions are listed below:

1. Metal lathe tools and equipment
2. Metal lathe procedures
3. Hand tools
4. Measuring instruments
5. Metal joining procedures

The Metal Lathe

1. When cutting threads on a lathe, what determines the relationship between the spindle speed and the number of threads per inch?
    A. motor speed and spindle speed
    B. spindle speed and feed bar speed
    C. lead screw speed and headstock spindle speed
    D. lead screw speed and feed bar speed

2. When making a facing cut, to get a smooth finish, you should:
    A. cut from outside in
    B. cut from inside out
    C. set tool 45° to surface
    D. set tool 90° to surface

3. What kind of lubricant would you use when taking a cut on cast iron?
    A. lube oil   C. gasoline
    B. water mixed with soda   D. none

4. The depth of thread being cut on a lathe is dependent upon the:
    A. adjustment of the cross slide
    B. positions of the quick-change gear levers
    C. alignment of the cutting tool with the lathe center
    D. adjustment of the thread cutting stop

5. Which way(s) can be used when cutting a taper?
    A. tailstock set over   C. using faceplate
    B. compound rest   D. use both A and B above

6. To convert taper per foot to taper per inch:
    A. multiply by 12
    B. divide by 12

C. add 12

D. subtract .200 and multiply by 4

7. To properly cut even numbered threads with a lathe, using the thread dial indicator, you should close the lathe split or half nut on:

    A. any line on the dial   C. odd numbered lines only

    B. even numbered lines only   D. any numbered half line

8. A left-hand or right-hand facing tool has a sharp point for the purpose of:

    A. machining necks   C. cutting outside threads

    B. machining square corners   D. cutting inside threads

9. To drill using the lathe, the drill must be mounted in the:

    A. headstock   C. lathe dog

    B. tailstock   D. drive plate

10. One complete revolution of the micrometer thimble will move the spindle:

    A. .001 inch   C. .025 inch

    B. .005 inch   D. .050 inch

11. In turning work between centers in a lathe, what must be clamped to the headstock end of the workpiece?

    A. chuck   C. drive plate

    B. lathe dog   D. steady rest

12. The difference between a regular lathe dog and a safety dog is that the latter has:

    A. a headless set screw   C. an exposed head screw

    B. a spring latch   D. a bent tail

13. When machining cast iron workpieces, which of the following fluids is most likely to be used?

    A. kerosene   C. mineral lard oil

    B. soluble oil   D. none of the above

14. When cutting threads on a lathe what do you use?

    A. compound rest

    B. cross feed with micrometer collar

    C. headstock

    D. apron

15. What degree angle is made on all lathe centers on the pointed end?

    A. 45°   C. 60°

    B. 29½°   D. 59°

16. When turning down a long, small diameter workpiece in a lathe, you should:

    A. make sure the dog is jammed in the faceplate

    B. use a steady rest

    C. allow for expansion at the tailstock

    D. do all of the above

17. The lathe tool shown here is a:
    A. cutting off tool
    B. left hand side facing tool
    C. right hand turning tool
    D. universal turning tool

18. What type of instrument would you use when centering up a piece of stock in a lathe?
    A. outside calipers   C. inside calipers
    B. micrometer   D. dial indicator

19. To cut a taper on a lathe, you can:
    A. set over the tailstock   C. use the compound rest
    B. use a taper attachment   D. do all of the above

20. When a lathe tool bit burns, it means that the:
    A. speed is too slow   C. material is too hard
    B. speed is too fast   D. material cannot be cut

21. If you were cutting off stock with a cut off tool blade and the stock tended to ride on top of the tool bit, you should:
    A. raise the tool bit
    B. lower the tool bit
    C. stop the lathe and tighten the chuck
    D. readjust the tailstock

22. The best procedure when filing a piece of metal in a lathe is to take:
    A. short even strokes   C. long fast strokes
    B. long slow strokes   D. short fast strokes

23. When a 1- to 2-inch micrometer reads .250, the micrometer indication is:
    A. 1¼ inch   C. 3¼ inches
    B. 2¼ inches   D. ½ inch

24. Each graduation on the micrometer barrel is equivalent to:
    A. .001 inch   C. .010 inch
    B. .025 inch   D. .100 inch

25. A depth of cut of 0.040 inch reduces the diameter of a lathe workpiece by:
    A. 0.020 inch   C. 0.080 inch
    B. 0.040 inch   D. 0.120 inch

26. When a workpiece is being faced in the lathe, the lathe tool bit must be set:
    A. at the work center   C. below the work center
    B. above the work center   D. with a micrometer

27. At what angle should the compound rest be set when cutting threads?
    A. 60°
    B. 29½° with the compound rest

C. 59°

D. 29° to the work

28. A follower rest is used on a lathe to prevent:

A. deflection of the work by the tool

B. improper centering of the work

C. irregular feed pressure in thread cutting

D. out-of-round turning of the work

29. A left-hand cutting tool cuts from:

A. left to right   C. middle outwards

B. right to left   D. left to right or right to left

30. For what purpose would you use a surface plate?

A. finding centers   C. cutting threads

B. lay out work   D. all of the above

31. A "dead center" for a lathe is so called because it:

A. fits dead center in the headstock

B. fits dead center in the tailstock

C. fits dead center in the workpiece

D. doesn't spin freely with the workpiece

32. A left-hand tool bit is one which is ground so that it will cut:

A. towards the tailstock   C. towards the cross-feed

B. towards the headstock   D. away from the cross-feed

33. The tool to use in checking a workpiece mounted in a four-jaw chuck to see if it is accurately centered is a:

A. surface gauge   C. center gauge

B. dial indicator   D. micrometer

34. The lathe tool shown is a:

A. threading tool

B. cutting off tool

C. right-hand facing tool

D. right-hand boring tool

35. The tool which is a combination drill and countersink is called:

A. boring bit   C. reamer

B. center drill   D. plug tap

36. To face work mounted in a lathe chuck, the top cutting edge of the tool bit must be set:

A. on the centerline of the work

B. slightly above the centerline of the work

C. below the work centerline

D. either A or B above

37. When a taper is being cut on a lathe with a taper attachment, the depth of the cut is adjusted with the:

A. swivel (slide) bar

B. cross-feed screw

      C. angle of the cutting tool

      D. tailstock taper adjustment

38. What would you use to determine the correct angle of a cutting tool or to find the correct center?

      A. drill gauge   C. nothing

      B. center gauge   D. all of the above

39. The operation of putting a nonslip surface on cylindrical work in a lathe is called:

      A. checkering   C. knurling

      B. cross-hatching   D. roughening

40. The lathe tool illustrated here is a:

      A. universal tool

      B. parting tool

      C. right-hand facing tool

      D. round nose turning tool

41. American National threads have an included angle of:

      A. 60°   C. 55°

      B. 29°   D. 47½°

42. The part of the metal lathe which turns the workpiece is the:

      A. tailstock   C. compound rest

      B. headstock   D. cross-feed

43. If you are machining a long workpiece between the centers of a lathe, you should:

      A. make sure the dog is jammed into the faceplate slot

      B. adjust tailstock center to allow for expansion

      C. use only the headstock

      D. use all of the above

44. In referring to threads, "pitch" is:

      A. the distance of the full length of the thread

      B. the distance from a point on one thread to a corresponding point on the next thread measured parallel to the axis

      C. the distance from the top of one thread to the bottom of the next thread

      D. the distance from the bottom of a head on a bolt to the first thread

45. If all the metals listed below are 2 inches in diameter, which is cut with the highest speed on the lathe?

      A. cast iron   C. aluminum

      B. machine steel   D. soft brass

46. When using the metal lathe to drill a hole in the end of a piece of stock, you would:

      A. hold the work in the headstock and move the tailstock with the drill

B. hold the work in the tailstock and move the headstock with the drill

C. hold the work in the headstock and move the compound rest with the drill

D. hold the work in between the headstock and tailstock and use the cross-feed

47. What would you use to check center to center readings, making sure stock is running true, checking tapers and checking to make sure there is no taper?

A. inside calipers   C. micrometer

B. outside calipers   D. dial indicator

48. Any short or sharp angled taper such as the 60° angle found on lathe centers, may be machined by use of the:

A. taper attachment   C. tailstock set over method

B. compound rest   D. all of the above

49. The micrometer screw has a pitch of:

A. 40 TPI   C. 75 TPI

B. 50 TPI   D. 100 TPI

50. When drilling holes larger than ½ inch, it is good practice to drill a small hole first. This is called the pilot hole, and the pilot drill should have a diameter:

A. slightly less than the web thickness of the large drill

B. equal to at least one-half the diameter of the large drill

C. slightly larger than the dead center or chisel edge of the large drill

D. small enough to ensure the maximum cut by the large drill

Machine Shop Procedures

1. When installing a new grinding wheel, always use:

A. blotting paper on each side of the wheel

B. copper gaskets on each side of the wheel

C. a torque wrench to tighten the nut

D. a dial indicator to center the wheel

2. The operation of "truing" a grinding wheel is known as:

A. centering   C. sizing

B. dressing   D. rounding

3. A scriber is made from:

A. carbon steel   C. tool steel

B. cold-rolled steel   D. hot-rolled steel

4. Extra strong (XS) pipe is identified as:

A. NPS (nominal pipe size)   C. schedule 80

B. schedule 40   D. schedule 120

5. A ¼ inch × 20 means:
    A. ¼ inch diameter, 20 threads overall
    B. ¼ inch diameter, 20 threads per inch
    C. ¼ inch diameter plus 20 thousands
    D. .005 inch diameter, 20 threads per inch

6. A tool used in cutting an external thread is called a:
    A. tap   C. reamer
    B. die   D. thread gauge

7. The smallest graduation on a machinist rule is:
    A. $^1/_8$ inch   C. $^1/_{32}$ inch
    B. $^1/_{16}$ inch   D. $^1/_{64}$ inch

8. The best chisel for cutting a keyway is the:
    A. round nose chisel   C. flat cold chisel
    B. diamond point chisel   D. cape chisel

9. The best instrument for measuring thousandths of an inch is the:
    A. caliper   C. micrometer
    B. tachometer   D. pyrometer

10. A street elbow has:
    A. male threads only
    B. has female threads only
    C. both male and female threads
    D. is a tubing fitting

11. Nominal pipe size refers to a dimension which is:
    A. inside diameter
    B. outside diameter
    C. not exact
    D. dimensions which apply to special applications

12. Pipe threads are tapered:
    A. to create a wedge fit
    B. to provide leak proof fitting
    C. to allow joints to be started easily
    D. so that standard threads will not fit pipe

13. One of the factors involved in the choice of a grinding wheel is:
    A. the kind of material to be ground
    B. the amount of stock to be removed
    C. the kind of finish required
    D. all of the above

14. The alignment of coupling faces can be checked:
    A. using an inside micrometer
    B. inserting a thermocouple
    C. inserting a feeler gauge between the coupling faces at various points around the circumference
    D. rotating and measuring to nearest permanent fitting

15. Removing the sharp edges from a piece of stock is referred to as:
    A. knurling   C. planning
    B. chamfering   D. turning
16. When tapping internal threads in a piece of stock, the diameter of the hole drilled for the threads is:
    A. larger than the tap diameter
    B. smaller than the tap diameter
    C. the same size as the tap diameter
    D. any of the above
17. An adjustable open end wrench is used with the force acting on:
    A. the movable jaw   C. the handle
    B. the solid jaw   D. adjusting screw
18. What is the center portion of the combination rule used for?
    A. level lines
    B. finding center on round stock
    C. scribing horizontal lines
    D. scribing vertical lines
19. Grinding wheels have a range of soft to hard abrasive materials depending on the use. Most manufacturers letter their wheels from A to Z. The hardest is marked:
    A. E   C. Z
    B. A   D. E1
20. The tool used to check external pipe threads is called a:
    A. plug gauge   C. pitch gauge
    B. thread gauge   D. ring gauge
21. A valve which is used to control flow and may be throttled is a:
    A. globe   C. gate
    B. plug lock   D. nonreturn
22. Before applying layout blue on a piece of metal, it must be:
    A. roughened   C. cleaned
    B. heated   D. cold
23. Tubing is measured by its:
    A. inside diameter   C. either
    B. outside diameter   D. none of the above
24. What would the face of a high temperature-high pressure valve disc be covered with?
    A. brass   C. stellite
    B. bronze   D. cast iron
25. The pressure remaining constant, a rise in temperature would cause a liquid to:
    A. contract   C. vaporize
    B. expand   D. condense
26. A close pipe nipple is one that is:

A. less than one half inch long

B. threaded on the entire length

C. shorter than the nipple's entire length

D. intended only for silver solder

27. Extra extra strong (XXS) pipe is identified as:

    A. NPS   C. schedule 80

    B. schedule 40   D. schedule 120

28. If you use a dry grinding wheel for sharpening tool bits, dip the end of the bit in water frequently to prevent:

    A. burning your fingers

    B. annealing the cutting edge of the bit

    C. hardening of the tip

    D. the tip from crystallizing

29. Soda added to water is used for cooling instead of plain water because:

    A. it reduces the amount of heat generated

    B. it improves the finish

    C. it overcomes rusting

    D. all of the above

30. When ordering bolts, the information necessary is:

    A. diameter and threads per inch

    B. diameter, threads per inch, and length

    C. diameter, threads per inch, length, and head size

    D. diameter, threads per inch, length, material, and head size

31. After a piece of pipe has been cut it is good shop practice to ream the burr from the end of the pipe. This is done to:

    A. make a taper for starting the die

    B. make a taper for starting the tap

    C. prevent the burr from restricting the flow in the pipe

    D. remove cutting tool marks

32. To join two pieces of pipe by turning, you would use a:

    A. union   C. nipple

    B. coupling   D. tee

33. The tool used to prepare copper tubing for fittings is the:

    A. reaming tool   C. flaring tool

    B. bending tool   D. file

34. The difference between a planer and a shaper is:

    A. the shaper cutting tool is fixed

    B. the planer cutting tool is fixed

    C. the workpiece is moved in a planer

    D. both B and C above

35. The most important factor relative to the physical properties of steel is the:

A. silicone content	C. manganese content
B. sulphur content	D. carbon content

36. If a hole in a piece of metal was ½ inch deep what would you use to measure the diameter accurately?

A. inside calipers	C. outside micrometer
B. telescoping gauge	D. inside micrometer

37. The jaws of a standard vise are:

A. soft	C. hard
B. semihard	D. semisoft

38. What is usually used to hold an impeller to a shaft?

A. lock nut	C. keyed and lock nut
B. press fit	D. keyed

39. The hand tool used for cutting threads on round stock is the:

A. stock and die	C. stock
B. die wrench	D. stock cutter

40. Standard pipe wall thickness is referred to as:

A. NPS	C. schedule 80
B. schedule 40	D. schedule 120

Metal-joining Procedures

1. A piece of steel that is reheated then cooled in still air is called:

A. tempered	C. annealed
B. normalized	D. quenched

2. Which of the following tests measures hardness by the penetration into metal?

A. Brinell	C. Brinell and Charpy
B. Charpy	D. Brinell and Rockwell

3. If muriatic acid is used as a flux, the soldered area must be cleaned thoroughly afterwards to prevent:

A. anyone touching it from getting burned
B. remaining acid from eating the metal
C. the acid from evaporating and the solder disintegrating
D. none of the above

4. Tool steel can be hardened by:

A. heating red hot and plunging into water
B. heating red hot and cooling in a blast of dry air
C. heating red hot and plunging into linseed or cottonseed oil
D. any of the above, depending on type and use

5. Soft solder melts at approximately:

A. 250°	C. 450°
B. 350°	D. 550°

6. Solder will not unite with a metal surface that has:
    A. grease on it   C. oxidation on it
    B. dirt on it   D. any of the above

7. Straight muriatic acid is often used as a flux on:
    A. galvanized iron   C. sheet steel
    B. cast iron   D. any of the above

8. What is the maximum acetylene pressure you would use?
    A. 2 PSI   C. 10 PSI
    B. 5 PSI   D. 15 PSI

9. Copper is annealed by heating to a cherry red color and:
    A. dousing in cold water   C. dousing in oil
    B. cooling slowly in air   D. dousing in hot water

10. If you were welding in a compartment on a ship's bulkhead, where would you place the fire watch?
    A. in the same compartment
    B. on the other side of the bulkhead being welded
    C. in the compartment below
    D. no fire watch is needed

11. When soldering, flux is used to:
    A. keep the solder from running off the metal
    B. keep the metal from getting too hot
    C. keep the tip of the soldering iron clean
    D. remove and prevent oxidation of the metals

12. The annealing of a cutting bit is usually done by what means?
    A. cooling of the cutting bit
    B. heating of the cutting bit from the grinder
    C. at the factory before you receive it
    D. none of these

13. The ability of a material to become permanently deformed without failure is known as:
    A. brittleness   C. ductibility
    B. hardness   D. elasticity

14. If you were welding in a compartment, the fire watch would be:
    A. in the same compartment   C. other side of bulkhead
    B. below the compartment   D. none needed

15. Brazing requires:
    A. hard solder   C. more heat
    B. soft solder   D. A and C above

16. What kind of lubricant would you use on an oxyacetylene regulator?
    A. lube oil   C. none
    B. machine oil   D. crude oil

17. The flux used for brazing is:
    A. muriatic acid   C. borax
    B. hydrochloric acid   D. zinc chloride

18. A brazed joint is:
     A. stronger than a soldered joint
     B. weaker than a soldered joint
     C. the same strength as a soldered joint
     D. three times as strong as a soldered joint
19. Special solders used for aluminum usually require:
     A. more heat
     B. less heat
     C. the same heat as copper wire
     D. the same heat as sheet metal
20. Another name for hydrochloric acid is:
     A. sulphuric acid   C. nitric acid
     B. muriatic acid   D. acetic acid
21. Soldering is the process of:
     A. holding two metals together by heating
     B. joining two metals by a third soft metal that is applied in a molten state
     C. holding two different kinds of metals together by heating
     D. joining two metals together by heating
22. One of the most important factors that is often overlooked when soldering is that:
     A. the surfaces to be soldered must be clean
     B. the two metals to be soldered must not be the same
     C. the two metals to be soldered must be the same
     D. all surfaces should be dipped in acid first
23. Sweating is the process of:
     A. soldering two different kinds of metal together
     B. separating two pieces of metal that have been soldered together
     C. tinning two surfaces, applying flux between them, holding the two together, and heating
     D. none of the above
24. Soft solder is made of:
     A. copper and zinc   C. tin and copper
     B. tin and lead   D. tin and zinc
25. The purpose of "tempering" is to make a metal:
     A. harder   C. less brittle
     B. softer   D. more brittle

Metal-cutting Tools

1. While grinding new cutting edges on a high speed drill you immerse it in cold water, what takes place?

    A. the 59° angle would change due to contraction
    B. cracks will form on the cutting edges
    C. the cutting surfaces will become annealed
    D. the cutting edges will become dull

2. Increasing the feed pressure on a drill as the drill point begins to break through the bottom of the workpiece will cause the drill to:
    A. break cleanly through the bottom of the workpiece
    B. cut an elongated hole in the bottom of the workpiece
    C. cut a tapered hole in the bottom of the workpiece
    D. dig into the workpiece and whirl it around

3. When drilling into cast iron which of the following is used?
    A. lard oil   C. soluble oil
    B. mineral oil   D. none of the above

4. An all hard hacksaw blade is best suited for work on:
    A. brass   C. cast iron
    B. tool steel   D. any of the above

5. In drill sizes:
    A. number 40 is larger than number 38
    B. number 38 is larger than number 36
    C. number 38 is larger than number 40
    D. both A and B above

6. Before drilling a hole in a piece of metal, the location of the hole center should be:
    A. marked with a center punch
    B. marked with chalk
    C. blued
    D. scribed

7. A hacksaw blade with 34 teeth per inch should be used for cutting:
    A. brass   C. heavy stock
    B. cast iron   D. thin wall tubing

8. A groaning sound from a drill tip as the drill is being fed into a metal workpiece indicates:
    A. overloading of the drill tip
    B. the drill is too large
    C. the drill speed is too slow
    D. underfeeding of the drill tip

9. When preparing to tap a hole, the drill size must be:
    A. smaller than the tap
    B. larger than the tap
    C. same size as the tap
    D. depends on the type of thread to be cut

10. A taper shank drill is removed from the drill press using a:
    A. drift pin   C. tang
    B. Morse taper   D. all of the above

11. A hacksaw blade can be placed in a frame in:
    - A. two positions
    - B. four positions
    - C. one position
    - D. three positions

12. Hacksaw blades are made of:
    - A. tool steel
    - B. high-speed steel
    - C. tungsten alloy steel
    - D. any of the above

13. If the lips on a drill point are of unequal length, the drill will wobble and:
    - A. wander from the hole center
    - B. jam in the hole and break
    - C. cut an oversized hole
    - D. over heat rapidly from rubbing

14. The term which refers to the number of teeth per inch in a hacksaw blade is:
    - A. set
    - B. rake
    - C. pitch
    - D. thread gauge

15. The length of a file is measured from:
    - A. end to end
    - B. point to heel
    - C. point to end
    - D. heel to end

16. A "pillar" file is used for:
    - A. filing slots
    - B. filing keyways
    - C. filing against a shoulder
    - D. any of the above

17. The cutting angle on a drill for drilling mild steel should be:
    - A. 39°
    - B. 49°
    - C. 59°
    - D. 69°

18. A drill bit has:
    - A. 4 flutes
    - B. 3 flutes
    - C. 2 flutes
    - D. no flutes

19. The "safe edge" of a file is:
    - A. the end opposite the handle
    - B. the one with the handle
    - C. the edge with no teeth
    - D. none of the above

20. Files are divided into two general classes called:
    - A. rough and smooth
    - B. large and small
    - C. single-cut and double-cut
    - D. flat shapes and round shapes

21. A hacksaw blade with 18 teeth per inch is best suited for cutting:
    - A. solid stock
    - B. cast iron
    - C. aluminum
    - D. any of the above

22. An all hard hacksaw blade is one that:
    - A. has a hard back and flexible teeth
    - B. has a flexible back and hard teeth

    C. has the entire blade hardened

    D. will only fit a solid frame hacksaw

23. Never use a file:

A. that is dirty	C. without oiling
B. without a handle	D. with a tang

24. The best file to use when finishing sharp corners or slots and grooves is the:

A. mill file	C. knife file
B. square file	D. jeweler's file

25. When drilling into a piece of steel, screeching and squeeling sounds occur. What is the reason?

    A. bit is dull

    B. bit is jammed into the work

    C. bit is oversize

    D. cutting speed too low

26. The part of a file that the handle fits on is the:

A. point	C. tang
B. heel	D. face

27. Rapid wear on the extreme outer cutting edges of a drill bit is an indication of:

    A. too much rake

    B. too much speed

    C. not enough speed

    D. margin is not wide enough

28. When using a drill press, the work should be held with:

A. the hand	C. a vise or clamp
B. a pair of pliers	D. gloves on

29. To remove metal stock rapidly with a file, use a:

A. double-cut bastard	C. double-cut coarse
B. rasp	D. A or C

30. For filing lead or babbitt, use a:

A. vixen file	C. lead float file
B. mill file	D. A or C

31. Which drill is the largest?

A. No. 14	C. Z
B. No. 80	D. 1

32. A tool used to finish drilled holes accurately to size is called a:

A. center drill	C. reamer
B. taper gauge	D. plug gauge

33. The hacksaw blade should be placed in the frame with:

    A. the teeth pointing forward

    B. the teeth pointing backward

    C. one end looser than the other end

    D. the teeth facing in any direction

34. A hacksaw blade with 14 TPI (teeth per inch) is best suited for cutting:
    A. cold-rolled steel   C. hot-rolled steel
    B. structural steel   D. any of the above

35. For a fine finish when draw filing, which type of file is preferred?
    A. double-cut file   C. bastard file
    B. single-cut file   D. second cut file

36. The proper cut of file to use when filing soft metal such as brass is the:
    A. smooth cut file   C. coarse or rough cut file
    B. second cut file   D. mill file

37. What is the correct lip clearance of a twist drill?
    A. 8° to 10°   C. 12° to 15°
    B. 10° to 12°   D. 15° to 18°

38. The size of a drill is stamped on the:
    A. web   C. margin
    B. shank   D. flute

39. The "tang" of a file is the part that:
    A. does the cutting   C. has no teeth
    B. fits into the handle   D. is opposite the handle

40. A "pillar" file has:
    A. one safe edge   C. two safe edges
    B. three safe edges   D. A or C

41. When using a hand hacksaw, pressure is applied only on the forward stroke:
    A. when cutting thin wall tubing
    B. when cutting carbon steel
    C. never, pressure is applied only on the return stroke
    D. at all times

42. For finishing a piece of work to size with a file, use a:
    A. double-cut fine-tooth file   C. mill file
    B. single-cut fine-tooth file   D. crossing file

43. When the lips of a drill are ground unevenly it will wobble and:
    A. overheat, and break the point
    B. cut an oversize hole
    C. make a continuous chip
    D. make noise

44. Which drill size is the smallest?
    A. No. 1   C. Z
    B. A   D. No. 80

45. To drill a hole in round stock on the drill press the workpiece should be held in a:
    A. collet chuck   C. vice grip
    B. clamp   D. "V" block

46. A twist drill gauge may be used to measure drill:
    A. length   C. clearance angle
    B. diameter   D. web thickness
47. The lip clearance of a drill should be approximately:
    A. 20° to 25°   C. 12° to 15°
    B. 5° to 10°   D. 15° to 20°
48. When drilling a hole for a taper pin, the drill to be used is:
    A. the smallest diameter of the taper
    B. the center taper diameter
    C. the largest diameter of the taper
    D. 75 percent of drill root diameter
49. All straight shanked twist drills must be mounted or held for drilling in a:
    A. drill socket   C. key type drill chuck
    B. tapered sleeve   D. Morse sleeve
50. If the point angle on a drill is less than 59°, the hole will:
    A. be too large
    B. take longer to drill
    C. will cut an undersized hole
    D. will not center properly

Machine Shop Devices

1. The best tool to use when opening a flanged joint is a:
    A. gasket cutter   C. scraper
    B. spud wrench   D. flange spreader
2. Which punch is used to remove a taper pin that is frozen?
    A. a drift punch   C. a center punch
    B. an aligning punch   D. a prick punch
3. When pipe is screwed in a properly tapped hole, it will give the correct fit when:
    A. the pipe cannot be turned
    B. all the threads are covered
    C. half the threads are covered
    D. all but 2 or 3 threads are covered
4. Tubing is sized by:
    A. allowed working pressure   C. nominal inside diameter
    B. cross section area   D. nominal outside diameter
5. Pipe from ⅛ inch to 12 inches diameter is sized by:
    A. wall strength   C. outside diameter
    B. nominal inside diameter   D. threaded diameter
6. Pipe is measured by its nominal:
    A. inside diameter

    B. outside diameter
    C. inside diameter from ⅛ inch to 12 inches, over 12 inches by
       its outside diameter
    D. inside diameter from ⅛ inch to 24 inches, over 24 inches by
       its outside diameter
7. An American Standard Taper pipe thread has a taper of _____
   inch per foot.
       A. ¼   C. ¾
       B. ½   D. 1
8. If you are cutting external threads by hand and start the die at an
   angle, the threads will:
       A. be out of round on the work
       B. be cut crooked on the work
       C. be rough, weak, and easily broken
       D. straighten out after the third revolution
9. The best chisel for cutting a keyway is the _____ chisel.
       A. round nose   C. diamond point
       B. flat cold   D. cape
10. When drilling holes completely through a metal plate, feed pres-
    sure on the bit should be eased as the bit breaks through the bot-
    tom of the hole to prevent:
       A. drill bit breakage   C. straining the spindle
       B. undersized holes   D. dulling the drill
11. Standard, extra strong, and double extra strong pipe all have the
    same:
       A. inside diameter   C. wall thickness
       B. outside diameter   D. wall strength
12. In which size is iron pipe NOT FOUND?
       A. ⅜ inch   C. ⅝ inch
       B. ½ inch   D. ¾ inch
13. To anneal a copper gasket, you should heat the gasket:
       A. and quench it in air
       B. to cherry red and quench it in water
       C. and let it cool slowly in air
       D. and carbonize it
14. Which material should be drilled at the highest speed?
       A. aluminum   C. copper
       B. medium cast iron   D. carbon steel
15. To get an accurate inside measurement of the diameter of a ½ inch
    hole, you should use a/an:
       A. depth micrometer   C. small hole gauge
       B. inside micrometer   D. inside spring caliper
16. The most accurate method of setting an inside caliper is to use
    a/an:

A. thread micrometer   C. scale

B. outside micrometer   D. dial indicator

17. In an oxygen acetylene welding outfit, the torch tip orifice size:

    A. depends on the hose length

    B. determines the amount of acetylene and oxygen fed to the flames

    C. can be varied by rotating the tip

    D. depends on the regulator flow rate

18. When securing an oxyacetylene cutting outfit for an extended period, you should close the:

    A. hand valves on the torch only

    B. cylinder valves only

    C. cylinder valves and close torch valves with 4 to 5 pounds of pressure in the hoses

    D. cylinder valves and close torch valves when pressure in hoses and regulators is zero

19. To check the thickness of a piece of thin shimstock before using it to make a bearing shim, you should use a:

    A. feeler gauge   C. machinist's rule

    B. micrometer   D. depth gauge

20. Before boring a blind tapered hole, you should:

    A. use a tapered reamer

    B. drill to the large diameter of the taper

    C. drill to the small diameter of the taper

    D. bore a straight hole

21. Acetylene should never be used at pressures above 15 PSI because:

    A. the relief valve will lift

    B. the fusible plug will blow out

    C. rapid depletion of acetylene is hazardous

    D. the slightest shock could cause an explosion

22. Oxygen and acetylene cylinders should always be stored:

    A. upright with the caps screwed on

    B. horizontal with the caps screwed on

    C. upright with the caps off

    D. horizontal with the caps off

23. For welding high carbon steels and nonferrous alloys such as monel, the best flame to use is termed a/an:

    A. oxydizing flame   C. nitriding fusion

    B. neutral flame   D. carburizing flame

24. While taking a rough cut on steel, if blue chips start coming off, you should:

    A. stop lubricating the tool

    B. reduce the cutting tool height

    C. reduce the tool feed or depth of cut

D. decrease the cross compound speed

25. When a lathe is used for thread cutting, the number of threads per inch produced is determined by the speed relationship between the _____ only.
    A. drive motor and spindle
    B. spindle and feed rod
    C. lead screw and head stock spindle
    D. lead screw and feed rod

26. A follower rest should be used with a lathe to machine:
    A. large diameter stock between centers
    B. threads on long slender shafts
    C. work mounted on the lathe carriage
    D. round stock to a finished dimension

27. A metal scriber should only be used to:
    A. remove packing   C. punch gasket holes
    B. mark on metal   D. clean file teeth

28. A tool for measuring or laying out angles is a:
    A. trammel   C. micrometer
    B. protractor   D. caliper rule

29. To safely change spindle speeds in a lathe, you must first:
    A. disengage the spindle clutch
    B. engage the feed change lever
    C. disengage the feed reverse lever
    D. stop the lathe rotation

30. Before the longitudinal carriage feed of a lathe is engaged, you must be sure the:
    A. spindle clutch is disengaged
    B. carriage clamp screw is loosened
    C. carriage stop screw is loosened
    D. thread dial indicator is zeroed

31. Which lathe operation is best done with the carriage locked in position?
    A. facing work held in a chuck
    B. turning work held between centers
    C. threading internal threads
    D. boring an angled hole

32. When coming to the end of a cut using a hand hacksaw, you should:
    A. stop applying the cutting fluid
    B. reduce cutting speed and pressure
    C. change to a finer cut blade
    D. increase cutting speed and pressure

33. Which of the following statements concerning braze welding is (are) true?
    A. braze welding is an exceptionally good method of repairing

malleable (special heat treated) iron
    B. a braze welded joint should be cooled immediately with cold
       water or forced air draft to reduce the intensity of the heat path
    C. repairs to working parts or containers used in chemical pro-
       cesses, especially strong alkaline solutions, are effectively
       accomplished with braze welding
    D. all of the above
34. A tailstock "dead" center is so called because it:
    A. is dead centered on the tailstock
    B. does not move
    C. is dead centered on the workpiece
    D. none of the above
35. The lathe steady rest is normally used for supporting one end of a:
    A. short heavy casting held in a three jaw chuck
    B. long workpiece for facing, drilling, and boring
    C. short workpiece being machined to an internal taper
    D. tubular workpiece being parted between centers
36. If you are taking a roughing cut on a steel workpiece in a lathe and
    see blue chips coming off that workpiece, you should:
    A. decrease the flow of lubricating oil to the tool
    B. reduce the cutting tool height above center
    C. reduce the tool feed or depth of cut
    D. decrease the cross compound speed
37. In a machine shop a center gauge is used for checking the angle of:
    A. drill points
    B. screw threads
    C. screw thread pitch
    D. 60 degree thread cutting tools
38. The rotating part of a micrometer is the:
    A. anvil   C. frame
    B. barrel   D. thimble
39. A micrometer screw has a pitch of _____ threads per inch.
    A. 40   C. 75
    B. 50   D. 100
40. The dead center of a lathe can be properly used only after the end
    of the workpiece has been:
    A. counter sunk   C. center drilled
    B. tapered   D. bored
41. Which statement is true regarding grades of pipe?
    A. steel pipe is manufactured in four common grades
    B. brass pipe is manufactured in three common grades
    C. copper pipe is manufactured in two common grades
    D. extra strong is normally associated with schedule 160 steel
       pipe

42. Which is the best definition of "tool feed" when referring to lathe work?
    A. the distance the tool advances with each revolution of the work
    B. the distance from the bottom of the cut to the uncut surface of the workpiece
    C. the distance the workpiece circumference moves past the cutting tool point in 1 minute
    D. the chip length that will be removed from the work in 1 minute

43. The graphite in a bearing lubricant of graphite grease acts as a:
    A. low temperature sealer
    B. moisture barrier
    C. filler to smooth surface irregularities
    D. coolant to carry away heat

44. The harder the metal, the greater should be the drill's:
    A. diameter   C. point angle
    B. lip clearance   D. cutting speed

45. If you are machining work between lathe centers and the lathe center starts to squeal, you should first:
    A. lubricate the centers
    B. stop the lathe
    C. change the cutting bit
    D. run the lathe at a lower speed

46. Increasing the pressure on a drill as it begins to break through the workpiece, will cause the drill to:
    A. break cleanly through the workpiece
    B. cut an elongated hole in the bottom of the workpiece
    C. form a tapered hole in the workpiece
    D. dig in and tend to whirl the workpiece around

47. When drilling blind holes with a drill press, the proper method of stopping the drill is by:
    A. moving the drill table
    B. using a depth stop
    C. adjusting the spindle return spring
    D. gauging chuck movement

48. Many micrometers are equipped with a ratchet stop on the end of the thimble to:
    A. click at each increment of measure
    B. prevent the user from closing the tool with too much force
    C. stop the spindle from sliding out of the barrel
    D. eliminate ratchet movement

49. The term which refers to the number of teeth per inch in a hacksaw blade is the:
    A. set   C. pitch
    B. rake   D. thread gauge

50. The difference between a common lathe dog and a safety lathe dog is that the latter:
    A. is more easily centered
    B. has a headless set screw
    C. has a spring loaded catch
    D. allows for misaligned center holes

51. When drilling metal, a squeaking sound indicates:
    A. the bit is too large for the hole
    B. the bit is not ground properly on the tip
    C. excessive force is being used
    D. a continuous chip is being taken by the bit

52. When drilling holes larger than ½ inch, you should drill a pilot hole first to:
    A. ensure the maximum cut by the larger drill
    B. provide a path for the dead center of the drill
    C. allow the use of a drill with a lesser lip clearance angle
    D. increase the speed of the cutting bit

53. When you are welding with an oxyacetylene outfit:
    A. open the acetylene valve until the hose pressure is 26 PSIG
    B. open the acetylene cylinder valve only ¼ to ½ turn and leave the wrench on the valve stem
    C. a leaking hose must be repaired by binding with tape
    D. a flashback of flame into the hose is normal

54. In an oxygen acetylene welding outfit, each cylinder has a regulator and two pressure gauges. One pressure gauge indicates cylinder pressure and the other indicates _____ pressure.
    A. tip   C. hose
    B. upstream   D. arc

55. The main difference between a common lathe dog and a safety lathe dog is that the latter:
    A. allows for misaligned center holes
    B. has a spring loaded catch
    C. has a headless set screw
    D. is more easily centered

56. What is the difference between a four jaw independent chuck and a three jaw universal chuck?
    A. the jaws on the three jaw chuck can be individually adjusted
    B. the jaws on the four jaw chuck can be individually adjusted
    C. the three jaw chuck will hold square, round, and irregular shapes in either a concentric or an eccentric position
    D. since the three jaw universal chuck is automatically self centering, it is always more accurate than the four jaw independent chuck

57. Fluxes are used when soldering to:
    A. decrease the melting point of the solder
    B. make the solder flow
    C. ensure proper tinning
    D. clean the joint area

58. Soldering fluxes help the soldering process by:
    A. softening the metals   C. removing oxides
    B. fusing the metals   D. hardening the metals

59. The taper produced by a lathe taper attachment is determined by setting the:
    A. guide (swivel) bar   C. tailstock off center
    B. automatic cross feed   D. compound rest angle

60. What types of classifications are given to short lengths of pipe called nipples?
    A. full threaded, half threaded, long, and short
    B. close, short, long, and tank
    C. standard, extra strong, double extra strong, and schedule 80
    D. cast, wrought, stainless, and brass

61. The degree to which the viscosity of an oil will change with a change in temperature is indicated by the _____ of the oil.
    A. weight designation   C. pour point
    B. viscosity index   D. floc point

62. If you are cutting off a piece of stock in a lathe and the workpiece tends to climb over the top of the cutting off tool, you should:
    A. increase the lathe spindle speed
    B. increase the height of the tool cutting edge
    C. stop the lathe and tighten the chuck
    D. stop the lathe and lubricate the dead center

63. When steel, cast iron, or other metal having scale on the surface is being turned, the first roughing cut should be taken:
    A. slowly to prevent tool chatter
    B. deep enough to get under the scale
    C. lightly to avoid dulling the tool
    D. rapidly in a continuous chip

64. Soft solders have relatively low melting points and consist mainly of _____ alloys.
    A. silver base   C. copper base
    B. lead base   D. nickel base

65. To remove a straight reamer from the work, you should:
    A. turn it clockwise and raise
    B. tap it out with a leather mallet
    C. turn it counterclockwise and raise
    D. work it side to side and raise

66. The drill size is marked on the:
    A. point   C. margin
    B. shank   D. flute
67. Which statement best defines depth of cut in lathe work?
    A. the distance of tool point advance with each revolution of the work
    B. the distance from the bottom of the cut to the uncut surface of the workpiece
    C. the distance the workpiece circumference moves past the cutting tool point in 1 minute
    D. The chip length that will be removed from the work in 1 minute
68. A depth of cut of .026 inch reduces the diameter on a workpiece in a lathe by _____ inch.
    A. 0.013   C. 0.052
    B. 0.026   D. 0.063
69. Two separate workpieces are to have a taper cut using the offset tailstock method. Both pieces are to have the same taper per inch. After the first piece is completed, the tailstock offset must be changed if there is a change in the:
    A. length of the workpiece   C. angle of the cutting tool
    B. diameter of the workpiece D. none of the above
70. For greater accuracy, some micrometers have a vernier scale which makes it possible to read in increments of _____ of an inch.
    A. five-thousandths   C. twenty-five thousandths
    B. ten-thousandths   D. one-fortieth
71. You will know that the correct torque value on a micrometer setting torque wrench is reached when:
    A. the scale is read on the handle
    B. the dial is read on the handle
    C. an audible click is heard and the handle releases
    D. a dial lights on the handle
72. A twist drill gauge can be used to measure the drill's:
    A. length   C. clearance angle
    B. diameter   D. web thickness
73. The taper produced by a lathe taper attachment is determined by setting the:
    A. guide (swivel) bar   C. tailstock off center
    B. automatic cross feed   D. compound rest angle
74. To properly cut odd numbered threads using the thread dial indicator, you should close the split or half nut on:
    A. any line on the dial
    B. any numbered line on the dial

      C. odd numbered lines only

      D. even numbered lines only

75. To properly cut even numbered threads, you should close the half nut on:

      A. any line on the dial   C. odd numbered lines only

      B. even numbered lines only   D. any unnumbered half line

76. Machine bolts are identified by their:

      A. weight   C. threads per millimeter

      B. diameter and length   D. threads per inch

77. What basic dimensions are used in describing machine bolts?

      A. diameter and length only

      B. diameter and cross section only

      C. diameter, length, and number of threads per inch

      D. diameter, head size, and shoulder length

78. What type nut should be used in a high vibration area?

      A. square   C. cap

      B. wing   D. castellated

79. The threaded pipe fittings called street elbows have:

      A. male threads only

      B. female threads only

      C. male and female threads

      D. interrupted threads on each end

80. Round, split dies are usually made adjustable to:

      A. allow threading on oversized stock

      B. control the diameter of threads cut

      C. to help start the die squarely on the round stock

      D. allow threading up to a shoulder

81. A "close nipple" is a piece of pipe that is:

      A. less than ½ inch long

      B. threaded on the entire length

      C. shorter than the nipple's outside diameter

      D. made only for silver soldering

82. If a drill press is being used to drill holes completely through a metal plate, feed pressure on the drill bit should be eased as the bit breaks the bottom of the hole to prevent:

      A. drill bit breakage   C. straining the spindle

      B. undersized holes   D. dulling the drill

83. A metal file that has become clogged with filings is said to be "pinned" and should be cleaned with a file:

      A. scraper   C. oilstone

      B. pick   D. dressing tool

84. To join two installed pipes which cannot be turned, you should use a pipe:

      A. nipple   C. coupling

      B. union   D. tee

85. One of the steps required to increase the drilling speed of a drill press is to:
     A. move the drive belt to a smaller diameter motor pulley
     B. move the drive belt to a smaller diameter spindle pulley
     C. change the terminal connections of the drive motor
     D. change to a larger diameter spindle
86. If a micrometer were opened a distance of 0.0001 inch, you would say the reading is _____ of an inch.
     A. one ten thousandth   C. one millionth
     B. ten one thousandths   D. ten millionths
87. Ferrous metals are metals which contain:
     A. no iron
     B. a large percentage of copper
     C. a large percentage of iron
     D. a large percentage of aluminum
88. A pipe or stillson wrench is properly used only on _____ objects.
     A. hexagonal   C. square
     B. round   D. flat
89. Which chisel should be used for cutting oil grooves?
     A. a diamond point chisel   C. a round nose chisel
     B. a flat cold chisel   D. a cape chisel
90. A flat chisel is properly used for cutting:
     A. inside corners   C. half-round grooves
     B. slots or keyways   D. flat stock
91. To set a divider to the proper radius, you should use a:
     A. micrometer   C. scale
     B. scribing circle   D. vernier caliper
92. Heavy pressure on the ends of a file will cause the work surface to be:
     A. tapered   C. rough
     B. smooth   D. rounded
93. Why are hacksaw blades installed with the teeth pointing away from the handle?
     A. to keep the blade from breaking
     B. so lubrication can flow down the teeth
     C. to keep the blade from overheating
     D. because cutting pressure is easier to apply on the forward stroke
94. When thread cutting, the number of threads per inch is determined by the speed between the:
     A. drive motor and spindle   C. lead screw and spindle
     B. spindle and feed rod   D. lead screw and feed rod
95. A follower rest should be used on a lathe to machine:

A. large diameter stock between centers
B. threads on long slender shafts
C. work mounted on the lathe carriage
D. round stock to a finished dimension

96. For mild steel and general work, the included angle of a drill point is:
    A. 29°   C. 118°
    B. 59°   D. 90°

97. A taper shank drill is removed from the spindle with a:
    A. taper punch   C. vice grip
    B. drill drift   D. leather mallet

98. A pipe or stillson wrench will function best when:
    A. the bite is taken midway up the jaw teeth
    B. the jaws are at the widest setting
    C. maximum pull is exerted with one hand
    D. an extension can be placed on the handle

99. To commence cutting threads on a metal lathe, you should engage the:
    A. feed change lever   C. back gear lever
    B. split or half nut   D. thread chasing dial

100. When you are drilling, which material does not have to be lubricated?
    A. tool steel   C. mild steel
    B. cast iron   D. cast steel

Answers to Multiple-Choice Questions for the Machinist

The metal lathe

1. C	14. B	27. D	40. D
2. B	15. C	28. A	41. A
3. D	16. C	29. A	42. B
4. A	17. B	30. B	43. B
5. D	18. D	31. D	44. B
6. B	19. D	32. A	45. C
7. A	20. B	33. B	46. A
8. B	21. A	34. B	47. D
9. B	22. B	35. B	48. B
10. C	23. A	36. A	49. A
11. B	24. B	37. B	50. D
12. A	25. C	38. B	
13. D	26. A	39. C	

Machine shop procedures

1. A	11. C	21. A	31. C
2. B	12. B	22. C	32. A
3. C	13. D	23. B	33. C
4. C	14. C	24. C	34. D
5. B	15. B	25. B	35. D
6. B	16. B	26. B	36. B
7. D	17. B	27. D	37. C
8. D	18. B	28. B	38. C
9. C	19. C	29. D	39. A
10. C	20. D	30. D	40. B

Metal-joining procedures

1. B	8. D	15. D	22. A
2. D	9. B	16. C	23. C
3. B	10. B	17. C	24. B
4. D	11. D	18. A	25. C
5. B	12. B	19. A	
6. D	13. C	20. B	
7. A	14. A	21. B	

Metal-cutting tools

1. B	14. C	27. B	40. D
2. D	15. B	28. C	41. D
3. D	16. C	29. D	42. B
4. D	17. C	30. D	43. B
5. C	18. C	31. C	44. D
6. A	19. C	32. C	45. D
7. D	20. C	33. A	46. B
8. A	21. D	34. D	47. C
9. A	22. C	35. B	48. B
10. A	23. B	36. C	49. C
11. B	24. C	37. C	50. B
12. D	25. A	38. B	
13. C	26. C	39. B	

Machine shop devices

1. D	8. B	15. C	22. A
2. A	9. D	16. B	23. D
3. D	10. A	17. B	24. C
4. D	11. B	18. D	25. C
5. B	12. C	19. B	26. B
6. C	13. C	20. C	27. B
7. C	14. A	21. D	28. B

Machine shop devices

29. D	47. B	65. A	83. B
30. B	48. B	66. B	84. B
31. A	49. C	67. B	85. B
32. B	50. B	68. C	86. A
33. A	51. B	69. A	87. C
34. B	52. B	70. B	88. B
35. B	53. B	71. C	89. C
36. C	54. C	72. B	90. D
37. D	55. C	73. A	91. C
38. D	56. B	74. B	92. D
39. A	57. D	75. A	93. D
40. C	58. C	76. B	94. C
41. C	59. A	77. C	95. B
42. A	60. B	78. D	96. B
43. C	61. B	79. C	97. B
44. C	62. B	80. B	98. A
45. B	63. B	81. B	99. B
46. D	64. B	82. A	100. B

CHAPTER TWELVE

Multiple-Choice Questions for the Electrician

The electrician works an 8-hour day and is responsible for all of the shipboard electrical maintenance. The duties of the electrician include the following:

*1. Perform electrical maintenance for the main and auxiliary generators, electrical switchboard, electrical distribution system, motors and controllers, winch, boom, and crane controls, and galley equipment.

2. Maintain an accurate and up-to-date work log and megger (megohmmeter) log.

3. Maintain an inventory of spare parts and order repairs and parts.

4. Perform a daily lamp and motor round.

*5. Perform electric cable and receptacle repairs in accordance with the U. S. Coast Guard regulations.

6. Maintain accurate and up-to-date copies of all of the electrical schematics.

7. Maintain the electrician's shop.

*8. Perform starting and testing operations of deck gear prior to arrival and departure.

About electrical machinery

Treat electric circuits as though they were "hot" until you are sure they are dead.

Before closing a switch be sure you know about the circuit. Don't electrocute a shipmate!

Do not bridge a fuse. Fuses are safety devices.

When working on motors or circuits, remove fuses or lock the switch open. Place a tag on the switch to warn others that the line is being worked on.

Ground the frame of portable electric tools before using them.

Stand on a dry rubber mat when working on electrical equipment.

Never use emery cloth on commutators of motors and generators.

Do not use portable electric lights or tools with loose or frayed connections.

Never neglect excessive sparking at the commutator or excessive heat in motors, generators, or switches.

---

*Routine off watch duties.

Realize that moisture and mechanical injury are the main causes of insulation failure.

Before using a steam or water hose in the engine room, take precautions to prevent steam or water from coming in contact with switchboards, generators, or other electrical equipment.

The topics covered by the multiple-choice questions in this chapter include: Electrical Theory; D.C. (Direct Current) Systems; A.C. (Alternating Current) Systems; Maintenance and Regulations; and Electrical Symbols. In addition, you should be prepared to answer multiple-choice questions on any of the following subjects:

1. Electrical theory
2. Electrical circuits
3. Ohm's Law
4. Batteries
5. Direct current generators
6. Direct current motors
7. Alternators
8. Alternating current motors
9. Electrical testing instruments
10. Transformers
11. Electrical maintenance and regulations
12. Electrical symbols

Electrical Theory

1. A stranded wire is given the same size designation as a solid wire if it has the same:
   A. cross-sectional area   C. overall diameter
   B. weight per foot   D. strength
2. Counter electromotive force is measured in:
   A. amps   C. volts
   B. ohms   D. coulombs
3. With other factors remaining constant, when the applied voltage is doubled, current flow in a given circuit will:
   A. double   C. be divided by two
   B. remain the same   D. be divided by four
4. The resistance of a copper wire to the flow of electricity:
   A. increases as the diameter of the wire increases
   B. decreases as the diameter of the wire decreases
   C. decreases as the length of the wire increases
   D. increases as the length of the wire increases

5. Which of the following formulas would solve for amperage?
    A. R divided by E   C. E divided by R
    B. R times E   D. R minus E

6. Which of the following expressions correctly states Ohm's Law?
    A. volts equal amps times resistance
    B. amps equal volts divided by resistance
    C. resistance equals volts divided by amps
    D. all of the above are correct

7. In a parallel circuit which of the following is the same throughout the circuit?
    A. impedance   C. voltage
    B. current   D. resistance

8. When using Ohm's Law, E divided by R would solve for:
    A. amperage   C. watts
    B. voltage   D. resistance

9. When using Ohm's law, E divided by I would solve for:
    A. amperage   C. resistance
    B. voltage   D. watts

10. A wire gauge is used to measure:
    A. insulation value   C. current carrying capacity
    B. size of wire   D. tensile strength

11. The unit of electrical current flow is the:
    A. amp   C. watt
    B. volt   D. ohm

12. The unit of electrical resistance is the:
    A. amp   C. volt
    B. watt   D. ohm

13. Volts times amps equals:
    A. kilowatts   C. ohms
    B. watts   D. watt-hours

14. The unit of electrical pressure is the:
    A. amp   C. watt
    B. volt   D. ohm

15. If the temperature varies with such conductors as copper, silver, and aluminum, which of the following statements is correct?
    A. as temperature increases, resistance increases
    B. as temperature decreases, resistance decreases
    C. as temperature increases, resistance decreases
    D. temperature has no effect on resistance

16. A circuit that does not provide a complete path for the flow of current is:
    A. an open circuit   C. a series circuit
    B. a closed circuit   D. a grounded circuit

17. In a series circuit the total current is:
    A. the same as that of the largest branch circuit
    B. the same throughout all parts of the circuit
    C. the same as that of the smallest branch circuit
    D. none of the above
18. Static electricity is most often produced by:
    A. pressure   C. magnetism
    B. heat   D. friction
19. The total resistance of a parallel circuit is *always*:
    A. larger than that of the branch with the greatest resistance
    B. equal to the sum of the individual branch resistance
    C. equal to the reciprocal of the sum of the individual branch
    D. smaller than that of the branch with the lowest resistance
20. Dielectric strength is the:
    A. opposite of potential difference
    B. ability of a conductor to carry large amounts of current
    C. ability of an insulator to withstand a potential difference
    D. strength of a magnetic field
21. If the resistance of a circuit is doubled and the applied voltage kept constant, the current will be:
    A. doubled   C. the same
    B. quadrupled   D. cut in half
22. If the length of a wire is doubled and the cross-sectional area is reduced to one-half, the change in resistance will be:
    A. halved   C. doubled
    B. quadrupled   D. quartered
23. The purpose of a rectifier is to:
    A. change A.C. to D.C.
    B. change D.C. to A.C.
    C. change the frequency of A.C. current
    D. change the voltage of D.C. current
24. Which is the smallest diameter wire?
    A. 18   C. 6
    B. 10   D. 4
25. In a D.C. series circuit, all the conductors have the same:
    A. power expended in them
    B. voltage drop across them
    C. resistance to the flow of current
    D. current passing through them
26. An increase in current:
    A. decreases temperature
    B. increases temperature
    C. has no effect on temperature
    D. will double the temperature

27. The horsepower of an 1,800 KW (kilowatt) motor is:
    A. 1,800   C. 2,412
    B. 2,142   D. 2,421
28. Soft iron is most suitable for use in a:
    A. permanent magnet   C. natural magnet
    B. temporary magnet   D. solid magnet
29. Residual magnetism is the magnetism:
    A. in a field coil
    B. in the motor
    C. remaining in a substance after it has been removed from a
       magnetic field
    D. gained in converting D.C. to A.C.
30. Magnetic flux is best insulated by:
    A. rubber   D. ceramic
    B. cambric   E. impossible to insulate
    C. porcelain
31. What happens in a series circuit when the voltage remains constant
    and the resistance increases?
    A. current decreases
    B. current increases
    C. current remains the same
    D. current increases by the square
32. The magnetic field around a current-carrying wire:
    A. moves in the direction of current flow
    B. is parallel to the current flow in the conductor
    C. exists at all points along the length of the wire
    D. exists only at the beginning of electron movement
33. Electric current is the flow of electrons through a conductor. This is
    commonly called:
    A. voltage   C. coulombs
    B. amperage   D. resistance
34. On megohm is equal to :
    A. 1,000 ohms   C. 100,000 ohms
    B. 10,000 ohms   D. 1,000,000 ohms
35. A multiconductor cable:
    A. has a number of separate circuits
    B. is a single circuit cable composed of a number of strands
    C. is a flexible cable to carry motor current
    D. is a special heating conductor
36. In D.C. circuits, power is expressed as the product of:
    A. volts and coulombs   C. volts and amperes
    B. ohms and amperes   D. amperes and coulombs

37. A mil is:
    A. 1/10 inches   C. 1/1,000 inches
    B. 1/100 inches   D. 1/1,000,000 inches

38. One kilowatt is equal to:
    A. 1.25 horsepower   C. 1.50 horsepower
    B. 1.33 horsepower   D. 2.00 horsepower

39. Defects in wiring which permit current to jump from one wire to another before the intended path has been completed are called:
    A. grounds   C. opens
    B. shorts   D. breaks

40. Which of the following is *not* a good conductor of electricity?
    A. copper   C. silver
    B. mica   D. aluminum

41. One horsepower equals:
    A. 1,000 watts   C. 100 watts
    B. 746 watts   D. 940 watts

42. The conductance of a conductor is the ease with which current will flow through it. It is measured in:
    A. ohms   C. henrys
    B. mhos   D. amperes

43. The electrical power in kilowatts used by a 220 volt motor drawing 15 amps is:
    A. 3.3   C. 3.8
    B. 3.6   D. 4.0

44. A horseshoe magnet has:
    A. one pole   C. four poles
    B. three poles   D. two poles

45. Retentivity is the power a metal has to retain:
    A. the current in a circuit
    B. magnetic lines of force
    C. electron flow within the circuit
    D. electricity when moving at high speeds

46. When selecting the size of wire to be used in a circuit, the most important item to consider is the:
    A. resistance of the circuit   C. amperage of the circuit
    B. voltage of the circuit   D. amount of wire to be used

47. If a wire is increased in circular mils:
    A. its size is larger in diameter
    B. its resistance is lower per foot
    C. its size is smaller in diameter
    D. A and B
    E. B and C

48. The following formula is used to compute power:
    A. $P = E^2R$ C. $P = I^2R$
    B. $P = R^2E$ D. $P = E \div R$

49. If the resistance of a circuit is doubled and the applied voltage kept constant, the current will:
    A. be increased fourfold   C. be cut in half
    B. be doubled in value   D. remain the same

50. Which of the following statements is true?
    A. like poles attract each other
    B. like poles repel each other
    C. unlike poles repeal each other
    D. none of the above

D.C. (Direct Current) Systems

1. How is a lead-acid cell tested?
    A. hydrometer   C. hogometer
    B. hygrometer   D. megometer

2. A 24-volt lead-acid storage battery consists of:
    A. 8 cells   C. 12 cells
    B. 6 cells   D. none of the above

3. If the charging rate to a battery was too high, it would:
    A. increase the terminal voltage
    B. increase the specific gravity
    C. increase the rate of hydrogen liberation
    D. decrease the terminal voltage

4. In a 12-volt battery there are how many cells?
    A. 2   C. 6
    B. 4   D. 8

5. If the specific gravity of a 12-volt battery at 80° is 1.225, the battery is:
    A. dead   C. partially charged
    B. fully charged   D. shorted

6. The state of charge of a nickel-cadmium battery is determined by the use of a (an):
    A. hydrometer   C. ammeter
    B. voltmeter   D. potentiometer

7. Batteries are rated for capacity in terms of:
    A. voltage   C. watt-hours
    B. amperage   D. ampere-hours

8. After having been given an equalizing charge, a lead-acid battery is considered fully charged when the specific readings of all cells taken at half-hour intervals show no change for:

    A. one hour   C. three hours

    B. two hours   D. four hours

9. What determines the voltage of a lead-acid cell?

    A. the type of electrolyte

    B. the strength of the electrolyte

    C. the size of the plates

    D. none of the above

10. Salt water in contact with storage batteries will develop:

    A. carbon dioxide   C. carbon monoxide

    B. nitrogen gas   D. chlorine gas

11. When a lead-acid storage battery discharges, what would be the effect on the electrolyte?

    A. specific gravity decreases

    B. specific gravity increases

    C. specific gravity remains the same

    D. none of the above

12. The lead plates in storage batteries are separated by:

    A. rubber   C. glass

    B. wood   D. any of the above

13. In cold weather the specific gravity of a battery:

    A. rises   C. remains the same

    B. lowers   D. none of the above

14. According to battery manufacturer's specifications, what hydrometer reading will be obtained from a fully charged portable lead-acid battery?

    A. 1.100 to 1.150   C. 1.280 to 1.300

    B. 1.180 to 1.182   D. 1.750 to 2.750

15. Dirty lead-acid type batteries should be cleaned off with:

    A. soap and water

    B. sodium chloride

    C. baking soda (sodium bicarbonate)

    D. potassium hydroxide

16. A fully charged battery reads from:

    A. 1.280 - 1.300   C. 1.050 - 1.350

    B. 1.025 - 1.075   D. 1.200 - 1.500

17. A dead cell of a lead-acid battery is checked by:

    A. megger   D. hydrometer

    B. hygrometer   E. ohmmeter

    C. test light

18. How many 1.5-volt batteries are required to supply a load of 12 volts if the batteries are connected in series?

    A. 12   C. 8

    B. 6   D. 10

19. How many 1.5-volt batteries are required to supply a load of 12 volts
if the batteries are connected in parallel?
  A. 12   C. 3
  B. 6   D. none of the above
20. The rating of a storage battery that delivers 15 amps for 12 hours is:
  A. 180 ampere hours   C. 27 ampere hours
  B. 150 ampere hours   D. 360 ampere hours
21. Which of the following items is necessary to keep a storage battery
in good operation?
  A. maintain proper specific gravity
  B. keep cool and well ventilated
  C. maintain proper level of electrolyte
  D. all of the above
22. What type of battery-charging circuit is used aboard ship to main-
tain storage batteries in a condition of readiness over long periods of
disuse?
  A. test discharge circuit
  B. quick charge circuit
  C. 20-amp charging rate circuit
  D. trickle charging circuit
23. H_2SO_4 is:
  A. sulphuric acid   C. hydraulic acid
  B. hydrochloric acid   D. muriatic acid
24. The total voltage and amperage of two 50-amp 6-volt batteries
connected in series is:
  A. 12 volts, 100 amps   C. 6 volts, 100 amps
  B. 12 volts, 50 amps   D. 6 volts, 50 amps
25. The total voltage and amperage of two 50-amp 6-volt batteries
connected in parallel will be:
  A. 6 volts, 100 amps   C. 12 volts, 100 amps
  B. 6 volts, 50 amps   D. 12 volts, 50 amps
26. The voltage of a battery is equal to the:
  A. efficiency of the number of cells times the resistance
  B. amperage of a single cell times the number of cells in series
  C. voltage of a single cell times the number of cells in series
  D. voltage of a single cell times the number of cells in parallel
27. Three 12-volt storage batteries connected in parallel will give you a
total voltage of:
  A. 12 volts   C. 36 volts
  B. 24 volts   D. 48 volts
28. Indicate the proper procedure for mixing battery electrolyte:
  A. use alkaline water, add water to acid
  B. use alkaline water, add acid to water

C. use distilled water, add water to acid

D. use distilled water, add acid to water

E. all of the above would be satisfactory

29. D.C. generators are classified according to the manner in which:

    A. they are used

    B. the field windings are connected to the load

    C. the armature circuit is connected to the load

    D. the field windings are connected to the armature circuit

30. The purpose of the commutator and brushes on a D.C. generator is to:

    A. change A.C. to D.C. current

    B. change D.C. to A.C. current

    C. neutralize armature reaction

    D. carry current to the outside circuit

31. When two D.C. generators operate in parallel, they are protected against motorizing by:

    A. blow out coils   C. undervoltage trips

    B. governor relay   D. reverse current trips

32. How is the rotation of a D.C. generator reversed?

    A. reverse field connections   D. both B and C

    B. switch brushes   E. none of the above

    C. switch armature leads

33. On a D.C. generator where is the pigtail located?

    A. feather spring   C. brush holder

    B. conductors   D. spiral adjusting spring

34. Which of the following D.C. generators has the largest percentage of voltage drop between no load and full load?

    A. stabilized shunt   C. shunt

    B. flat compounded   D. under compounded

35. A D.C. generator that has a voltage rise from no load to full load is said to be:

    A. under compounded   C. flat compounded

    B. over compounded   D. under flat compounded

36. If a D.C. generator was rotated in the wrong direction, it would fail to come up to voltage because the:

    A. brushes would burn out

    B. generator would burn out

    C. armature field would oppose the field current

    D. circuit breaker would not energize

37. A generator operates on the principle that:

    A. when a field revolves, current is generated

    B. when an armature revolves, a magnetic field is induced

C. voltage is induced when a conductor cuts a magnetic flux

D. a small voltage in the primary produces high voltage in the secondary because of the large number of coils in the secondary

38. With an increase in loat on a flat-compounded D.C. generator, the voltage will:

A. increase   C. remain the same

B. decrease   D. reduce to half

39. D.C. generators are rated in:

A. KVA   C. Kw

B. KwA   D. HP

40. The voltage output of a compound D.C. generator is adjusted by a rheostat placed:

A. in series with the shunt field

B. in series with the series field

C. across the series field

D. across the shunt field

41. If two generators are connected in series:

A. voltage is added and current stays the same

B. current is added and voltage stays the same

C. both current and voltage stay the same

D. none of the above

42. A generator interpole always has the same polarity as the:

A. pole following it   C. opposite main pole

B. pole preceding it   D. none of the above

43. Interpoles are connected in:

A. series with the armature

B. series with the shunt field

C. parallel with the armature

D. parallel with the series field

44. A D.C. compound-wound generator that has a voltage drop from no load to full load is said to be:

A. under compounded   C. flat compounded

B. over compounded   D. none of the above

45. The part of a D.C. generator into which the working voltage is induced is the:

A. yoke   C. armature

B. field poles   D. commutator

46. The proper sequence for securing a D.C. generator in parallel operation is to:

A. open the circuit breaker, reduce the current to zero, and secure the driving unit

B. open the circuit breaker, secure the driving unit, and cut in resistance to the field

C. reduce current to near zero, open circuit breaker, and switch and secure the driving unit

D. reduce the current to near zero, secure the driving unit, and open circuit breaker and switches

47. Interpoles or commutating poles are connected in compound D.C. generators in:

A. series with the shunt field

B. series with the series field

C. series with the armature

D. series with shunt and series field

E. series with the armature but in parallel with each other

48. The only type of compound generator commonly used aboard ship is the:

A. over compounded   C. stabilized shunt

B. flat compounded   D. cumulative compounded

49. What are commutators made of?

A. soft copper bars insulated with mica

B. hard drawn copper bars insulated with mica

C. soft solid copper with cutaway slots for mica

D. hard drawn solid copper with cutaway slots for mica

50. A shunt-wound generator is one in which the field windings are in parallel with the:

A. armature   C. commutator

B. brushes   D. field poles

51. An "exciting current" is required to:

A. build up a dead circuit

B. create a magnetic field

C. excite a synchronous motor

D. build up the voltage in a battery

52. Which of the following are *not* in a D.C. commutator and armature?

A. interpole   C. copper bars

B. mica   D. vee ring

53. If the brushes in a generator are not positioned in the neutral plane, sparking may occur between the brushes and the:

A. yoke   C. armature windings

B. commutator   D. field pole windings

54. A rheostat is a device that regulates the strength of an electric current by:

A. varying the resistance in the circuit

B. varying the voltage in the circuit

C. increasing magnetic field in the circuit

D. varying the current in the circuit

55. Which of the following is *not* found on a D.C. generator?
    A. pigtails   C. stationary armature
    B. brushes   D. brush holders

56. Which of the following will *not* cause a generator to vibrate?
    A. misalignment   C. loose pigtails
    B. loose bolts   D. faulty speed governor

57. Most generators will withstand an overload of:
    A. 15 percent   C. 30 percent
    B. 25 percent   D. 35 percent

58. A series-wound generator has the field windings in series with the:
    A. brushes   C. commutator
    B. armature   D. field poles

59. The pole pieces mounted in a D.C. generator are built up of sheet steel laminations riveted together to:
    A. fit the curvature of the frame
    B. reduce eddy current losses
    C. allow for necessary air gap
    D. allow for easy assembly

60. What is the primary reason for commutating poles in a D.C. generator?
    A. aid in commutation
    B. increase field strength
    C. neutralize armature reaction
    D. prevent sparking of the brushes

61. Sparking and grooving of commutator may be caused by:
    A. overload   C. wrong type of brushes
    B. strength of field   D. any of the above

62. The voltage of a D.C. generator depends on which of the following?
    A. speed of armature
    B. strength of field
    C. number of armature conductors
    D. all of the above

63. To correct the polarity of a generator, you should:
    A. rotate armature
    B. lift brushes and rotate armature
    C. lift brushes and apply D.C.
    D. lift brushes and run generator

64. Which of the following groups of motors are D.C. motors?
    A. compound and synchronous
    B. series and induction
    C. series, shunt, and compound
    D. induction and synchronous

65. A series-wound motor is used to run a pump driven with a belt. If the belt breaks, the motor will:
    A. overspeed and run out of control
    B. stop
    C. slow down
    D. keep running at the same speed

66. If more resistance is applied to the shunt field of a D.C. motor, the motor speed will:
    A. decrease
    B. increase
    C. remain constant
    D. brake down to a stop

67. A shunt motor would be best suited for:
    A. constant speed results
    B. an anchor windlass
    C. a cargo winch
    D. any of the above

68. If the resistance is increased in the shunt field of a motor, the motor will:
    A. speed up
    B. slow down
    C. run at same speed
    D. stop

69. Which of the following is the distinguishing feature of a shunt motor?
    A. it has a high starting torque
    B. a load will not affect it if running at high speed
    C. it has a stable speed through a wide load range
    D. it will not drop in speed if overloaded

70. Which of the following will *not* cause a hot motor bearing?
    A. insufficient lubrication
    B. loose brushes
    C. overload
    D. misalignment

71. When the polarity of the D.C. line is reversed, what does it do to the motors connected?
    A. rotation stays the same
    B. rotation is reversed
    C. they stop
    D. speed will decrease

72. A D.C. series motor should always be mechanically coupled to the load in order to:
    A. increase torque
    B. facilitate cooling
    C. increase efficiency
    D. prevent excessive speed

73. D.C. motors are provided with starters and controllers to:
    A. provide local control for the motor
    B. improve power factor
    C. provide good speed control at light loads
    D. start motor at less than line voltage

74. The handle on a faceplate starter is returned to the off position by a:
    A. solenoid
    B. spring
    C. switch
    D. push button

75. The handle on a faceplate starter is held in the operating position by:
    A. solenoid   C. switch
    B. spring   D. push button

76. The advantage of D.C. motors over A.C. motors is the fact that they:
    A. are less expensive
    B. require less maintenance
    C. can be started across the line
    D. offer a better means of controlling speed

77. To reverse a D.C. compound motor:
    A. change any two of the three leads
    B. interchange armature leads
    C. interchange armature and field leads
    D. put one lead to ground

78. Below normal speeds of cargo-winch at average load would indicate failure of the:
    A. control fuse   C. overload relay
    B. brake solenoid   D. accelerating contactor

79. A starting resistance used with a large D.C. motor should gradually be:
    A. cut out of the field circuit as the motor picks up speed
    B. cut into the armature circuit as the motor picks up speed
    C. cut out of the armature circuit as the motor picks up speed
    D. cut into the field circuit as the motor picks up speed

80. Starting resistors are used in conjunction with D.C. motors to:
    A. reduce the heavy starting current
    B. start the motor in the desired direction
    C. keep the motor from gaining speed too rapidly
    D. prevent excessive counter EMF from being developed

81. If the load was suddenly released from a shunt motor, it would:
    A. continue to operate at the same speed
    B. speed up
    C. slow down
    D. stop

82. In a compound-wound motor, part of the line current flows through the:
    A. frame   C. interpoles
    B. stator   D. shunt field coils

83. What is the distinguishing feature of a shunt motor?
    A. high starting torque
    B. will not drop in speed if overloaded
    C. stable speed through a wide load range
    D. load will not affect it if running at high speed

84. To reverse a D.C. compound motor:

    A. put one lead to ground
    B. interchange armature leads
    C. change any two of the three leads
    D. interchange armature and field leads

85. What would cause one bar of a commutator to blacken?
    A. open coil   C. shorted coil
    B. closed coil   D. grounded coil

86. If the load was removed from a series-wound motor, it would:
    A. slow down   C. speed up
    B. stop   D. remain at the same speed

87. Brushes are normally seated to a commutator by:
    A. filing them down to proper size
    B. using emery cloth to fit them
    C. using fine sandpaper on them
    D. not using anything; they are preset at the factory

88. What would you use to clean a commutator?
    A. soap and water
    B. light oil
    C. low pressure dry air with an electrical solvent
    D. pencil eraser

89. Which of the following will cause generator brushes to burn?
    A. brushes not in neutral plane
    B. generator overload
    C. weak brush springs
    D. all of the above

90. If a commutator is slightly out of round you would:
    A. discard armature
    B. take a cut with lathe tool with commutator in place
    C. use a file
    D. apply heat

91. When the armature coils of a D.C. motor cut through the magnetic field, the voltage induced is known as:
    A. load EMF   C. effective EMF
    B. counter EMF   D. applied EMF

92. Armature cores are laminated to:
    A. increase the lines by force
    B. increase the magnetism
    C. cut down on losses by eddy currents
    D. decrease heat losses

93. High mica between commutator bars is removed by:
    A. removing   C. undercutting
    B. burning   D. chiseling

94. New brushes are fitted by:

A. drawing sandpaper between brush and commutator
B. drawing crocus cloth between brush and commutator
C. drawing emery cloth between brush and commutator
D. using a half round file to shape them

95. Annular grooves around the circumference of a commutator indicate:
    A. improper brushes
    B. high mica
    C. improper brush staggering
    D. open armature circuit

96. What is *not* part of maintenance work on brushes and commutators?
    A. check for high mica
    B. staggering brushes
    C. lift brushes and apply coat of mineral oil
    D. replace worn brushes

97. The proper color for a commutator is:
    A. dark brown   C. glazed chocolate
    B. shiny brown   D. reddish brown

98. If the manufacturer's specifications for brush pressure are not known, a safe pressure would be:
    A. 2 to 3 PSI   C. 1 to 1½ PSI
    B. 1 to 3 PSI   D. none of the above

99. A proper method to determine if commutator brushes are properly spaced is:
    A. measuring the brush rigging bars
    B. using a paper template indicating proper brush position
    C. using a fish or hook scale to equalize all spring tensions
    D. scribing the commutator at each brush and shifting the commutator to the proper position

100. Commutator segments are made of:
    A. zinc   C. copper
    B. brass   D. nickel

A.C. (Alternating Current) Systems

1. Impedance in an A.C. circuit is:
    A. combined effects of X_L and X_C
    B. combined effects of resistance, X_L and X_C
    C. resistance to flow of current due to inductance
    D. resistance to flow of current due to capacitance

2. The unit of measurement for inductive reactance is the:
    A. ohm   C. ampere
    B. volt   D. henry

3. A capacitive circuit causes:
    A. voltage to lead current
    B. current to lead voltage
    C. current and voltage to be in phase
    D. current and voltage to be in step

4. In a three-phase circuit the phases are:
    A. 360° apart   C. 160° apart
    B. 180° apart   D. 120° apart

5. The unit hertz is equivalent to:
    A. revolutions per minute   C. revolutions per second
    B. coulombs per second   D. cycles per second

6. Alternating current may be changed to direct current by the use of a:
    A. transformer   C. capacitor
    B. rectifier   D. resistor

7. Which of the following waveforms represents the current and voltage supplied by a ship's A.C. generator?
    A. exponential wave   C. square wave
    B. sawtooth wave   D. sine wave

8. The ratio of real power to apparent power is the:
    A. safety factor   C. design factor
    B. power factor   D. A or C

9. In the accompanying illustration the power factor meter would indicate:
    A. unity   C. lead
    B. lag   D. no indication

10. What is the purpose of a synchroscope?
    A. parallel an A.C. generator with a D.C. generator
    B. synchronize propulsion motor with propulsion
    C. parallel A.C. generators
    D. parallel D.C. generators

11. Inductance is the property of an electric circuit that:
    A. opposes any change in the applied voltage through that circuit
    B. opposes any change in the current through that circuit
    C. aids any change in the applied voltage through that circuit
    D. aids any change in the current through that circuit

12. In preparation for putting an A.C. generator in parallel with one which is on the bus, the synchroscope is observed turning in the slow direction. This indicates:
    A. voltage and current are out of phase
    B. the oncoming generator is running slower than the bus

C. the generator which is on the bus is running slower than the oncoming generator

D. the synchroscope is not turned on

13. The frequency of the alternating current generated by a synchronous generator is governed by the speed and the:

    A. full excitation   C. power factor

    B. load   D. number of poles

14. How is the rotating field of an alternator excited?

    A. slip rings

    B. slip rings insulated from shaft

    C. slip rings uninsulated from shaft

    D. separate D.C. excitation

    E. none of the above

15. Why is a reverse power relay put in an A.C. generator circuit?

    A. to prevent it from acting as a motor

    B. to prevent overload

    C. to prevent overspeed

    D. all of the above

    E. none of the above

16. Chattering of the alternator brushes can usually be eliminated by:

    A. decreasing the brush tension

    B. dressing and polishing the collector rings

    C. decreasing the load

    D. changing the position of the brushes

17. The load rating of an A.C. generator is determined by the;

    A. internal heat it can withstand

    B. load it can carry continuously

    C. load it is capable of supplying

    D. overload it can carry for a specified time only

18. With an increase in load on an alternator, to maintain the voltage the automatic voltage regulator will:

    A. cut resistance into the armature

    B. cut resistance out of the armature

    C. cut resistance into the field

    D. cut resistance out of the field

    E. change the number of poles

19. Which of the following is *not* found on A.C. generators?

    A. slip rings   C. brushes

    B. commutator   D. field coils

20. Another name for an A.C. generator is:

    A. a dynamometer   C. an alternator

    B. a dyamotor   D. any of the above

21. An A.C. armature is *always* the:

    A. rotating part of the generator

    B. stationary part of the generator

    C. conductor into which voltage is induced

    D. conductor through which D.C. exciter current flows

22. The power factor of an A.C. generator may be said to be in unity when:

    A. the kilowatts developed equal the voltage

    B. the kilowatts developed equal the current

    C. voltage is maximum at the same time current is minimal

    D. voltage and current reach maximum values simultaneously

23. When using an A.C. generator on a three-phase, four-wire system, the neutral wire:

    A. maintains equal current in each phase

    B. maintains equal power in each phase

    C. maintains equal voltage in each phase

    D. has current flow when the loads are unbalanced

24. With A.C. generators, the revolving armature-type generator is not generally used because:

    A. it would be too difficult to parallel

    B. too much D.C. excitation would be required

    C. excessive weight would be required for the unit

    D. heavy voltage slip rings and brushes would be required

25. The voltage output of an A.C. generator is controlled by:

    A. varying the D.C. exciter voltage

    B. varying the reluctance of the air gap

    C. regulating the speed of the prime mover

    D. shorting out part of the armature windings

26. The rating of an alternator, as given on its nameplate, is 800 Kw, 0.8 power factor. The significance of this rating is that the alternator:

    A. always operates at 0.8 power factor

    B. can supply an 800 Kw, 0.8 lagging power factor load at rated voltage

    C. is fully loaded at 800 Kw, any power factor

    D. efficiency is highest with an 800 Kw, 0.8 power factor load

27. A reverse power relay is used to;

    A. reverse the rotation of a motor

    B. protect the generator from a power reversal

    C. change A.C. to D.C. or D.C. to A.C.

    D. reverse the rotation of a generator

28. Synchronization means:

    A. phase difference   C. equal speeds

    B. time for time   D. cycle for cycle

29. The proportion of the kilowatt load handled by one of a group of paralleled alternators may be increased by increasing its:

    A. reactive current   C. field excitation

    B. voltage output   D. governor setting

30. Excitation for an A.C. generator can be taken from a:

    A. battery   C. converter

    B. separate exciter   D. any of the above

31. The load rating of an A.C. generator is determined by the:

    A. internal heat it can withstand

    B. load it can carry intermittently

    C. load it is capable of supplying

    D. overload it can carry for a specified time only

32. Except for the power limitation of the turbine the maximum load carried by a generator is limited by the:

    A. relay settings   C. field current

    B. generator voltage   D. temperature rise

33. If you have two alternators in parallel and one is not working properly, and one alternator cannot handle the load, what would you do?

    A. change any two of the three leads

    B. increase the D.C. voltage to exciter

    C. speed up one alternator

    D. cut out some of the branch circuits and secure the faulty alternator

34. Synchronous converters are used to:

    A. change A.C. to D.C.

    B. change D.C. to A.C.

    C. change synchronous to induction

    D. change induction to synchronous

35. If a synchroscope is placed in a circuit in which the frequency of the incoming alternator is equal to that of the bus, the pointer will:

    A. rotate at a constant velocity in the slow direction

    B. oscillate continuously between the fast and slow directions

    C. rotate at a constant velocity in the fast direction

    D. remain stationary

36. Field excitation, where required, is *always* supplied from a (an):

    A. magneto

    B. attenuating amplifier

    C. direct current source

    D. alternating current source

37. Rather than have six leads coming from a three-phase A.C. generator, you can:

    A. tie the leads from each phase together in series

    B. tie the leads from each phase together in parallel

    C. have one lead from each phase connected together

    D. have any 3 leads connected together to get 2-lead output

38. Which of the following types of A.C. motors is employed for propulsion modern ship installations?

    A. wound-rotor   C. synchronous

    B. squirrel cage   D. universal

39. An operation characteristic which appears on the name plates of shipboard A.C. motors is the:

    A. type of winding   C. temperature rise

    B. input Kw   D. locked rotor torque

40. One very important advantage of A.C. over D.C. motors is that:

    A. A.C. motors are self-grounding

    B. alternating current is more powerful than direct current

    C. for a given power, A.C. motors are smaller than D.C. motors

    D. by using resistor banks, you can obtain much finer control with A.C.

41. What type of motor makes up the greatest part of the load of three-phase A.C. shipboard power systems?

    A. synchronous   C. repulsion

    B. squirrel cage induction   D. wound-rotor induction

42. What is the difference between a three-phase and a single-phase motor?

    A. a three-phase motor is self-starting and a single-phase motor requires auxiliary means of starting

    B. a three-phase motor requires auxiliary means of starting and a single-phase motor is self-starting

    C. a three-phase motor is used only for small horsepower and a single-phase motor is used only for high horsepower

    D. none of the above

43. The type of A.C. motor used for high-starting torque and low-starting current is the:

    A. synchronous motor   C. squirrel-cage motor

    B. wound-rotor motor   D. compound-wound motor

44. Reversing direction of rotation of the propeller on a turbo-electric vessel is achieved by:

    A. reversing the frequency supply from generator to motor

    B. reversing the direction of rotation of the main turbine

    C. interchanging two of the three conductors between generator and motor

    D. changing the position of circuit contacts to cut in reversing coils on the motor

45. Increasing the number of poles in an induction motor:

    A. increases the field speed

    B. decreases the field speed

      C. decreases the motor's rated torque

      D. causes the frequency of line E to drop

46. Increasing the frequency of the voltage applied to an induction motor causes the:

      A. field speed to decrease   C. rotor torque to decrease

      B. field speed to increase   D. stator current to increase

47. The synchronous speed of a 6-pole 60-cycle induction motor is:

      A. 900 RPM   C. 1,800 RPM

      B. 1,200 RPM   D. 3,600 RPM

48. Which of the following A.C. motors has its rotor energized by D.C.?

      A. synchronous   C. repulsion

      B. squirrel-cage   D. wound-rotor

49. The purpose for squirrel-cage windings in a synchronous motor is to:

      A. provide a means for starting

      B. make balancing more precise

      C. produce a higher power factor

      D. eliminate arcing between the stator and the rotor

50. The direction of rotation of a split-phase induction motor can be reversed by:

      A. reversing the starting winding leads

      B. reversing the main winding leads

      C. reversing the leads of one phase

      D. reversing any two leads

51. A synchronous motor differs from an induction motor in that it:

      A. is not self-starting

      B. requires an A.C. and D.C. power supply

      C. may be used for power factor correction

      D. all of the above

52. An advantage of a wound rotor motor over an induction motor is:

      A. high starting torque with low starting current

      B. much cooler operation

      C. much cheaper

      D. it doesn't require a starter

53. The rotor winding of a squirrel-cage motor consists of:

      A. a series winding connected to slip rings

      B. metal bars and end rings

      C. form-wound coils

      D. salient field poles

54. The most common type of starter used on board ship for A.C. motors is the:

      A. secondary capacitor   C. autotransformer

      B. primary resistor   D. across-the-line

55. An across-the-line starter gives:

A. high speed   C. slow starting power

B. poor voltage control   D. maximum torque

56. The speed of a synchronous motor is varied by:
    A. changing the voltage to the motor
    B. changing the frequency or the number of poles
    C. by inserting resistance into the rotor
    D. by inserting resistance into the stator

57. All of the following will cause an induction motor to run hot except:

    A. grounded stator   C. clogged ventilation duct

    B. shorted stator   D. high power factor

58. When a synchronous motor is unloaded it would:

    A. speed up   C. maintain speed

    B. slow down   D. stop

59. Synchronous motor speed is controlled by:
    A. field excitation
    B. generator voltage
    C. varying frequency or number of poles
    D. rheostat control

60. Switching which 2 power leads to a three-phase motor will reverse the direction of rotation?

    A. L1 and L2 only   C. L1 and L3 only

    B. L2 and L3 only   D. any two leads

61. What is meant by the slip of an induction motor?
    A. change of speed under load
    B. difference in the speed of the rotor to the speed of the magnetic field
    C. difference in the speed of the rotor and frequency
    D. difference in the speed of the rotor and speed of the generator
    E. none of the above

62. How is speed changed in a 2-speed induction motor?
    A. vary the number of poles
    B. vary the frequency
    C. vary the voltage
    D. vary resistance in rotor circuit

63. Which term designates across-the-line starters that automatically restart the motor after a temporary power failure?

    A. emergency run   C. low-voltage protection

    B. step-back relay   D. low-voltage release

64. Two types of instrument transformers are:

    A. auto and power   C. step-up and step-down

    B. potential and current D. potential and high voltage

65. In a transformer, if:
    A. primary voltage increases, current increases
    B. primary voltage increases, current decreases

    C. secondary voltage increases, current decreases

    D. secondary voltage decreases, current decreases

66. The 3 principal parts of a transformer are its:

    A. core, primary windings, and secondary windings

    B. primary windings, load, and magnetic flux

    C. primary windings, secondary windings, and magnetic flux

    D. mutual induction, magnetic flux, and windings

67. On a transformer, to increase the voltage from the primary winding to the secondary winding:

    A. increase the windings in the primary

    B. reduce the windings in the primary

    C. reduce the winding in the secondary

    D. use a permanent winding

68. A step-up transformer:

    A. raises voltage and decreases amperage

    B. raises voltage and amperage

    C. decreases voltage and amperage

    D. decreases voltage and increases amperage

69. Transformers are used with:

    A. D.C. current   C. A.C. current

    B. A.C. or D.C. current   D. synchronous current

70. When 120 volts are supplied to a 4-to-1 step-down transformer, what would be the voltage in the secondary winding?

    A. 10 volts   C. 30 volts

    B. 130 volts   D. 120 volts

71. A step-down transformer lowers:

    A. voltage and amperage

    B. voltage and increases amperage

    C. amperage and increases voltage

    D. none of the above

72. What is found in the primary of a transformer if the secondary is stepped up?

    A. fewer coils   C. magnet

    B. more coils   D. high voltage

73. If the secondary of a transformer is stepped down, the primary will have:

    A. fewer turns   C. twice as many turns

    B. more turns   D. half as many turns

74. There are three classes of transformers. Which is *not* correct?

    A. iron core   C. auto-tran

    B. air core   D. parallel

75. This diagram represents a motor
    starter of what type?
    A. compensating time
    B. across the line
    C. shunt time delay
    D. transformer

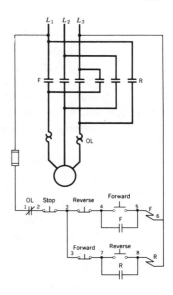

Maintenance and Regulations

1. Low voltage release as used on motor starting equipment has which
   of the following characteristics?
   A. it trips the circuit contactor when motor starts to overspeed
   B. it requires manual resetting upon restoration of normal
      power
   C. it uses a phase sensitive relay to trip contacts in series with
      the holding coil of the starter
   D. it allows the motor to restart upon restoration of normal
      voltage

2. From the diagram, if number one was a blown
   fuse, how is a jump test made using a voltage
   tester?
   A. connect probes A to C
   B. connect probes A to D
   C. connect probes B to C
   D. connect probes B to D

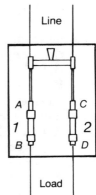

3. The load between two steam-driven alternators operating in parallel may be adjusted by varying:
    A. the speed of the alternators
    B. the field strength of the machines
    B. the power factor of the alternators
    D. steam supply to the prime movers

4. When would you ground an electric hand tool?
    A. when it is a D.C. machine
    B. when it is an A.C. machine
    C. any machine that operates on over 100 volts
    D. only when working on wet steel plates

5. All of the following operating characteristics are listed on the nameplates of motors used aboard ship except the:
    A. temperature rise   C. horsepower
    B. input kilowatts   D. operating voltage

6. A wattmeter shows the:
    A. voltage
    B. amperage
    C. combined volts and amps or load delivery
    D. resistance

7. A probable cause for a turbo-generator tripping out on overspeed is a sudden:
    A. loss of field excitation   C. total loss of load
    B. large increase in load   D. loss of steam pressure

8. An ammeter is connected in a circuit in:
    A. series parallel   C. series
    B. parallel   D. contact

9. Which of the following are protected from motorization by reverse power relays?
    A. alternators   C. motor-generator sets
    B. exciters   D. amplidynes

10. A 500-volt "megger" is being cranked at the required speed for taking readings. If the ground lead and the test prong are touched together, what will the "megger" reading be?
    A. 0   C. 500 ohms
    B. 250 volts   D. 500 volts

11. The correct phase rotation of a three-phase alternator can be checked with a:
    A. dynamometer   C. three-phase motor
    B. power factor meter   D. polyphase voltmeter

12. A voltmeter is connected in a circuit in:
    A. parallel   C. series
    B. series parallel   D. relay

13. To keep the current through a D.C. voltmeter as low as possible, the moving coil circuit is provided with a (an):
    A. series inductor   C. high series resistance
    B. external shunt   D. high parallel resistance

14. When the lifeboat master switch is in the off position:
    A. the solenoid is deenergized, and the brake is on
    B. the solenoid is energized, and the brake is off
    C. the solenoid operates the emergency switch
    D. the brake is not operated by the solenoid switch

15. Except for the power limitation of the turbine, the maximum load carried by a generator is limited by the:
    A. relay settings   C. field current
    B. generator voltage   D. temperature rise

16. If the needle on a megger does *not* return to zero, what is the cause?
    A. out of calibration
    B. needle bent
    C. normal operation
    D. external adjustment is necessary

17. A galvanometer is used to measure:
    A. small voltage   C. large currents
    B. small currents   D. both A and B

18. The power supply for a megger is obtained from:
    A. any 115 volt D.C. circuit   C. flashlight batteries
    B. any 115 volt A.C. circuit   D. a magneto

19. A megger measures:
    A. volts   C. resistance
    B. amps   D. insulation resistance

20. Which could you use to locate a grounded coil in a synchronous motor?
    A. voltmeter   C. multimeter
    B. frequency meter   D. megohmmeter

21. The purpose of connecting a rheostat in series with the shunt field of a D.C. generator is to adjust:
    A. line current   C. field current
    B. generator voltage   D. bus voltage

22. A shorted coil can be detected by:
    A. high resistance   C. overheated coil
    B. low resistance   D. both B and C

23. A circuit that has one wire in contact with the hull of a ship is a:
    A. short circuit   C. series circuit
    B. closed circuit   D. grounded circuit

24. A synchroscope is used to:
    A. parallel A.C. generators
    B. parallel D.C. generators

C. synchronize propulsion motor and generator

D. none of the above

25. A multimeter contains a voltmeter and:

A. wattmeter

B. frequency meter

C. ammeter and ohmmeter

D. ohmmeter and milliammeter

26. Which of the following connections would be most likely to injure the instrument attached?

A. an ammeter in series in the circuit

B. a voltmeter connected across the line

C. an ammeter connected across the line

D. a voltmeter in series with the line

27. If a voltmeter is connected across a line, it must be protected with a:

A. shunt

B. high resistance coil in the armature circuit

C. low resistance coil in the armature circuit

D. shunt and a coil of high resistance

28. An ohmmeter measures:

A. voltage   C. resistance

B. insulation resistance   D. amperage

29. Using a multimeter, you *cannot* zero the indicator when touching the prods together in the resistance position. This will normally indicate that:

A. new batteries are needed

B. the shunt has gone bad

C. the meter coil is open

D. the indicator is bent or stuck

30. When positive and negative lines are in contact and the current bypasses the load, it is called a (an):

A. open circuit   C. proper connection

B. short circuit   D. positive contact

31. When a bar-to-bar test is made with a volt-ohmmeter an open coil will be indicated by:

A. high reading on open bars and lower on the others

B. the same reading as across bars and slightly lower on others

C. a lower reading on open bars and slightly higher on others

D. a zero reading across open bars and higher on others

32. A short circuit is:

A. an electrical leak

B. two grounded wires

C. unwanted current with low resistance

D. all of the above

33. An open coil can be detected by:
    A. high resistance   C. watts
    B. low resistance   D. resistance

34. Current measuring instruments must always be connected in:
    A. series with the circuit   C. series parallel connection
    B. parallel with the circuit   D. shunt

35. If a fuse blows the circuit, it becomes a (an):
    A. parallel circuit   C. closed circuit
    B. open circuit   D. grounded circuit

36. A frozen motor is a motor in which the:
    A. bearings have overheated   C. fields have been reversed
    B. rotor will not turn   D. contactor will not close

37. A motor with a locked rotor may:
    A. burn out the field winding
    B. cause the motor contactor to trip out
    C. burn out motor supply leads
    D. all of the above

38. You can test a motor field for an open condition with a (an):
    A. ammeter   C. voltmeter
    B. megger   D. wattmeter

39. Damp armature windings will cause:
    A. reduced voltage   C. overheating
    B. reduced current   D. increased resistance

40. All electric cables run through watertight bulkheads must be:
    A. welded on both sides of the bulkhead
    B. installed with watertight packing glands
    C. grounded on both sides of the bulkhead
    D. fitted with unions on each side of the bulkhead

41. A "dead board" is:
    A. a board with no power
    B. a board with no switches
    C. a board with no circuit breaker
    D. none of the above

42. If a splice is necessary, where should it be made?
    A. where it can't be seen   C. in a junction box
    B. out of reach   D. overhead only

43. The safety factor in using a double pole switch is the fact that:
    A. both line wires are dead when switch is turned off
    B. it can be replaced easily
    C. it will stand greater loads
    D. it can be used on any voltage

44. Which of the following is a consequence of reversing the phase sequence?

A. single-phase motors will run backward
B. three-phase motors will not start
C. three-phase motors will run backward
D. single-phase motors will not start

45. Rubber or asbestos varnished cambric insulated power and light cables are not allowed in sizes smaller than:

   A. no. 14   C. no. 18
   B. no. 12   D. no. 16

46. The magnetic field in a three-phase squirrel-cage induction motor is established by the:

   A. induced current in the rotor windings
   B. stator windings and the three-phase supply voltage
   C. laminated steel core and the aluminum conductors in the rotor
   D. movement of the poles around the rotor

47. Dead front switch boards shall be used on D.C. boards when the voltage is above:

   A. 110   C. 220
   B. 250   D. 115

48. When the ground indicator light comes on, you should:

   A. go to the distribution panel and open circuits one by one until light goes out
   B. check wiring from the main switchboard
   C. visually check the main feeders for burned spots
   D. check insulation resistance of the main lines

49. What will happen to an operating D.C. generator's voltage when the field resistance is increased?

   A. voltage will decrease
   B. voltage will increase
   C. voltage will remain the same
   D. voltage will oscillate, then increase

50. The navigation lighting branch circuits are equipped with:

   A. 3 amp fuses   C. 10 amp fuses
   B. 5 amp fuses   D. 15 amp fuses

51. Renewable link fuses:

   A. are used on circuits above 50 volts
   B. are used on circuits above 250 volts
   C. are used on D.C. circuits
   D. shall not be used aboard ship

52. Most wiring aboard ship from the switchboard to the panel boxes and branch circuits is installed by:

   A. Romax cable
   B. single conductor wire

C. the knob and tube system

D. armored cable multiconductor

53. In a three-wire system, the ground wire is:

    A. red   C. green

    B. white   D. black

54. What protective device is used on a "dead front" switchboard to take the place of the fused knife switch on a "live front" board?

    A. open type circuit breaker

    B. motor operated circuit breaker

    C. enclosed type circuit breaker

    D. a fusestat

55. The reason why an equalizer bus is used with compound generators operated in parallel is that it:

    A. regulates the degree of compounding

    B. places the shunt fields in parallel

    C. prevents any motor action from developing in any of the machines

    D. divides the load equally

56. The usual function of disconnect switches in a high voltage circuit is to:

    A. open or close the circuit under load

    B. isolate from live buses equipment not in service

    C. maintain continuity of service should the breakers fail

    D. open the circuit in the event of overload

57. Branch lighting circuits are allowed to carry:

    A. 880 watts

    B. 1200 watts

    C. 2440 watts

    D. no maximum wattage but circuit must be limited to 30 amps

58. Horizontal cable supports should be placed every:

    A. 14 inches   C. 18 inches

    B. 24 inches   D. 12 inches

59. In the following list of instruments, which is not correctly stated?

    A. megger is used to register high resistance

    B. wattmeter is used to measure power

    C. voltmeter is connected with high resistance to the needle

    D. ammeter is connected across the circuit

    E. ohmmeter measures resistance

60. When selecting the size of wire to be used in a circuit, the most important item to consider is the:

    A. resistance of the circuit   C. amperage of the circuit

    B. voltage of the circuit   D. amount of wire to be used

61. You would be standing on a rubber mat when you are:

    A. cleaning a commutator
    B. in front of a switchboard paralleling generators
    C. changing fuses
    D. all of the above
62. It is advisable to close a knife switch firmly and rapidly because then there is less:
    A. danger of shock to the operator
    B. chance of making an error
    C. mechanical wear of the contacts
    D. likelihood of arcing
63. Which of the following devices prevents overload on a generator?
    A. rheostat   C. fusestat
    B. circuit breaker   D. any of the above
64. The limiting factor in the use of a direct switching starter is the relationship between:
    A. current and voltage
    B. generator capacity and fuses used
    C. starting current and circuit breaker
    D. starting current and generator capacity
65. Emergency generators can be stopped with the:
    A. overvoltage trip   C. manual trip
    B. overspeed trip   D. undervoltage
66. The general alarm phones are powered by what type system?
    A. I.C.   C. 115V D.C.
    B. 440V A.C.   D. 24V D.C.
67. The safest solvent to use for cleaning an electric motor is:
    A. carbon tetrachloride   C. carbon dioxide
    B. diluted muriatic acid   D. trichloride ethylene
68. Under voltage release device is undesirable and dangerous when used in control of motors in some types of service because:
    A. it will automatically restart the motor without attention after normal voltage is restored
    B. the motors must be restarted manually after every step
    C. such a device will disconnect the motor only after an overload has been sustained for a dangerous period of time
    D. such a device may open the circuit on a short time overload
69. All electrical indicating and alarm systems should be inspected frequently for:
    A. oil soakage   C. grease in switch boxes
    B. loose connections   D. broken or sagging cables
70. Of the following, the least undesirable practice if a specified wire size is *not* available for part of a circuit is to:
    A. use two wires of ½ capacity in parallel as a substitute
    B. use the next larger size

    C. use a smaller size wire if the length is short

    D. reduce the size of the fuse and use smaller wire

71. When tightening a terminal screw connection, the end of the wire should pass around the screw in the same direction as the screw is turned so that:

    A. the wire will act as a locknut

    B. the screw can be removed more easily

    C. any pull on the wire will tighten the screw

    D. the wire will not turn off

72. The capacity of no. 14 rubber insulated wire is:

    A. 20 amps   C. 25 amps

    B. 15 amps   D. 30 amps

73. A "dead front" board is a board with:

    A. insulated switches and no open terminals

    B. no switches on it

    C. no circuit breaker

    D. no safety handrail or rubber mat

74. A limit switch is used on a piece of electrical apparatus to shut off the power when:

    A. the travel reaches a definite limit

    B. the current exceeds a definite limit

    C. the voltage is below a definite limit

    D. the resistance frequently exceeds a definite limit

75. Before handling or making any connections, a capacitor should be:

    A. checked as to its polarity

    B. shorted out with a jumper

    C. coated with lacquer or varnish

    D. sandpapered to remove oxides from the terminals

76. In accordance with Coast Guard Regulations, each group of receptacles for refrigerated containers must:

    A. have a switch near the receptacles that disconnects all power to those receptacles

    B. have a sign stating that the disconnected switch should be opened before cables are disconnected from the receptacles

    C. be designed for circuit breaking service

    D. all of the above

77. In accordance with Coast Guard Regulations, each electric cable for an intrinsically safe system must be:

    A. 2 inches (50 mm) or more form other intrinsically safe circuits

    B. partitioned by a nongrounded, nonferrous barrier from other non-intrinsically safe electric cables

    C. a shielded cable

    D. all of the above

78. Coast Guard Regulations require emergency diesel starting sys-

tems to have sufficient capacity to provide for at least:
    A. three continuous starting sequences
    B. six consecutive cranking cycles
    C. nine repeated starts under load
    D. consecutive cranking periods of 5 seconds
79. In accordance with Coast Guard Regulations, the minimum number of consecutive cranking cycles an emergency diesel generator's starting system must be capable of providing is:
    A. two   C. six
    B. three   D. eight
80. What is one requirement of Coast Guard Regulations concerning emergency diesel engines?
    A. the fuel must have a flash point not less than 75°F
    B. emergency diesel engines must be capable of operating under full load not less than 30 seconds after cranking
    C. the starting battery must produce 12 consecutive cranking cycles
    D. emergency diesel engines must operate satisfactorily up to a 22.5 degree list
81. Which statements is/are correct for decks and bulkheads which are penetrated by electrical cables?
    A. if properly installed, stuffing tubes will prevent progressive flooding where cables pierce watertight bulkheads
    B. bushings having rounded edges and a bearing surface of at least 0.25 inch in length are required for all cables that pass through deck beams
    C. where cables pierce main vertical zone bulkheads, arrangements must be made to ensure that the fire resistance of the bulkhead is not impaired more than 10 percent
    D. all of the above
82. According to Coast Guard Regulations (46 CFR 111), if a section of power cable is damaged:
    A. it may be renewed in part by splicing in a new section
    B. the cable must be renewed in kind for its entire length
    C. the damaged section may only be repaired by use of a junction box if the entire cable is not to be renewed
    D. as long as it does not supply a vital system, it may be left as is indefinitely, provided its supply circuit breaker is secured and tagged
83. Coast Guard Regulations require that the emergency lighting and power system:
    A. emergency generator must be tested under load before sailing
    B. must be tested and inspected weekly and the date recorded
    C. batteries must be tested annually and the date recorded

      D. must be capable of sustaining the emergency load for 48 hours

84. Coast Guard Regulations state that a source of emergency lighting and power on a cargo vessel must be the _____ switchboard.

      A. emergency generator supply to the emergency

      B. emergency generator supply to the main

      C. battery supply to the main

      D. turbogenerator supply to the emergency

85. Coast Guard Regulations require that the construction and operation of ship's service generators adhere to the code of the:

      A. Underwriter's Laboratories, Inc.

      B. American Bureau of Shipping

      C. manufacturer

      D. A.M.E.

86. A storage battery for an emergency lighting and power system must have capacity to:

      A. close all watertight doors three times

      B. open all watertight doors four times

      C. open and close all watertight doors in six consecutive cycles within a 20-second period

      D. none of the above

87. Coast Guard Regulations state that a continuous trickle charge supplied from the ship's service power system is required for batteries supplying power to the:

      A. emergency power system for the radar

      B. portable radios for the lifeboats

      C. radios installed in the lifeboats

      D. emergency power and lighting systems

88. Coast Guard Regulations require each receptacle outlet to have a grounding pole only if it:

      A. operates at 100 volts or more

      B. is in a location exposed to the weather

      C. is in a location accessible to other than qualified personnel

      D. is connected to a D.C. source

89. According to Coast Guard Regulations, which of the following is true concerning portable electric cord and fixture wire aboard ship?

      A. solderless crimp-on splices with outside insulators are permitted

      B. soldered Western Union splices with latex tape are permitted

      C. splices or taps are not permitted in cable runs longer than 30 feet

      D. no splices or taps are permitted

90. Which of the following is/are true concerning electric power operated watertight door systems?

A. each motor-driven door must use the main bus as its source of power

B. each distributing panel for the system must be on the lowest level, where berthing quarters are located

C. Distribution panels must not have a means of locking to permit quick activation

D. each system must have a separate branch circuit

91. According to Coast Guard Regulations, the power supply for the general alarm system must be a storage battery with sufficient capacity to supply the general alarm system continuously for a period of at least _____ hours.

A. 3   C. 8

B. 6   D. 12

92. Coast Guard Regulations (46 CFR 111), require each motor controller to have a wiring diagram located:

A. on the inside of the controller door

B. in the engineering department office

C. in the spare parts locker

D. all of the above

93. Which of the following is/are true concerning the contact makers used in general alarm systems?

A. each must be a normally open, spring-return-to normal, enclosed, watertight switch

B. each must close its contacts when the operating handle is rotated in a counterclockwise direction through an arc of ninety degrees

C. each must have the "off" and "on" positions clearly stenciled or conspicuously posted on a nearby bulkhead

D. all of the above

94. In accordance with Coast Guard Regulations, the emergency generator set aboard an 1800-gross ton tank ship in ocean service must be capable of supplying an emergency source of power for a minimum period of:

A. 12 hours

B. 12 hours or twice the time of the vessel's run, whichever is the least

C. 36 hours

D. 36 hours or twice the time of the vessel's run, whichever is the least

95. Coast Guard Regulations prohibit the use of portable electric cord or fixture wire aboard ship if the wire or cord is smaller than:

A. 12 AWG   C. 16 AWG

B. 14 AWG   D. 18 AWG

96. Coast Guard Regulations (46 CFR 112), require automatic shutdown of an emergency diesel generator if the:

    A. cooling water temperature is high

    B. engine overspeeds dangerously

    C. oil pressure is excessive

    D. exhaust temperature is high

97. When power ventilation is required in a battery compartment, Coast Guard Regulations require:

    A. the power ventilation system to be separate from ventilation systems for other spaces

    B. electric ventilation motors to be inside the vent duct

    C. electric ventilation motors to be inside the compartment

    D. all of the above

98. In accordance with Coast Guard definitions a "non-sparking fan" means a fan that cannot produce sparks that will ignite a flammable mixture and has:

    A. blades and housing of nonferrous material

    B. blades and housing of corrosion resistant steel

    C. ferrous blades and housing with one-half inch or more designed tip clearance

    D. any of the above

99. Which protective device do Coast Guard Regulations require of a motor controller which is to be manually started following a power failure?

    A. overload protection   C. low voltage protection

    B. low voltage release   D. reverse current protection

100. If a steering motor becomes overloaded, the:

    A. overload condition will trip the motor off the line

    B. overload condition will be indicated visually in the engine room

    C. motor running indicator will begin to flash on and off

    D. standby steering pump will start automatically and come on the line

Electrical Symbols

1. The symbol shown is:

    A. diode

    B. rotary switch

    C. potentiometer

    D. A and B above

2. The symbol shown is a:

    A. coil

    B. transformer (air core)

    C. condenser

    D. condenser (air core)

3. This is the electrical symbol for:
   A. shunt
   B. fuse
   C. contact
   D. splice

4. This electrical symbol represents a:
   A. transformer
   B. buzzer
   C. bell
   D. relay

5. This electrical symbol stands for:
   A. a generator
   B. a motor
   C. a push button switch
   D. a knife switch

6. This symbol represents a normally:
   A. closed switch
   B. open switch
   C. open contactor
   D. closed contactor

7. This symbol represents:
   A. D.C. motor
   B. D.C. generator
   C. two-line conductor
   D. none of the above

8. This symbol represents a:
   A. shunt-wound motor
   B. series-wound motor
   C. universal motor
   D. compound wound motor

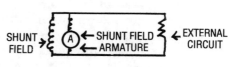

9. This symbol represents a:
   A. compound wound motor
   B. series-wound motor
   C. shunt-wound motor
   D. overcompounded motor

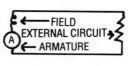

10. This schematic diagram represents:
   A. an open circuit
   B. a grounded circuit
   C. a closed circuit
   D. a parallel circuit

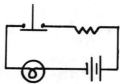

11. Which of the following valves could a rheostat be compared with?
   A. globe valve   C. throttle valve
   B. check valve   D. safety valve

12. This represents a:
    A. double splice
    B. "T" tap
    C. pigtail splice
    D. Western Union splice

13. This electrical symbol represents a:
    A. circuit breaker
    B. transformer iron core
    C. thermostat
    D. variable resistor

14. Small switches are classified as:
    A. rotary   C. tumbler
    B. push button   D. all of the above

15. What does this symbol stand for?
    A. lamp
    B. fuse
    C. ground
    D. connection

16. This symbol represents a:
    A. double-pole, single-throw switch
    B. double-throw, single-pole switch
    C. double-pole, double-throw switch
    D. none of the above

17. Another name for an over current protection device is a:
    A. magnetic breaker   C. fuse
    B. thermal breaker   D. all of the above

18. Components A and F in the figure Static exciter, below, are:
    A. linear inductors   C. diodes
    B. transformers   D. auto transformers

19. Components T1, T2, and T3 in the figure Static exciter, below, are:
    A. linear inductors   C. diodes
    B. transformers   D. motor field windings

20. Excitation for the generator field in the figure Static exciter, below, comes from:
    A. L1 and L2   C. CR1
    B. T 1 and T2   D. generator output leads

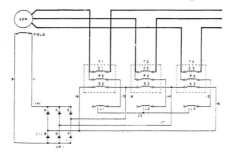

21. This symbol represents a: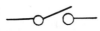
    A. two-way switch
    B. single-throw switch
    C. fuse
    D. double-throw switch
22. This symbol represents a:
    A. triple pole multithrow switch
    B. triple-throw triple pole switch
    C. triple pole double-throw switch
    D. triple pole single-throw switch
23. T.P.S.T. stands for:
    A. triple pole standard terminal
    B. triple pole single-throw switch
    C. temporary pole standard terminal
    D. tandem pole single-throw switch
24. This electrical symbol represents a:
    A. rheostat
    B. thermal element
    C. variable resistor
    D. circuit breaker
25. This symbol represents a normally:
    A. open switch
    B. open contactor
    C. closed switch
    D. closed contactor
26. D.P.D.T. stands for:
    A. duplex pole dead throw switch
    B. double-pole single-throw switch
    C. double-pole double-throw switch
    D. direct power to direct terminal
27. This symbol represents a:
    A. normally open contactor
    B. normally closed switch
    C. normally open switch
    D. normally closed contactor
28. This symbol represents:
    A. battery
    B. ground
    C. rheostat
    D. contactor
29. This electrical symbol represents a:
    A. balance relay
    B. series relay

C. main control switch

D. thermocouple

30. This circuit represents a:

    A. series circuit

    B. parallel circuit

    C. series parallel circuit

    D. none of the above

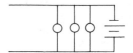

Electrical Review

1. If the approximate voltage to be measured in a circuit is not known, you should:

    A. use the lowest voltage range on the voltmeter

    B. connect the meter in series with the circuit

    C. calibrate the meter before using it

    D. use the highest voltage range on the voltmeter

2. A device which normally prevents an action occurring until all other required conditions are met is a/an:

    A. limit   C. modulator

    B. monitor   D. interlock

3. Equal power factors on paralleled AC generators are maintained by an automatic:

    A. voltage regulator   C. reverse current relay

    B. reverse power relay   D. governor control switch

4. If less resistance is applied to the shunt field of a DC motor, the motor speed will:

    A. decrease   C. remain constant

    B. increase   D. brake down to a stop

5. What occurs during the charging of a lead-acid storage battery?

    A. negative plates change to lead peroxide

    B. positive plates change to lead peroxide

    C. both plates change to lead peroxide

    D. both plates change to lead sulfate

6. If the excitation of one of two alternators operating in parallel is increased, the:

    A. power factor will change in the lagging direction

    B. power factor will change in the leading direction

    C. kilowatt load will be greatly increased

    D. ampere load will be greatly decreased

7. In a series wound motor, the current that goes through the field also goes through the:

    A. armature   C. cargo boom

    B. motor shaft   D. bell housing

8. A DC ammeter is always connected:
   - A. in series with a circuit
   - B. in parallel with a circuit
   - C. with internal shunts only
   - D. without regard to polarity
9. The force that causes free electrons to move in a conductor as an electric current is called _____ force.
   - A. resistant
   - B. an electromotive
   - C. inductive
   - D. dielectric
10. When a transformer is used to step down the voltage, the low voltage winding is:
    - A. part of the core
    - B. the primary
    - C. not insulated
    - D. the secondary
11. A Zener diode is placed in parallel with a load. You measure the voltage across the Zener and find that it does not change as the current through the load is increased. This means that the Zener diode:
    - A. is open
    - B. is shorted
    - C. is working as it should
    - D. does not regulate as it should
12. A salinity indicating system functions by measuring the:
    - A. electrical inductance of water
    - B. electrical conductivity of water
    - C. specific gravity of water
    - D. hydrogen ion concentration of water
13. In order to increase the range, a resistance would be placed in series with which of the following instruments?
    - A. DC voltmeter
    - B. DC ammeter
    - C. frequency meter
    - D. power factor meter
14. Prior to starting an AC generator prime mover, the voltage regulator cut out switch should be placed in the:
    - A. manual position
    - B. bus neutral position
    - C. raise voltage position
    - D. transfer position
15. What type of battery charging circuit is used to maintain a wetcell lead-acid storage battery in a fully charged state over long periods of disuse?
    - A. normal charging circuit
    - B. quick charging circuit
    - C. trickle charging circuit
    - D. high ampere charging circuit
16. A ground can be defined as an electrical connection between the wiring of a motor and its:
    - A. shunt field
    - B. circuit breaker
    - C. metal framework
    - D. interpole
17. External shunts are sometimes used with ammeters to:

    A. increase meter sensitivity

    B. permit shunts with larger resistances to be utilized

    C. prevent damage to the meter movement from heat generated by the shunt

    D. provide a compact meter with a virtually unlimited range

18. Before measuring an unknown resistance with an ohmmeter, you should:

    A. adjust the meter's pointer to mid-scale

    B. change the meter's batteries

    C. center the meter's pointer at infinity

    D. short the test leads and calibrate the meter

19. When an alternator governor control switch is moved to "raise," this will:

    A. raise the no-load speed setting of the governor

    B. raise the percentage of speed droop

    C. lower the no-load speed setting of the governor

    D. lower the percentage of speed droop

20. Which statement is true concerning the operating characteristics of a squirrel cage motor?

    A. rotor slip is dependent on the motor load

    B. an increase in motor load results in less slip

    C. a decrease in rotor speed results in less generated current

    D. a decrease in rotor speed produces a weaker magnetic field

21. An accidental path of low resistance which passes an abnormal amount of current is known as a/an:

    A. open circuit   C. polarized ground

    B. short circuit   D. ground reference point

22. Upon failure of the normal power supply, the emergency generator is placed on the line by the:

    A. bus tie feeder

    B. automatic bus transfer device

    C. line connection feeder

    D. power failure alarm bus

23. When securing an AC generator, you should first:

    A. trip the generator circuit breaker

    B. switch the voltage regulator to "manual"

    C. decrease the field excitation to minimum

    D. reduce the load on the unit

24. When using an ohmmeter to test a diode, you find a low resistance in both the forward and reverse bias directions. What would this indicate about the diode?

    A. open diode   C. good resistive quality

    B. shorted diode   D. good capacitive quality

25. The capacity of a lead-acid storage battery is measured in:

    A. volts   C. farads
    B. ampere-hours   D. amps

26. When placed in a magnetic field, what material will have the highest permeability?
    A. glass   C. soft iron
    B. bakelite   D. aluminum

27. The output voltage of a 440 volt, 60 hertz, AC generator is controlled by the:
    A. prime mover speed   C. load on the alternator
    B. exciter output voltage   D. number of poles

28. Any electric motor can be constructed to be _____ proof.
    A. short   C. explosion
    B. ground   D. overload

29. What is the main difference between a relay and a contactor?
    A. contactors control current; relays control voltage
    B. a relay is series connected; a contactor is parallel connected
    C. contactors can handle heavier loads than relays
    D. contactors are made from silver; relays are made from copper

30. A fullwave rectifier has one diode burned out in an open condition. The output is:
    A. zero   C. fullwave rectified
    B. halfwave rectified   D. equal to the AC input

31. Motor controller or starter contacts may become pitted and welded together if the contacts:
    A. open under loaded conditions
    B. close slowly with light pressure
    C. open too quickly and arc
    D. close quickly with proportionate pressure

32. Under normal conditions, the speed of a two-speed, squirrel-cage induction motor is changed by varying the:
    A. frequency of the applied voltage
    B. resistance in the rotor circuit
    C. number of field poles
    D. amplitude of the applied voltage

33. A loud buzzing noise at the contacts of a magnetic controller could indicate:
    A. weak contact spring pressure
    B. misalignment of magnet faces
    C. excessive line current
    D. mechanical binding

34. An AC circuit contains capacitance in series. If the line voltage remains constant the capacitive reactance value can be varied by changing the:
    A. line frequency

    B. resistance

    C. number of commutating poles

    D. number of interpoles

35. When you are using an ohmmeter to test a diode, a low resistance is found in both the forward and reverse bias directions. What does this indicate about the diode?

    A. good capacitive quality   C. shorted diode

    B. good resistive quality   D. open diode

36. High vacuum diodes, gas filled diodes, and germanium semiconductor diodes may all be used as:

    A. potentiometers   C. power sources

    B. rectifiers   D. photocells

37. The insulation resistance of electrical machinery should be tested for lowest normal insulation values:

    A. immediately after shutting down the machine

    B. every time the brush rigging is adjusted

    C. immediately after starting up the machine

    D. every 30 days whether the machine is in use or not

38. The most inefficient method of voltage reduction from the standpoint of power loss is a/an _____ in series with the load.

    A. capacitor   C. capacitor and inductor

    B. inductor   D. resistor

39. A degree of control over the speed of a slip ring induction motor can be obtained by:

    A. adjusting governor linkage

    B. changing the number of phases to the motor

    C. inserting resistance into the stator circuit

    D. inserting resistance into the rotor circuit

40. The Wheatstone bridge is a precision instrument used to measure:

    A. inductance   C. resistance

    B. capacitance   D. amperage

41. The greatest detrimental effect on idle electrical equipment such as cargo pump motors is:

    A. loss of residual magnetism

    B. absorption of moisture in the insulation

    C. insulation varnish flaking

    D. dirt collecting on the windings

42. What must be done before a voltage tester may be used to test the three line fuses of a three-phase motor?

    A. the fuses must be removed from the circuit

    B. the starter must be placed in the STOP position to stop the motor

    C. the three line connections in the motor terminal box must be disconnected and tagged

      D. nothing need be done as long as the motor is running no
         more than lightly loaded

43. The cycles per second of the alternating current from the alternator aboard your boat are determined by:
    A. the speed of the engine driving the alternator
    B. the resistance applied to the field rheostat
    C. the synchronous speed of induction
    D. the adjustments made to the voltage regulator

44. The counter EMF of a DC motor is zero when the:
    A. armature has just begun to turn
    B. armature is not turning
    C. motor is almost up to rated speed
    D. motor is at rated speed

45. A semiconductor that decreases in resistance with an increase in temperature is known as a:
    A. resistor   C. diode
    B. thermistor   D. thermopile

46. The ratio of the effective value of the counter EMF in volts to the effective value of the current in amperes is called:
    A. impedance factor   C. inductive reactance
    B. capacitive reactance   D. root mean square

47. What is the device used with the repulsion start-induction run motor to convert its rotor into a squirrel cage type rotor?
    A. capacitor   C. shaded coil
    B. short circuit necklace   D. interpoles

48. As load is added to an AC generator with constant field excitation the prime mover slows down:
    A. lowering frequency and lowering generated voltage
    B. increasing frequency and increasing generated voltage
    C. increasing frequency and lowering generated voltage
    D. lowering frequency and increasing generated voltage

49. A characteristic of an induction motor with a low resistance rotor winding is:
    A. high starting voltage   C. high slippage
    B. high starting current   D. low starting voltage

50. A loud buzzing noise in an AC controller is probably caused by:
    A. poor contact with the overload relay
    B. a wrong size heater
    C. a broken shading coil
    D. abnormal starting current

51. What is the overall result of increasing the load on the secondary of a transformer?
    A. decrease in the primary voltage
    B. increase in the primary voltage

      C. decrease in the primary current

      D. increase in the primary current

52. In trouble-shooting a circuit in a console, you find that a resistor may be faulty, and you are going to use an ohmmeter to check its value. What precaution must be observed in doing so?

      A. correct polarity must be observed

      B. meter leads must not be twisted

      C. the resistor must be isolated

      D. the meter must be placed in series to the circuit

53. The counter EMF of a DC motor is maximum when the:

      A. motor is at rated speed

      B. armature is not turning

      C. motor is almost up to rated speed

      D. armature has just begun to turn

54. Magnet chatter or pumping in a magnetic contactor can be caused by:

      A. dirt or grease on pole faces

      B. mechanical interference in the contacts

      C. chattering contacts on the control relay

      D. magnetic lockout of the contacts

55. If the "high level" and "low level" alarms both come on for the same address of a control console, the most likely problem is a/an:

      A. sensor failure   C. low level

      B. failed alarm   D. extremely high level

56. A transformer works on the principle of:

      A. self induction   C. mutual induction

      B. attraction and repulsion   D. increasing power

57. Before measuring an unknown resistance with an ohmmeter, you should:

      A. center the meter's pointer at infinity

      B. change the meter's batteries

      C. short the test leads and calibrate the meter

      D. adjust the meter's pointer to mid-scale

58. A burned-out LED (light emitting diode) would be indicated by:

      A. excessive input   C. excessive illumination

      B. a slight glow in the crystal   D. no illumination

59. Under normal conditions, the speed of a 2-speed squirrel cage induction motor is changed by varying the:

      A. frequency of the applied voltage

      B. resistance in the rotor circuit

      C. number of field poles

      D. amplitude of the applied voltage

60. Magnetic controller contacts may become welded together during operation because of:

      A. an open coil

    B. low contact pressure

    C. excessive ambient temperature

    D. excessive magnet gap

61. If a transformer is connected to a D.C. source, which part of the transformer will overload?

    A. the contacts   C. the secondary

    B. the primary   D. the core

62. The resistance of most conducting materials changes due to temperature change. The resistance of copper will:

    A. increase as temperature decreases

    B. decrease as temperature decreases

    C. remain the same between 20°F and 110°F

    D. remain the same between 20°C and 110°C

63. You are checking a capacitor with an ohmmeter. Which reading tells you that the capacitor is short-circuited?

    A. the capacitor show charging, but the final resistance reading is appreciably less than normal

    B. the reading goes practically to zero and stays there

    C. the capacitor shows no charging action but just reads very high resistance

    D. the pointer moves quickly to low resistance side of the scale and then slowly recedes toward infinity

64. The instantaneous reduction in voltage resulting from an increase in load before the automatic voltage regulator can correct it in an AC generator is called voltage:

    A. droop   C. dip

    B. drop   D. regulation

65. A characteristic of a wound-rotor induction motor with a high resistance rotor winding is:

    A. low starting torque   C. high speed

    B. high starting torque   D. low starting voltage

66. You place a Zener diode in parallel with a load. You measure the voltage across the Zener and find that it does not change as the current through the load is increased. This means that the Zener diode:

    A. is working as it should

    B. is shorted

    C. is open

    D. does not regulate as it should

67. Voltage generated by most AC generators is brought from the machine to the bus by means of:

    A. brushes on a commutator

    B. brushes on slip rings

    C. slip rings on a commutator

D. direct connections from the stator

68. What will happen to the alternator frequency if the load is removed from a turbogenerator whose governor has a 3 percent speed droop?

    A. it will remain unchanged

    B. it will decrease approximately 3 percent

    C. it will become variable

    D. it will increase

69. Reversing any two of the three rotor leads on a wound-rotor induction motor will:

    A. increase motor performance

    B. decrease motor performance

    C. reverse the motor rotation

    D. have no effect on the direction of rotation or motor performance

70. What will happen if a single element fuse is used to replace a blown dual element fuse in a motor controller circuit?

    A. the fuse blows when the motor is started

    B. the fuse works but overheats at high motor loads

    C. the motor runs at reduced voltage

    D. the motor runs normally

71. A hydrometer measures specific gravity by comparing the:

    A. density of a substance in water with the density of the same substance in air

    B. differences in weight between water and the liquid measured

    C. mass of substance measured with the density of the same substance

    D. buoyancy of an object in water with the buoyancy of the same object in the liquid being measured

72. The unit of apparent power in a purely inductive circuit is called the:

    A. KVA   C. EMF

    B. VAR   D. WATT

73. A grounded switch or cable will be indicated by a megohmmeter reading which is:

    A. at infinity

    B. at zero

    C. unsteady in the high range

    D. unsteady in the low range

74. As a general rule, the first troubleshooting action to be taken in checking faulty electric control apparatus is to:

    A. draw a one line diagram of the circuitry

    B. test all fuses and measure the line voltage

    C. take megger readings

    D. insulate the apparatus from ground

75. The most common type of AC service generator found aboard ship is the:

    A. electromagnetic field-revolving armature-type

    B. electromagnetic field-oscillatory armature-type

    C. armature-oscillatory electromagnetic field-type

    D. armature-rotating electromagnetic field-type

76. The main purpose of the auxiliary winding on a split-phase, single-phase motor is to:

    A. limit the starting current

    B. increase the starting current

    C. start the motor

    D. keep the motor running in the event the main winding should fail

77. The load sharing characteristics of two diesel generators operating in parallel are mostly dependent on their governors' _____ settings.

    A. load limit   C. speed limit

    B. idle speed   D. speed droop

78. What type of rotor is used in split-phase motors?

    A. drum   C. squirrel cage

    B. salient pole   D. wound rotor

79. Tightly knit braid should be used with a printed circuit board when:

    A. conductor flexibility is required

    B. desoldering components in the circuit

    C. electrically produced magnetic fluxes would cause inaccuracies in adjacent components

    D. reactance in the circuit must be kept to a minimum

80. To conduct an in-circuit test of a transistor, you should use a/an:

    A. transistor voltmeter   C. ohmmeter

    B. impedance meter   D. solid state device

81. Copper is often used as an electrical conductor because it:

    A. has high resistance at low temperatures

    B. has a highly polished surface

    C. is able to pass current with little opposition

    D. holds insulation together well

82. When can the engine room take throttle control away from the bridge?

    A. at any time

    B. only with the Master's permission

    C. after a ten-minute delay

    D. only when the throttle is placed in stop

83. A dual-element fuse is most frequently used in which of the following circuits?

    A. lighting circuit   C. electric heater circuit

    B. motor circuit   D. radar circuit

84. Of what significance is ambient temperature in relation to the service life of electronic components?

    A. ambient temperature should be as high as possible to drive off moisture

    B. increased ambient temperature decreases the service life of electronic components

    C. ambient temperature is not significant as long as the relative humidity is kept low

    D. a reduced ambient temperature causes a corresponding reduced service life

85. The torque produced by the motor when the shaft is blocked and rated voltage is applied to the stator is known as the:

    A. locked-rotor torque   C. breakdown torque

    B. pullout torque   D. true margin

86. Electrical leads and insulation on a motor should be painted with:

    A. heat-resisting enamel   C. insulating varnish

    B. heat-resisting aluminum   D. insulating white lead

87. What should be done to prevent moisture damage to electrical apparatus during extended periods of idleness?

    A. fill the motor housing with CO_2 to inert the space

    B. strap silica gel around the commutator

    C. place heat lamps in motor housings

    D. cover with a canvas tarpaulin

88. A constant output voltage from an AC generator is maintained by the:

    A. prime mover governor   C. voltage regulator

    B. exciter generator   D. reverse power relay

89. Amortisseur windings are installed in a synchronous motor to:

    A. reduce eddy current losses

    B. produce a higher power factor

    C. provide a means for starting

    D. eliminate arcing between the stator and the rotor

90. Electric strip heaters are used in motor controllers to:

    A. prevent freezing of movable contacts

    B. keep the components at their design ambient temperature

    C. prevent condensation of moisture

    D. minimize resistance in internal circuits

91. Which statement about copper wire sized by AWG numbers is correct?

    A. number 12 AWG wire has a higher current rating than 10 AWG wire

    B. number 12 AWG wire at 250C has more resistance per 1000 ft than 10 AWG wire at 250C.

    C. number 10 AWG wire has a higher dielectric strength than 12 AWG wire

    D. number 12 AWG wire is larger than number 10 AWG wire

92. Normally, the first step in troubleshooting a transistor circuit card is to:
    A. carefully remove the transistors from the card
    B. give the circuit an initial test with a signal generator
    C. test for continuity with a low voltage DC supply
    D. visually inspect the card
93. An unknown resistance in a circuit is to be tested using the volt-meter/ammeter method. The meters should be connected such that:
    A. both meters are in series with the resistance
    B. both meters are in parallel with the resistance
    C. the ammeter is in series and the voltmeter is in parallel with the resistance
    D. the ammeter is in parallel and the voltmeter is in series with the resistance
94. How is the DC output obtained from a brushless exciter?
    A. from collector rings mounted on the armature
    B. from the semiconductor rectifier mounted on the exciter ar-mature
    C. directly from the commutator by induction
    D. from a semiconductor rectifier mounted on the stator
95. In general, polyphase induction motors can be started on full line voltage by means of _____ starters.
    A. compensator   C. across-the-line
    B. autotransformer   D. primary-resistor
96. The open-circuit voltage of a fully charged lead-acid cell is _____ volts.
    A. 1.5   C. 2.0
    B. 1.8   D. 2.3
97. You are testing armature coils by applying low voltage. A short circuit will be indicated by a:
    A. high voltage reading while the other readings have an equal or lower value
    B. low or zero voltage reading while the other coils have higher readings
    C. changing voltmeter reading while the other coil readings are steady
    D. steady voltmeter reading while the other coil readings are steady
98. Which of the following characteristics is most critical in determin-ing the size of cable to be used in a particular circuit?
    A. voltage rating
    B. weight per unit length
    C. current rating
    D. resistance per unit length

99. What is the purpose of the capacitors on the output of the power supplies used in today's consoles?

    A. the act as a permanent load

    B. they filter out ripple

    C. they prevent overloads

    D. they increase the output frequency

100. The electrolyte used in a nickel-cadmium battery is _____ hydroxide.

    A. potassium   C. sodium

    B. cadmium   D. calcium

101. The device which most commonly utilizes the principle of electromagnetic induction is the:

    A. diode   C. transistor

    B. transformer   D. rheostat

102. An operating characteristic which appears on the nameplates of shipboard AC motors is:

    A. the type of winding   C. temperature rise

    B. input kilowatts   D. locked rotor torque

103. Low horsepower polyphase induction motors can be started with full line voltage by means of _____ starters.

    A. primary-resistor   C. autotransformer

    B. across-the-line   D. compensator

104. What item is normally installed on a large turbine electric propulsion alternating current generator?

    A. temperature detector coils inserted in the stator slots for measuring stator temperature

    B. a CO_2 fire extinguishing system

    C. electric space heaters to prevent condensation of moisture

    D. all of the above

105. A magnetic blowout coil in a DC contactor functions to:

    A. open contact rapidly

    B. prevent contact melting

    C. adjust opening spring tension

    D. provide "snap-action" in the contactor

106. What device measures pressure and converts it into an electrical signal?

    A. transducer   C. transformer

    B. reducer   D. rectifier

107. Grounds found in electrical machinery due to insulation failure are usually caused by:

    A. deterioration due to age   C. vibration

    B. excessive heat   D. all of the above

108. Which statement is true concerning the maintenance of solid-silver contacts in relays and auxiliary control circuits?

A. when necessary, they should always be dressed with a wire wheel

B. they should be filed with a fine-cut file when projections end beyond the contact surface

C. when black silver oxide is present, it should always be removed from the contact surface with coarse sandpaper

D. if necessary, they should be held together with moderate pressure while emery paper is drawn between the contacts

109. While you are starting a main propulsion synchronous motor as an induction motor, the ampere meter pegs out at maximum and then returns to the proper value after synchronization. This means the:

A. motor has started properly

B. field windings are grounded

C. slip rings are dirty

D. power transmission cables are grounded

110. AC circuits contain resistance, inductance, and capacitance. The capacitive reactance of a circuit is expressed in:

A. ohms   C. henrys

B. mhos   D. farads

111. Which is a true statement about the circuits in a sound-powered telephone system?

A. the ringing circuit is composed of one common wire to ground.

B. the common talking circuit is composed of two ungrounded wires.

C. the calling circuit has two ungrounded wires connected to each station.

D. the talking and calling circuits are electrically dependent.

112. Which motor is fitted with an instantaneous overload relay?

A. fan   C. winch

B. pump   D. machine tool

113. A molded-case circuit breaker provides protection against short circuits by using a/an:

A. electromagnet   C. arc quencher

B. shading coil   D. burn away strip

114. Which statement is correct concerning an analog device and a digital device?

A. the variables in digital systems are fixed quantities, and the variables in analog systems are continuous quantities

B. there are no basic differences between the two systems

C. analog devices are superior in accuracy compared to digital devices

D. Operations in a digital device are performed simultaneously

115. Heat sinks are frequently used with:

A. power transistors C. gating circuits

B. vacuum tubes   D. all of the above

116. Battery rooms must be well ventilated to:
     A. prevent sulphation during discharge
     B. supply oxygen
     C. dissipate explosive gases
     D. prevent moisture formation

117. The alarm system for an engine order telegraph uses small selsyn motors attached to the indicators. The alarm sounds when the rotors are:
     A. in synchronous position, no current is flowing, and the relays are open
     B. in synchronous position, no current is flowing, and the relays are closed
     C. not synchronized, current is flowing, and the relays are open
     D. not synchronized, current is flowing, and the relays are closed

118. The frequency of an operating alternator is controlled by the:
     A. relative speed of the rotor poles
     B. number of turns of wire in the armature coil
     C. strength of the magnets used
     D. output voltage

119. What does a wound-rotor induction motor have which a squirrel cage motor does *not*?
     A. slip rings   C. a centrifugal switch
     B. end rings   D. end plates

120. The current at which a magnetic-type overload relay tends to trip may be decreased by raising the plunger further into the magnetic circuit of the relay. This action:
     A. reduces magnetic pull on the plunger and requires more current to trip the relay
     B. reduces magnetic pull on the plunger and requires less current to trip the relay
     C. increases magnetic pull on the plunger and requires more current to trip the relay
     D. increases magnetic pull on the plunger and requires less current to trip the relay

121. Protection against sustained overloads in molded-case circuit breakers is provided by a/an:
     A. overvoltage release   C. thermal overload relay
     B. thermal acting trip   D. current overload relay

122. A tubular fuse should always be removed from a fuse panel with:
     A. a screwdriver   C. any insulated object
     B. a pair of insulated pliers D. fuse pullers

123. One of the factors which determines frequency of an alternator is controlled by the:

    A. number of turns of wire in the armature coil

    B. number of magnetic poles

    C. strength of the magnets used

    D. output voltage

124. A generator has been exposed to water, and you are checking the safety of operation. You should:

    A. check for shorted coils with a growler

    B. take moisture readings with a hydrometer

    C. test insulation values with a megger

    D. ground the commutator or slip rings and run it at half load for 12 hours

125. Which best describes a compound-wound DC generator that has a higher voltage at no load than at full load?

    A. flat-compounded   C. under-compounded

    B. over-compounded   D. terminal-compounded

126. The speed of a three-phase, squirrel-cage, induction motor operating from a fixed frequency system is varied by changing the:

    A. number of phases to the motor

    B. number of stator poles

    C. locked rotor current

    D. resistance of the rotor winding

127. An across-the-line starter is used for which application?

    A. reduced-current starting of large motors

    B. low torque starting of small motors

    C. low resistance starting of DC motors

    D. full-voltage starting of smaller motors

128. An adjustable resistor whose resistance can be changed without opening the circuit in which it is connected is called a:

    A. bleeder resistor   C. bridge

    B. rheostat   D. vable shunt strip

129. Why are D.C. series motors used extensively for electric drives on winches?

    A. they are constant speed

    B. they operate at high speeds when under heavy loads

    C. they don't require a controller

    D. they are designed to operate in a stalled condition

130. The purpose of the heat sink frequently used with transistors is to:

    A. prevent excessive temperature rise

    B. compensate for excessive doping

    C. increase the reverse current

    D. decrease the forward current

131. The variable resistance placed in the rotor circuit of a form-wound induction motor provides for _____ control.

    A. speed   C. voltage

    B. frequency   D. starting torque

132. Local action in a dry cell or lead-acid battery is the process whereby:
    A. hydrogen gas is liberated
    B. the electrolyte compensates for overcharging
    C. potassium hydroxide absorbs carbon dioxide from the air
    D. the battery becomes discharged without being connected to a load

133. The RMS value of a sine-wave current may also be expressed as the _____ value.
    A. average
    B. maximum
    C. effective
    D. instantaneous

134. On tank vessels with an electrically driven capstan, the motor should be meggered periodically to test:
    A. insulation resistance
    B. eddy currents
    C. capacitance
    D. armature reactance

135. The speed of a squirrel cage induction motor is determined by the:
    A. diameter of the stator
    B. number of stator poles
    C. rotor winding resistance
    D. rotor conducting bar's resistance

136. A reverse current relay prevents DC generator motorization by:
    A. automatically redirecting the load
    B. automatically speeding up the prime mover
    C. automatically securing the exciter generator
    D. tripping the circuit breaker

137. Larger sizes of wire are made in the form of a cable consisting of several small strands to:
    A. obtain the flexibility required for easy handling
    B. reduce the overall weight of the wire run
    C. reduce the number of supports needed for a horizontal over-heat run
    D. all of the above

138. The first requirement for logical troubleshooting is the ability to:
    A. collect all available data on a casualty
    B. recognize normal operation
    C. identify the probable cause of a symptom
    D. isolate the faulty component

139. Violent gassing from a lead-acid battery while it is being charged indicates that the:
    A. plate separators are grounded
    B. battery compartment ventilation is inadequate
    C. electrolyte specific gravity is too low
    D. charging rate is too high

140. You should use an ohmmeter to measure:
    A. current flow in a circuit
    B. voltage between two points in a circuit
    C. circuit continuity
    D. power
141. The voltage of an alternator is normally controlled by varying the:
    A. prime mover speed
    B. field strength
    C. number of conductors in series per winding
    D. number of poles
142. Under normal conditions, the speed of a 2-speed squirrel cage induction motor is changed by varying the:
    A. frequency of the applied voltage
    B. resistance in the rotor circuit
    C. number of field poles
    D. amplitude of the applied voltage
143. Magnetic controller contacts may become welded together during operation because of:
    A. an open coil
    B. low contact pressure
    C. excessive ambient temperature
    D. excessive magnet gap
144. If a transformer is connected to a D.C. source, which part of the transformer will overload?
    A. the contacts   C. the secondary
    B. the primary   D. the core
145. One method of testing for a reversed shunt field coil in a DC generator or motor is by connecting the field to a direct current source reduced from the fields rated voltage and then testing for polarity using a/an:
    A. iron bar across each field
    B. magnetic compass placed near each field
    C. test lamp across adjacent fields
    D. copper jumper across the interpole connections
146. The rate at which heat is produced in a DC circuit is equal to:
    A. P/R   C. E/I
    B. I2R   D. IR/t
147. A basic meter movement responds to the current that flows through its coil. This meter movement may be used as a/an:
    A. voltmeter by placing a resistance in parallel with the coil
    B. ohmmeter by placing another meter movement in parallel with the coil
    C. wattmeter by pacing a battery in parallel with the coil
    D. ammeter by placing a low resistance in parallel with the coil

148. When power is restored after a complete power failure, a steering pump motor will:
    A. have to be restarted   C. restart automatically
    B. have to be reset   D. trip its overload relays

149. What is a characteristic of an ungrounded distribution system?
    A. accidental contact between one line and ground does not cause an outage
    B. double ground faults on different phases will not cause an outage
    C. ground detection systems are unnecessary
    D. accidental contact between one line and ground will always cause an outage

150. In a compound-wound motor, part of the line current flows through the:
    A. interpoles   C. shunt field coils
    B. stator   D. frame

151. You can determine if a circuit breaker is tripped by:
    A. examining for the position of the handle
    B. checking for the warm breaker
    C. looking for a burned-out link
    D. any of the above

152. The standard method of controlling the output voltage of a 440-volt, 60Hz, AC generator is accomplished by adjusting the:
    A. prime mover speed
    B. number of poles
    C. alternator field excitation
    D. load on the alternator

153. The air gap in induction motors should be checked periodically with a feeler gauge to guard against an unequal air gap and:
    A. decreased motor magnetizing current
    B. hysteresis losses
    C. increased power factor
    D. mechanical damage to the rotor

154. Due to the operating characteristics of the system, time lag fuses (or dual-element fuses) are necessary for use in _____ circuits.
    A. main lighting   C. emergency lighting
    B. motor starting   D. general alarm

155. A motor controller contains three push buttons labeled "start,", "jog," and "stop." When the jog button is pushed, the motor:
    A. will run continuously after the "jog" button is released
    B. will run until the "jog" button is released
    C. cannot start until both the "jog" and "start" buttons are pushed
    D. cannot stop unless the "stop" button is pushed

156. Which of the following precautions should you take when securing propulsion generators and motors for an extended period of time?
     A. disconnect the brush pigtails from their contacts and circulate air through the units.
     B. disconnect the brush pigtails from their contacts and discharge carbon dioxide into the units to keep them dry.
     C. lift the brushes from commutator collector rings and use the built-in heater to prevent moisture accumulation.
     D. lift the brushes from commutator or collector rings and circulate cool dry air through the units.

157. Nonadjustable molded case circuit breakers are classified by frame size, ampere rating, and interrupting capacity. The frame size is expressed in:
     A. degrees centigrade   C. amperes
     B. circular mils   D. volts

158. A voltage relay with the addition of an air bleed or a dash-pot to slow down or delay the action of its contacts is often used for:
     A. sequence control   C. acceleration control
     B. low-voltage release   D. all of the above

159. Which solid AWG wire size has the least cross-sectional area?
     A. 12 AWG   C. 16 AWG
     B. 14 AWG   D. 18 AWG

160. A lead-acid battery is considered fully charged when the:
     A. electrolyte gases freely
     B. battery charger ammeter indicates a positive reading
     C. terminal voltage reaches a constant value at a given temperature
     D. specific gravity of all cells reaches the correct value and no longer increases over a period of 3 to 4 hours

161. Which of the following is true concerning a polyphase synchronous propulsion motor?
     A. the motor is started as an induction motor
     B. resistance is gradually added to the rotor circuit
     C. the starting current is held below the rated current
     D. the field winding is energized for starting purposes only

162. Where a thermal-acting breaker must be used in an area of unusually high, low, or fluctuating temperatures, an ambient compensating element must be used consisting of a:
     A. cylindrical spring on the contact arm
     B. conical spring on the contact arm
     C. second bimetal element
     D. second electromagnet

163. What could be an application for a silicon controlled rectifier?

    A. to provide DC power for a main propulsion motor

    B. for use as a voltage reference diode

    C. for sensing flame in an automated burner

    D to eliminate power supply hum

164. In an AC synchronous motor turboelectric power plant, propeller speed is controlled by varying the:

    A. turbine speed

    B. electric coupling field strength

    C. number of energized main motor poles

    D. propulsion generator field strength

165. The frequency of an AC generator is adjusted by means of the:

    A. main alternator field rheostat

    B. exciter field rheostat

    C. prime mover governor control

    D. equalizing reactor

166. The purpose of a commutator in a DC motor is to:

    A. reverse the flow of current through the armature

    B. reverse the flow of current in the field poles

    C. reduce the reluctance of the magnetic path through the motor

    D. shift the neutral running plane of the brushes to prevent sparking

167. Humming or buzzing electric contacts is a symptom of:

    A. low voltage   C. a circuit ground

    B. power failure   D. a circuit overload

168. Capacitance in an AC circuit will:

    A. stop current flow once the capacitor is fully charged

    B. allow current flow in only one direction

    C. oppose any change in circuit voltage

    D. rectify the current

169. An ohmmeter test for back-to-forward resistance in a transistor should read roughly what ratio?

    A. 100:1   C. 1000:1

    B. 500:1   D. 5000:1

170. If an induction motor were run at 90 percent rated voltage:

    A. there would be an increase in starting torque

    B. starting current would increase slightly

    C. synchronous speed would decrease slightly

    D. the slip would increase

171. You are troubleshooting a magnetic controller and find the contacts are welded. The most probable cause is:

    A. excessive operation at low load

    B. high ambient temperature

    C. low voltage on the operating coil

    D. high voltage on the operating coil

172. The function of a step-down potential transformer is to reduce load:
    A. voltage and current
    B. voltage and increase line current
    C. current and increase line voltage
    D. power

173. To avoid damaging the components of a printed circuit board when testing it with a DC volt-ohmmeter, you should:
    A. ground the board
    B. avoid reversing the polarity of the leads
    C. isolate sensitive components with heat sinks
    D. all of the above

174. When you check the specific gravity of battery electrolyte with a hydrometer, you should know that:
    A. the battery is fully charged when the float sinks deepest into the electrolyte sample
    B. the battery is discharged when the float floats highest in the electrolyte sample
    C. a hydrometer reading is inaccurate if taken immediately after water is added to the cell
    D. warm temperature will raise the specific gravity of the electrolyte

175. A resistor in parallel to the output of a power supply:
    A. is a temperature compensator
    B. corrects power factor
    C. prevents excessive currents
    D. aids in output voltage regulation

176. With both ends of a three conductor cable disconnected and arranged so the conductors do not touch each other, an ohmmeter reading of zero ohms between the ends of a conductor would indicate that the conductor:
    A. has continuity   C. resistance is infinity
    B. has a partial ground   D. is short-circuited

177. The electrolyte used in a nickel-cadmium battery is:
    A. diluted sulfuric acid   C. lead sulfate
    B. potassium hydroxide   D. zinc oxide

178. An accidental path of low resistance which passes an abnormal amount of current is known as a/an:
    A. open circuit   C. polarized ground
    B. short circuit   D. ground reference point

179. Three factors responsible for the change in voltage as load is applied to an AC generator running with constant speed and excitation are resistance drop in the armature circuit, change in flux, and change in the:

A. armature winding speed
B. inductance load drop
C. coil pitch factor
D. armature reactance voltage drop

180. The speed of a wound-rotor induction motor is:
    A. fixed by the number of field poles
    B. varied by a rheostat control
    C. synchronous speed at full load
    D. synchronous speed at no load

181. If you hear a loud buzzing noise coming from a magnetic controller for a motor, you should:
    A. assume that the motor is operating at a full load
    B. assume that the controller is operating normally
    C. notify the electrician or watch officer of the problem
    D. feel the outside of the casing with your hand to see if it's hot

182. The purpose of the autotransformers used with the starters of large AC motors is to provide:
    A. increased voltage for starting
    B. increased torque for starting
    C. reduced voltage for starting
    D. speed control

183. A solid state circuit is not working. You should FIRST:
    A. change all transistors
    B. check all the resistors
    C. wiggle all components for loose connections
    D. check the DC operating voltage

184. The purpose of a short circuit forcing module (short time trip) installed in a branch line is to provide:
    A. high speed clearance of low impedance short circuits in the branch
    B. continuity of service on main bus under short circuit conditions in a branch
    C. isolation of short circuits by selective tripping of branch circuit breakers
    D. all of the above

185. Which is a function of voltage regulators used with AC generators?
    A. to cut out generators when they are no longer needed
    B. to cut in generators automatically as they are needed
    C. to divide the KW load equally between generators operating in parallel
    D. to divide reactive current between generators operating in parallel

186. In an AC generator, direct current from a separate source is passed through windings of the rotor:

    A. by means of slip rings and brushes
    B. by means of a commutator
    C. by means of a rotating bar magnet
    D. to minimize the danger of arc over

187. The purpose of a cage rotor winding placed on the rotor of a synchronous motor is to:
    A. provide excitation to the DC field
    B. start the machine as an induction motor
    C. contribute extra torque at synchronous speed
    D. prevent the machine from falling out of step

188. Motor controllers are seldom troubled with grounds because:
    A. the auxiliary contacts have a high resistance connection
    B. the contactors and relays are mounted on a nonconducting panel
    C. the resistor banks are composed of individual series-connected units
    D. there are separate switches for the motor and the control

189. In an induction motor with a cage rotor, the full load stator current is approximately _____ times the running current.
    A. two   C. five
    B. three   D. nine

190. A single-phase induction motor that has a relatively high starting torque is the _____ motor.
    A. shaded pole   C. capacitor-start
    B. wound-rotor   D. resistance-start

191. When you are choosing a battery for a particular application major consideration should be given to the battery's:
    A. amp-hour capacity
    B. terminal polarity
    C. stability under charge
    D. ambient temperature rise

192. The rated temperature rise of an electric motor is the:
    A. average temperature of any given latitude
    B. normal temperature rise above the standard ambient at rated load
    C. average temperature rise due to resistance at 10 percent overloaded
    D. permissible difference in the ambient temperature of the motor due to weather

193. What is the preferred method of cleaning dust and foreign particles from electrical equipment?
    A. wiping   C. vacuum suction
    B. compressed air   D. cleaning solvent

194. In an AC generator connected to the bus, as the load and power factor of the load changes, these changes are reflected by changes

in the armature reaction of the generator. These changes in armature reaction are compensated for by the:

A. governor speed droop setting   C. balance coil

B. voltage regulator   D. phase-balance relay

195. A delayed-action fuse is most frequently used in which circuit?

A. lighting circuit   C. electric heater circuit

B. motor circuit   D. radar circuit

196. A semiconductor is a material with a:

A. conductivity higher than a normal conductor

B. conductivity higher than a normal insulator

C. conductivity lower than a normal insulator

D. high conductivity at low temperatures

197. A soft iron core with wire coiled around it and a direct current passing through the wire is the description of a simple:

A. magnetic shield   C. piezoelectric device

B. electromagnet   D. electromagnetic domain

198. To properly use a hook-on volt-ammeter when checking current flow, you must FIRST:

A. de-energize the circuit to allow for connecting the instrument in series

B. hook the jaws of the instrument around the insulated conductor

C. connect the voltage test leads to the appropriate terminals

D. short the test leads and calibrate the instrument to zero

199. Autotransformer starters or compensators are sometimes used with polyphase induction motors to:

A. reduce the voltage applied to the motor during the starting period

B. increase the voltage for "across the line starting"

C. provide a back-up means of voltage regulation for emergency starting

D. allow the voltage to be either stepped up or down depending on the application to ensure full torque

200. A common type of protective covering used on electrical conductors is:

A. plain paper   C. silver sheathing

B. fibrous braid   D. babbit sheathing

Answers to Multiple-Choice Questions for the Electrician

Electrical theory

1. A	4. D	7. C	10. B
2. C	5. C	8. A	11. A
3. A	6. D	9. C	12. D

13. B	23. A	33. B	43. A
14. B	24. A	34. D	44. D
15. A	25. D	35. A	45. B
16. A	26. B	36. C	46. C
17. B	27. C	37. C	47. D
18. D	28. B	38. B	48. C
19. D	29. C	39. B	49. C
20. C	30. D	40. B	50. B
21. D	31. A	41. B	
22. B	32. C	42. B	

D.C. systems

1. A	26. C	51. B	76. D
2. C	27. A	52. A	77. B
3. C	28. D	53. B	78. D
4. C	29. D	54. A	79. C
5. C	30. A	55. C	80. A
6. B	31. D	56. C	81. A
7. D	32. D	57. B	82. D
8. D	33. C	58. B	83. C
9. B	34. D	59. B	84. B
10. D	35. B	60. D	85. C
11. A	36. C	61. D	86. C
12. D	37. C	62. D	87. C
13. A	38. C	63. C.	88. C
14. C	39. C	64. C	89. D
15. C	40. A	65. A	90. B
16. A	41. A	66. B	91. B
17. D	42. B	67. A	92. C
18. C	43. A	68. A	93. C
19. D	44. A	69. C	94. A
20. A	45. C	70. B	95. C
21. D	46. C	71. B	96. C
22. D	47. C	72. D	97. C
23. A	48. C	73. D	98. C
24. B	49. B	74. B	99. B
25. A	50. A	75. A	100. C

A.C. systems

1. B	6. B	11. B	16. B
2. A	7. D	12. B	17. A
3. B	8. B	13. D	18. D
4. D	9. A	14. B	19. B
5. D	10. C	15. A	20. C

21. C	35. D	49. A	63. D
22. D	36. C	50. A	64. B
23. D	37. C	51. D	65. C
24. D	38. C	52. A	66. A
25. A	39. C	53. B	67. B
26. B	40. C	54. D	68. A
27. B	41. B	55. D	69. C
28. D	42. A	56. B	70. C
29. D	43. B	57. D	71. B
30. D	44. C	58. C	72. A
31. A	45. B	59. C	73. B
32. D	46. B	60. D	74. D
33. D	47. B	61. B	75. B
34. A	48. A	62. A	

Maintenance and regulations

1. D	26. C	51. D	76. D
2. C	27. B	52. D	77. C
3. D	28. C	53. C	78. B
4. C	29. A	54. C	79. C
5. B	30. B	55. D	80. D
6. C	31. A	56. B	81. A
7. C	32. D	57. D	82. A
8. C	33. A	58. A	83. B
9. A	34. A	59. D	84. A
10. A	35. B	60. C	85. B
11. C	36. B	61. D	86. A
12. A	37. D	62. D	87. D
13. C	38. B	63. B	88. A
14. A	39. C	64. C	89. D
15. D	40. B	65. C	90. D
16. C	41. A	66. A	91. C
17. D	42. C	67. D	92. A
18. D	43. A	68. A	93. A
19. D	44. C	69. B	94. A
20. D	45. A	70. B	95. D
21. B	46. B	71. D	96. B
22. D	47. B	72. B	97. A
23. D	48. B	73. A	98. D
24. A	49. A	74. A	99. C
25. D	50. A	75. B	100. B

Electrical symbols

1. A	9. B	17. D	25. C
2. B	10. C	18. C	26. C
3. B	11. C	19. B	27. D
4. C	12. D	20. C	28. B
5. C	13. B	21. B	29. B
6. C	14. D	22. D	30. B
7. C	15. D	23. B	
8. D	16. C	24. C	

Electrical review

1. D	34. A	67. D	100. A
2. D	35. C	68. D	101. B
3. A	36. B	69. D	102. C
4. A	37. A	70. A	103. C
5. B	38. D	71. D	104. B
6. A	39. D	72. B	105. B
7. A	40. C	73. B	106. A
8. A	41. B	74. B	107. D
9. C	42. B	75. D	108. B
10. D	43. A	76. C	109. A
11. C	44. B	77. D	110. A
12. B	45. B	78. C	111. B
13. A	46. C	79. B	112. C
14. A	47. B	80. BC	113. A
15. C	48. A	81. C	114. A
16. C	49. B	82. A	115. A
17. C	50. C	83. B	116. C
18. D	51. D	84. B	117. D
19. A	52. C	85. A	118. A
20. A	53. A	86. C	119. A
21. B	54. C	87. C	120. D
22. B	55. A	88. C	121. B
23. D	56. C	89. C	122. D
24. B	57. C	90. C	123. B
25. B	58. D	91. B	124. D
26. C	59. C	92. D	125. B
27. B	60. B	93. C	126. C
28. C	61. B	94. B	127. C
29. C	62. B	95. C	128. B
30. B	63. B	96. C	129. D
31. B	64. C	97. B	130. A
32. C	65. B	98. C	131. D
33. B	66. A	99. B	132. D

133. C	150. C	167. A	184. D
134. A	151. A	168. C	185. D
135. B	152. C	169. B	186. A
136. D	153. D	170. D	187. B
137. A	154. B	171. C	188. B
138. B	155. B	172. B	189. C
139. D	156. C	173. B	190. C
140. C	157. C	174. C	191. A
141. B	158. D	175. D	192. B
142. C	159. D	176. A	193. C
143. B	160. D	177. B	194. B
144. B	161. A	178. B	195. B
145. B	162. C	179. D	196. B
146. B	163. A	180. B	197. B
147. D	164. A	181. C	198. B
148. C	165. C	182. C	199. A
149. A	166. A	183. D	200. B

CHAPTER THIRTEEN

Multiple -Choice Questions for the Deck Engineer

The topics covered by the multiple-choice questions include: Equipment Operations; Deck Machinery; and Electrical Procedures. The subjects covered in the questions are listed below:

1. Valves, piping, and fittings
2. Pumps
3. Hydraulics
4. Deck machinery
5. Electrical testing equipment
6. Maintenance of electrical equipment

Equipment Operations

1. The size of flexible hoses used in hydraulic systems is indicated by:
   - A. the inside diameter
   - ✓B. a number designation
   - C. a color code
   - D. the outside diameter
2. How can you decrease the chance of contaminating the hydraulic fluid when you are working on machinery?
   - ✓A. clean fittings before you disconnect them
   - B. place drip pans under leaky fittings
   - C. seal any cracks in lines with Permatex
   - D. coat all threads with graphite and oil
3. The nameplate on a reciprocating pump reads 7″ × 6″ × 4″. What is the proper order?
   - A. liquid cylinder, stroke, steam cylinder
   - B. stroke, liquid cylinder, steam cylinder
   - C. steam cylinder, stroke, liquid cylinder
   - ✓D. steam cylinder, liquid cylinder, stroke
4. A pump is said to have "negative suction head" when the pump is located:
   - A. between the suction and discharge
   - B. below the liquid supply
   - ✓C. above the liquid supply
   - D. any of the above
5. The pump-packing gland should be:
   - ✓A. slack enough to allow slight leakage of fluid
   - B. slightly cocked

C. brought up tight so as not to allow any leakage

D. fitted with a relief valve

6. The volute pump is one in which the impeller:

    A. discharges into a gradually widening channel

    B. has stationary diffuser vanes

    C. produces no kinetic energy

    D. all of the above

7. Standard pipe is labeled:

    A. schedule 40   C. schedule 120

    B. schedule 80   D. schedule 160

8. Double extra strong (XXS) pipe is labeled:

    A. schedule 40   C. schedule 120

    B. schedule 80   D. schedule 160

9. To secure a reciprocating pump, you would close in the following order:

    A. steam exhaust valve, drains, suction and discharge, steam inlet

    B. suction and discharge, steam inlet and exhaust, and open drains

    C. steam inlet and exhaust, suction and discharge, and open drains

    D. suction and discharge, exhaust, drains, and inlet

10. What kind of lubrication is used on reciprocating pumps?

    A. engine oil   C. graphite and oil

    B. oil mixed with kerosene   D. beeswax

11. The valve on the bilge suction of the main circulator must be a:

    A. globe valve   C. nonreturn valve

    B. gate valve   D. angle valve

12. Thread compound is used on:

    A. bolt threads   C. valve steam threads

    B. threaded flanges   D. stuffing box gland nuts

13. How do you measure sheet metal thickness?

    A. micrometer   C. wire gauge

    B. machinist rule   D. surface plate

14. Sleeve bearings should not be excessively lubricated because:

    A. the bearing will overheat

    B. you will have to flush the bearing sooner than usual

    C. dirt will accumulate inside the bearing

    D. the motor will develop excessive slip

15. With a reciprocating pump, excessive vibration may be caused by:

    A. misalignment

    B. liquid plunger packing too tight

    C. cushion valves not set properly

    D. any of the above

16. The flinger ring, fitted on the pump shaft, is used to:
    A. lubricate the packing
    B. seal the suction side
    C. prevent leakage of fluid into bearing housing
    D. prime the pump when first starting

17. To measure the pitch of a threaded bolt, you could use a:
    A. telescoping gauge   C. thread micrometer
    B. screw pitch gauge   D. depth gauge

18. What should you do to a grinding wheel whose face is grooved and uneven?
    A. replace it   C. use a wheel dresser
    B. turn it around   D. ask the first assistant

19. After cutting a piece of tubing that you are going to flare, you should:
    A. remove inside burrs with a reamer
    B. rough up the tube end with a file
    C. flare the tube before removing any burrs
    D. crimp the tube end to slip on the fitting

20. What should you do with a chisel that has a mushroom head?
    A. remove the ragged edges by grinding
    B. do not strike the mushroomed portion
    C. use only light hammer blows with the chisel
    D. knock off the ragged edges with a hammer

21. How would you check the rudder angle indicator on the bridge?
    A. on the dock   C. with the steering gear
    B. on the wheelhouse   D. with all of the above

22. When checking rudder angle indicator from bridge to steering gear you turn the wheel hard left and right, back and forth and the rudder moves sluggishly, what might be the cause?
    A. wrong telemotor   C. too high a voltage
    B. using wrong power cable   D. air in the system

23. With a reciprocating pump, failure to deliver liquid may be caused by:
    A. pump not being primed
    B. discharge head too high
    C. liquid plunger packing worn
    D. any of the above

24. A pump is said to have "positive suction head" when the pump is:
    A. located above the liquid supply
    B. located below the liquid supply
    C. located in a separate compartment
    D. lower than the discharge

25. To set a divider to the proper radius, you should use a:
    A. micrometer   C. scale
    B. scribing circle   D. vernier caliper

26. Before reassembling any machinery, you should:
    ✓ A. replace all bearings regardless of length of service
    B. apply a heavy coat of oil to all mating surfaces
    C. clean any corroded surfaces and file all burrs smooth
    D. coat all parts with allemite grease
27. When removing a broken bolt, you should first try to:
    A. saw the bolt off flush with the job surface
    ✓ B. loosen the bolt by soaking it with penetrating oil
    C. fracture the bolt with a prick punch and hammer
    D. remove the bolt by heating the surrounding surface
28. How would you measure the thickness of *shim* stock?
    A. inside micrometer   C. outside caliper
    ✓ B. outside micrometer   D. feeler gauge
29. A file which has its teeth pinned may be:
    A. heated   ✓ C. cleaned with a file card
    B. cleaned with a wire brush D. cleaned with an acid
30. Pinning of a file may be prevented by:
    A. greasing the file teeth
    B. rubbing chalk on the file teeth
    ✓ C. dipping the file in solvent prior to use
    D. it cannot be prevented
31. Flax fibers are generally useful as a packing material because they:
    A. are very abrasive   ✓ C. are strong and durable
    B. never leak   D. cannot absorb moisture
32. Small leaks in gaskets should be taken up immediately after installation because:
    ✓ A. the leak will probably worsen in time
    B. the gasket may not seal itself for several hours
    C. leakage will result in severe flange distortion
    D. small leaks cause the pipeline to creep
33. Extra strong (XS) pipe is labeled:
    A. schedule 40   C. schedule 120
    ✓ B. schedule 80   D. schedule 160
34. What is schedule 80 extra strong?
    A. steel   C. sheet metal
    ✓ B. pipe   D. hard drawn copper
35. "Groaning" in the steam end of the reciprocating pump may result from:
    A. cylinder misalignment   C. too tight packing
    B. broken piston rings   ✓ D. all of the above
36. The follower plate is found on which of the following parts of a reciprocating pump?
    A. valve chest   C. snifter valve
    ✓ B. steam chest   D. liquid plunger

37. To accurately cut the proper size gasket for installation in a pipeline, you should use:
  A. tin snips   ✓C. a gasket cutter
  B. a jackknife   D. a ball peen hammer
38. What type gasket would be used in a steam line?
  A. rubber   ✓C. metallic and asbestos
  B. rubber and metal   D. all of the above
39. A gate valve installed in a pipeline should be:
  ✓A. used in either the fully closed or fully open position
  B. installed with the stem down
  C. used for steam service only
  D. used to throttle or regulate the flow of liquid
40. A packing hook is used to remove packing from a valve to:
  A. prevent damaging the valve seat
  ✓B. prevent damaging the valve stem
  C. allow the bonnet to be removed easier
  D. avoid removal of the hand wheel
41. When starting a positive displacement pump, the *first* valve to open should be the:
  ✓A. suction valve   C. discharge valve
  B. drain valve   D. steam valve
42. You should *never* use what type of packing on a pump shaft?
  A. asbestos   ✓C. wire inserted
  B. flax   D. graphite
43. Two pieces of pipe of unlike sizes may be joined together by the use of a:
  A. union   ✓C. reducing coupling
  B. coupling   D. adapter
44. To facilitate the removal of a pump for repair, the suction and discharage piping might be fitted with a (an):
  A. adapter   C. coupling
  ✓B. union   D. bushing
45. A nominal dimension such as IPS (iron pipe size) is:
  ✓A. close but not exact
  B. actual standard measurement
  C. standard pipe
  D. extra strong
46. The best way to support a large pipe while removing a section is:
  A. have several fellow workers hold it
  ✓B. support with a chain fall and guide with lines
  C. tie a safety line on and stand back
  D. let it drop
47. Severe leakage of the hydraulic system of the winch could cause:

    A. failure of pump to build suction
    B. clogged filters
    C. overheating of fluid
    D. damage to pump motor

48. The hydraulic motor/pump is making unusual noises:
    A. call the chief
    B. add hydraulic fluid
    C. shut down the system
    D. locate the source of the noise and shut down

49. Lint from cleaning rags can be harmful to a hydraulic machine because lint:
    A. can cause rusting of internal parts
    B. causes the hydraulic fluid to break down
    C. clogs filters and promotes leakage
    D. solidifies and causes cracked lines

50. The most common type of hydraulic pump used in winches is:
    A. centrifugal   C. radial piston type
    B. reciprocating   D. double acting

51. The gear, screw, and lobe pumps are all classified as:
    A. variable stroke pumps
    B. multistage pumps
    C. positive displacement pumps
    D. triple-ported pumps

52. Lantern rings on a pump serve which of the following purposes?
    A. give added starting torque
    B. lubricate pump bearings
    C. lubricate and seal pump packing
    D. act as a vent

53. What type of valve is used to direct the flow of hydraulic fluid?
    A. relief valve   C. directional control valve
    B. check valve   D. pressure control valve

54. What determines the overall strength of rubber hydraulic hose?
    A. layers of rubber impregnated cotton braid
    B. layers of wire braid
    C. layers of cotton braid
    D. number of layers of braid

55. Use extreme care in the use of rags to clean hydraulic system due to:
    A. danger of lint
    B. loose cloth
    C. their cleanliness
    D. frequent failure to remove rags after repair

56. If the hydraulic fluid in the system gets low and there is none of the proper type available:

A. shut down the system

B. use the type which closely matches the required type

C. use lube oil of same viscosity

D. check manufacturer's instruction book

57. What would a centrifugal pump with a volute and diffuser do to the liquid pressure?

A. increase   C. keep the same

B. decrease   D. none of the above

58. What is the purpose of a relief valve?

A. to fill 2 tanks at the same time

B. to use pump at a higher pressure

C. to return liquid to suction side if discharge valve is closed

D. all of the above

59. The accumulator serves the purpose of:

A. bleed air from system

B. automatic purge device

C. storage of liquid under pressure

D. pressure relief device

60. Hydraulic hoses are identified by:

A. ID

B. number designation

C. pressure they will withstand

D. the outside sheath

61. What precaution should you take if you have to remove an old gasket from a flange by scraping?

A. knock the old gasket with a sledge hammer before trying to scrape it

B. heat the flange faces with a torch before trying to remove the old gasket

C. gouge the flange face slightly so you can insert a paint scraper

D. remove the old gasket carefully and avoid scratching the mating flange surfaces

62. Insulation on deck steam piping must be installed securely because:

A. loose insulation causes steam leaks

B. deck steam lines are subject to vibration

C. steam driven machinery cannot run with loose insulation

D. loose insulation prevents pipe expansion

63. The best feature of a globe valve is the ability to:

A. allow movement of liquid with no restriction to flow

B. throttle the valve to control flow

C. permit flow in one direction only

D. A and B only

64. An arrow cast into the valve body indicating the direction of flow is common to:
    A. gate valves only   C. check valves only
    B. globe valves only   D. globe and check valves

65. If the relief valve on the discharge side of a hydraulic pump lifts:
    A. the strainer is plugged
    B. the pump is defective
    C. the discharge line is blocked
    D. the pump is air bound

66. The advantage of a centrifugal pump as compared with a reciprocating pump is that:
    A. discharge is continuous
    B. it has no internal valves
    C. upon accidental closing of discharge valve, excessive pressure will not build up
    D. all of the above are true

67. Suitable clearance should be left between the ends of packing rings to allow for:
    A. easy removal   C. air pockets
    B. expansion   D. all of the above

68. If you are given the job of adding hydraulic fluid to a mooring winch and you are not certain about what type of fluid to use, you should:
    A. add fluid that is the same color as the fluid in the reservoir
    B. add turbine oil because it is always a good substitute
    C. add any oil that has the same viscosity as the hydraulic fluid
    D. ask the first assistant or check the winch manufacturer's instruction book

69. The part of a rubber hydraulic hose that determines the overall strength of the hose is the:
    A. inner tube   C. outer cover
    B. braid   D. outer armor

70. Flax and hemp packing is used for which application?
    A. high temperature   C. lube oil
    B. low temperature   D. fuel oil

71. Leaking fluid at a pump shaft indicates:
    A. loose packing
    B. worn packing
    C. leaking packing
    D. excessive internal pressures

72. To decrease pump wear:
    A. a suction strainer is used
    B. pump is run at very low speed
    C. run pump only when necessary
    D. inspect monthly

73. High pressure steam line gaskets are made of:
    A. wire inserted rubber   C. plastic
    B. cloth   ✓D. metal

74. Joints in pipelines must be properly aligned before you make them up because:
    ✓A. excessive strain on the joints will result if they are misaligned
    B. misalignment permits excessive expansion
    C. the pipe will be completely clocked by even the slightest amount of misalignment
    D. condensate accumulates rapidly when flanges are not properly aligned

75. The tool used to remove a ball bearing from the shaft of a motor is called a:
    A. slugging wrench   C. drift pin
    ✓ B. wheel puller   D. come-along

Deck Machinery

1. The spring set electrically operated brakes used with deck machinery operate on the fail-safe principle because the brakes are automatically applied by spring action if the:
    A. lowering speed of the load is excessive
    B. brake suffers any mechanical failure
    C. load placed on the winch is too great
    ✓D. electric power to the winch fails

2. The speed control lever on some steam winches is held in neutral position by:
    A. a brake   ✓C. an automatic latch
    B. a compound gear   D. a spur gear

3. The clutch-band of a constant tension mooring winch must be set up tight enough to drive the winch drum and should slip only when:
    ✓ A. excessive loads are placed on the winch
    B. minimum pull is being exerted by the winch
    C. automatic operation of the winch is desired
    D. wire is being retrieved at the maximum rate

4. On a steam driven anchor windlass, the clutch is used to:
    A. regulate the speed
    B. hold the anchor
    ✓ C. engage and disengage the wildcat
    D. regulate the angle of the warping heads

5. Mechanical hand brake mechanisms incorporated in boat handling winches must be able to:
 A. automatically control the gravity lowering speed
 B. mechanically control the boat raising rate under power
 C. hold the load suspended during lowering
 D. automatically stop the boat if the centrifugal brake fails

6. The oil in a cargo winch gear box should be sampled periodically to:
 A. prevent the gear box from leaking
 B. prevent the oil from becoming inflammable
 C. make sure it has not become contaminated
 D. make sure the motor bearings are lubricated

7. The screw threads on the brake linkage of an anchor windlass:
 A. must be lubricated and maintained in good condition
 B. never require any maintenance
 C. are unimportant because they have no effect on braking
 D. are engaged only in emergency situations

8. How would you set the valves on a steam anchor windlass?
 A. set pistons on dead center with the valves centered over the ports
 B. set eccentric at 10° lead and pistons at 90° to dead center
 C. set eccentric at 90° and piston at 10°
 D. put piston at dead center and set eccentric at 90°

9. The valves on steam cargo winch engines are made:
 A. with lap and lead   C. without lead only
 B. without lap or lead   D. without lap only

10. When starting a hydraulic winch system under normal conditions, the pressure controls for the axial piston hydraulic motor should be set for:
 A. minimum pressure   C. purge and vent
 B. neutral stroke   D. maximum torque

11. What is the purpose of the neck bushing in a steam pump?
 A. compensates for piston wear
 B. aids in sealing the stuffing box
 C. seals the steam valve
 D. protects the neck on the slide valve rod

12. A compression grease cup puts the grease into the bearing by:
 A. capillary action   C. gravity
 B. spring pressure   D. hydraulic pressure

13. Overheating of the hydraulic fluid in an electrohydraulic anchor windlass indicates pump cavitation caused by a (an):
 A. overload on the pump motor
 B. low fluid viscosity around the shaft seal
 C. low fluid level in the reservoir
 D. high oil level in the sump

14. In order for a variable stroke radial-piston pump to function, which of its parts is moved off center?

    A. nonrevolving ring

    B. floating ring (reaction ring)

    C. cylinder body

    D. central cylindrical valve (pintle or spindle valve)

15. Wildcats and warping heads:

    A. run in either direction

    B. run in the direction of windlass

    C. reverse when the windlass reverses

    D. do all of the above

16. An electrohydraulic windlass is controlled by the operation of a handwheel which:

    A. controls the speed of the electric motor

    B. controls the output of the electrohydraulic unit

    C. operates the devil's claw

    D. disconnects the warping heads

17. When an electrical power is removed from the windlass the anchor is locked by:

    A. an electrical braking device

    B. a powerful spring actuated braking device

    C. operating the brake lever

    D. operating the handwheel

18. If there is an accumulation of air in an electrohydraulic steering system, it will be indicated by:

    A. the motor running continuously

    B. the rudder not responding to the signals

    C. excessive pressures on the rams

    D. the relief valves lifting

19. The hydraulic system of a deck winch has been drained, flushed, and refilled with hydraulic fluid. An erratic knocking noise from the hydraulic motor when the winch is started would indicate:

    A. the fluid is too cold

    B. air trapped in the system

    C. clogged suction line fluid filters

    D. abrasive matter circulating in the oil

20. After working on deck steam lines, you can prevent damage to machinery from water hammer by:

    A. installing a steam strainer in all exhaust lines

    B. opening machinery throttle valves rapidly

    C. draining the steam piping before operating any machinery

    D. preheating the steam lines before you operate machinery

21. To safely lubricate a crankshaft bearing with a grease gun on an operating steam winch, you should:

   A. slow the winch down
   B. stop the winch
   C. make sure your sleeves are rolled up
   D. be sure you are grounded

22. Prior to operating a hydraulic crane:
   A. the hydraulic system must undergo a transmission check
   B. the system must be warmed up for a few minutes
   C. the crane must be operated on electrical power
   D. have chief check controls

23. The most practical method of fixing a hot winch motor bearing of the sealed type is to:
   A. add grease through the zerk fitting
   B. allow the winch to run at slow speeds only
   C. replace the bearing with a new one
   D. apply a light oil to the bearing housing

24. When a cargo winch is lowering a heavy load, the slowest speed should be used to:
   A. prevent loss of lubrication
   B. allow down clutching
   C. prevent overloading of cables
   D. produce a minimum impact upon landing

25. The brake of a cargo winch is:
   A. automatically applied when power to the winch is lost
   B. automatically set when the winch motor control is moved to stop
   C. applied by strong springs
   D. all of the above

26. The wildcat may be referred to as a (an):
   A. mooring line tender   C. auxiliary cargo winch
   B. anchor chain lifter   D. all of the above

27. If a lifeboat winch lowers too rapidly, what should you do?
   A. adjust centrifugal brake
   B. tighten the hand friction brake
   C. engage motor friction brake
   D. remove some of the weight

28. On a constant tension warping winch or anchor windlass to prevent the brake lining from sticking to the drums, you should:
   A. remove the glazed surface
   B. release the friction pad from the drum when not in use
   C. polish the drum every two months
   D. lubricate with a little oil

29. The vertical windlass is installed with the motor and reduction gear located below deck. The capstan now takes the place of the:

A. clutch   C. constant tension winch
B. warping head   D. wildcat

30. At dock side or in a lock the ship's position may be maintained automatically by the use of a:

A. gypsy winch   C. vertical capstan
B. constant tension winch   D. A and C above

31. A valve installed in a hydraulic system to direct the flow of fluid is called a:

A. relief valve   C. directional control valve
B. reservoir valve   D. power valve

32. In the event of failure of the hydraulic steering engine, the ship may be steered by a:

A. come-along   C. hand pump
B. chain fall   D. standby electrical system

33. What inspection should you make while you are warming up a steam winch?

A. make sure that the steam is at the proper temperature
B. listen for any unusual noises coming from the winch
C. thoroughly grease the brake band if one is installed
D. open the throttle valve wide when you first start the winch

34. In the majority of electrohydraulic steering systems, if electric power is lost, the rudder:

A. stays in the same position it was before the power loss
B. swings left or right 35°
C. causes the hydraulic relief valve(s) to open
D. returns to the midships position

35. What device is used to control the speed and direction of rotation of a steam powered windlass?

A. hydraulic motor   C. hand lever
B. electrohydraulic pump   D. electric motor

Electrical Procedures

1. Which of the following instruments is used to test capacitors?

A. voltmeter   C. wattmeter
B. megger   D. ohmmeter

2. A "megger" is:

A. an instrument for measuring current
B. a hand-cranked A.C. generator
C. a hand-cranked D.C. generator
D. a meter for measuring the thickness of insulation

3. A megger is used to measure:

A. kilohms   C. milliohms
B. megohms   D. microhms

4. The power supply for a megger is obtained from:
    A. any 115 volt D.C. circuit   C. flashlight batteries
    B. any 115 volt A.C. circuit   D. a magneto

5. If the pointer of a megger does not come back to "zero" when the unit is not in use:
    A. the megger is out of calibration
    B. the megger is operating normally
    C. the hairsprings are burned out
    D. the pointer is stuck

6. Counter EMF is measured in:
    A. amps   C. volts
    B. ohms   D. coulombs

7. One kilowatt is equal to:
    A. 1.25 horsepower   C. 1.50 horsepower
    B. 1.33 horsepower   D. 2.00 horsepower

8. When troubleshooting a magnetic controller and the contacts are welded, it may be the result of:
    A. high ambient temperature
    B. prolonged overload
    C. high voltage operating coil
    D. low voltage operating coil

9. An ohmmeter measures:
    A. voltage   C. resistance
    B. insulation resistance   D. amperage

10. Which of the following materials would you use to clean a commutator?
    A. sandpaper   C. emery cloth
    B. oil cloth   D. monk's cloth

11. A voltmeter is connected in a circuit in:
    A. parallel   C. series
    B. series parallel   D. relay

12. You are told to measure the insulation resistance of some feeders. To do this you would use a:
    A. megger   C. magneto test
    B. bell test   D. field service engineer

13. Copper is often used as an electrical conductor because it:
    A. has high resistance at low temperatures
    B. has a highly polished surface
    C. is able to pass current with little opposition
    D. holds insulation together well

14. Large D.C. motors can be automatically started by which type starters?
    A. definite-time element   C. counter EMF
    B. current limiting shunt   D. all of the above

15. What type motors are used on hoisting cranes?
     A. single-phase   C. three-phase
     B. two-phase   \   —D. D.C. motors
16. Portable power hand tools are grounded to the:
     ⌐ A. body   C. field
     B. armature   D. switch
17. An ammeter is connected in a circuit in:
     A. series parallel   — C. series
     B. parallel   D. contact
18. An operating characteristic which appears on the nameplates of
     shipboard A.C. motors is the:
     A. type of winding   ⌐ C. temperature rise
     B. input KW   D. locked rotor torque
19. A short in a D.C. motor would be detected by:
     A. brush sparking   C. blackened bars
     B. ground lights   ⌐D. A or C
20. It is advisable to close a knife switch firmly and rapidly because then
     there is less:
     A. danger of shock to the operator
     B. chance of making an error
     C. mechanical wear of the contacts
     ⌐D. likelihood of arcing
21. If the needle on a megger does *not* return to zero, what is the cause?
     A. out of calibration
     B. needle bent
     ⌐ C. normal operation
     D. external adjustment is necessary
22. If you reversed the field and armature leads of a motor, it would:
     A. burn out   ⌐ C. run in the same direction
     B. run backwards   D. stall
23. A leaky gasket on a controller box will result in:
     A. loss of power   C. defective motor
     ⌐ B. corrosion   D. open solenoid
24. What condition can result if dirt and grease are allowed to accumu-
     late between the commutator segments of a motor?
     ⌐A. a partial short circuit
     B. a dead short circuit
     C. misalignment of the motor unit
     D. overspeeding of the motor
25. A short circuit may be measured by:
     — A. ammeter or megger   C. dynamometer or megger
     B. voltmeter or megger   D. ammeter and ohmmeter
26. To measure the voltage across a load you would connect:

A. a voltmeter across the load
B. an ammeter across the load
C. a voltmeter in series with the load
D. an ammeter in series with the load

27. Movable cams on controllers serve what purpose?
    A. change resistance   C. operator control handle
    B. change motor connection   D. open controller housing

28. An open coil can be detected by:
    A. high resistance   C. watts
    B. low resistance   D. both B and C

29. A shorted coil can be detected by:
    A. high resistance   C. overheated coil
    B. low resistance   D. resistance

30. Which of the following would cause one bar of a commutator to blacken?
    A. grounded coil   C. an open coil
    B. shorted coil   D. any of the above

31. A short circuit may be measured by:
    A. ammeter or megger   C. dynamometer or megger
    B. voltmeter or megger   D. ammeter and ohmmeter

32. What type of motor is used near tank tops or vents on deck?
    A. waterproof   C. leakproof
    B. dustproof   D. explosionproof

33. If the secondary of a transformer has more windings (turns) than the primary, the transformer is:
    A. step-up   C. wye
    B. step-down   D. delta

34. If a D.C. motor failed to start, the cause could be:
    A. a short circuit in the armature
    B. blocked motor ventilating ports
    C. blown fuses in the power supply
    D. high starting voltage

35. Batteries which are maintained in a fully charged state by being constantly on charge are said to be on what type charge?
    A. initial   C. continuous
    B. trickle   D. equalizing

36. A generator has been exposed to water. Which of the following instruments would be used to determine if it is safe to operate?
    A. a megger   C. a hydrometer
    B. a voltmeter   D. a wattmeter

37. Damp armature windings will cause:
    A. reduced voltage   C. overheating
    B. reduced current   D. increased resistance

38. A characteristic of D.C. power systems and controls is:
    A. light weight
    B. high motor starting torque
    C. low maintenance
    D. simplified design and construction

39. Sparking at the brushes of a running motor could be caused by:
    A. excessive vibration in the brush holder
    B. moisture in the field windings
    C. excessive brush pressure
    D. high motor torque

40. Another name for an over current protection device is a:
    A. magnetic breaker   C. fuse
    B. thermal breaker   D. all of the above

41. A "dead board" is:
    A. a board with no power
    B. a board with no switches
    C. a board with no circuit breaker
    D. none of the above

42. A circuit that has one wire in contact with the hull of the ship is a:
    A. series circuit   C. short circuit
    B. grounded circuit   D. closed circuit

43. D.P.D.T. stands for:
    A. duplex pole dead throw switch
    B. double-pole single-throw switch
    C. double-pole double-throw switch
    D. direct power to direct terminal

44. The insulation resistance of a transformer winding is readily measured with:
    A. a wattmeter   C. a megger
    B. an ammeter   D. a Kelvin bridge

45. The resistance of two 60 amp 6 volt batteries connected in series is:
    A. 15 ohms   C. .10 ohms
    B. .20 ohms   D. .25 ohms

46. Sparking and grooving of commutator may be caused by:
    A. overload   C. wrong type of brushes
    B. strength of field   D. any of the above

47. One horsepower equals:
    A. 1,000 watts   C. 100 watts
    B. 746 watts   D. 940 watts

48. The handle on a surface plate controller is returned to the "off" position by a:
    A. strong spring   C. manually
    B. solenoid   D. contactor

49. The voltage of a D.C. generator depends on which of the following?
    A. speed of armature
    B. strength of field
    C. number of armature conductors
    D. all of the above

50. If a three-phase motor develops an open in one of its phases, what will happen?
    A. it will continue to run if it has a low load
    B. it will develop greater torque
    C. it will immediately stop and then can be restarted
    D. it will immediately stop and can't be restarted

51. How are the ammeter and the voltmeter properly connected in a circuit?
    A. both meters are connected in series with the line
    B. they can be connected either in series or parallel with the line and read correctly
    C. the ammeter must be connected in series with the line and the voltmeter connected across the line or in parallel with the circuit
    D. the voltmeter is connected in series with the line and the ammeter connected across the line or in parallel with the circuit

52. When used for taking resistance measurements, a volt-ohm milli-ammeter powered by:
    A. a hand-cranked generator
    B. internal storage batteries
    C. the current in the circuit being tested
    D. a step-down transformer

53. High mica between commutator bars is removed by:
    A. removing   C. undercutting
    B. burning   D. chiseling

54. A galvanometer is used to measure:
    A. small voltage   C. large currents
    B. small currents   D. both A and B

55. To test an armature for grounds, you could use a (an):
    A. voltmeter or megger   C. ammeter or megger
    B. voltmeter or ammeter   D. ammeter or dynamometer

56. The Wheatstone Bridge is an instrument that may be used to measure:
    A. voltage   C. resistance
    B. current   D. conductance

57. A megger measures:
    A. volts   C. resistance
    B. amps   D. insulation resistance

58. A short circuit is:
    A. an electrical leak
    B. two grounded wires
    C. unwanted current with low resistance
    ⁓ D. all of the above
59. A megger is always used on a:
    A. grounded circuit   C. live circuit
    B. short circuit   ⁓D. deenergized circuit
60. When a D.C. motor fails to start and you are troubleshooting, the first thing to check is:
    A. motor windings for obvious shorts
    ⁓ B. fuses and circuit breaker
    C. motor controller leads for continuity with a megger
    D. motor controller leads for opens with a megger

Machinery Troubleshooting and Procedures

1. If the hydraulic pump on an anchor windlass is overheating, the cause may be:
    A. excessive pump speed
    B. excessive pump outlet pressure
    C. low discharge pressure
    D. low pump speed
2. Hydraulic fluid in a windlass pump can overheat due to cavitation caused by:
    A. an overload on the pump motor
    B. a low fluid level in the reservoir
    C. a low fluid viscosity around the shaft seal
    D. a high oil level in the sump
3. If the cover gasket of the winch master control switch deteriorates, it could result in:
    A. overheating of the winch motor
    B. contamination of the lube oil
    C. sparking at the motor brushes
    D. rapid corrosion of switch components
4. The hydraulic system on a deck winch was serviced, and upon starting a knocking noise comes from the hydraulic motor. The cause could be:
    A. the fluid is cold
    B. air in the system
    C. clogged suction line filters
    D. abrasives in the hydraulic oil
5. On a steam driven anchor windlass, the clutch is used to:

    A. regulate the speed at which the anchor chain pays out

    B. hold the anchor securely in the hawsepipe

    C. engage and disengage the wildcat from the engine

    D. regulate the speed of the warping heads

6. Steam spur gear anchor windlasses used on large tankers have a hand brake of the _____ type.

    A. pump brake   C. whelp brake

    B. screw compression   D. toggle brake

7. Turbulence in hydraulic system piping and equipment causes:

    A. fluid vibration   C. erratic pressure

    B. energy losses   D. mechanical damage

8. Energy losses which occur in a hydraulic system are ultimately absorbed by the:

    A. reservoir expansion chamber

    B. flexible piping

    C. atmosphere as heat

    D. fluid as friction

9. With an increase in temperature, the volume of hydraulic fluid:

    A. contracts

    B. remains the same

    C. remains constant if pressure decreases

    D. expands

10. A ground in a wire outside the engine room would be indicated by:

    A. impossible to locate

    B. bright ground lamp on the switchboard

    C. dim ground lamp on the switchboard

    D. a ground indicator at the branch box

11. When the indicator on a cartridge type filter in a hydraulic system reads "by-pass," you must:

    A. replace the filter

    B. reduce the load

    C. bypass the cartridge

    D. bypass the filter

12. What is the most common type gauge used aboard ship?

    A. steam gauge   C. vacuum

    B. bourdon tube   D. pressure

13. When repairing the steam valves on a reciprocating pump, the first thing that must be done is:

    A. move the piston to the lower ⅓ of the cylinder

    B. measure the steam parts

    C. disconnect the valve linkage

    D. bar the piston to the bottom of the cylinder

14. An O-ring seal in a hydraulic system will begin to leak when it has lost its fit due to:

A. compression set or wear
B. low fluid pressure
C. high fluid temperature
D. excessive vibration

15. The major source of chemical contaminants in hydraulic fluid is:
    A. microscopic steel shavings
    B. abrasive waste
    C. antioxidant compounds
    D. oxidation by-products

16. Hydraulic machinery failures are commonly caused by misalignment and:
    A. hydraulic fluid contamination
    B. excessive fluid friction
    C. turbulent fluid flow
    D. fluid pressure surges

17. Overheating of a hydraulic system can be caused by:
    A. excessive discharge pressure
    B. deterioration of the hydraulic fluid
    C. insufficient internal pump slippage
    D. fluctuating discharge pressure

18. Why are D.C. series motors used extensively for electric drives on winches?
    A. they are constant speed
    B. they operate at high speeds when under heavy loads
    C. they don't require a controller
    D. they are designed to operate in a stalled condition

19. The full torque electric brake on an electric cargo winch functions to:
    A. act as a backup in case the mechanical brake fails
    B. automatically hold the load if current is lost
    C. automatically govern the lowering speed of the load
    D. automatically govern the hoisting speed of the load

20. The cams on the drum switch of a cargo winch:
    A. control the winch brake
    B. control the winch motor speed
    C. control the clutch setting
    D. none of the above

21. Overheating of a hydraulic system can be caused by:
    A. low fluid viscosity   C. both a and b
    B. high fluid viscosity   D. none of the above

22. Which problem can be caused by using a hydraulic fluid with a viscosity higher than specified?
    A. seal deterioration
    B. fast response and hunting

      C. increased power consumption

      D. oil film breakdown

23. After installing a new hydraulic pump, what special attention should be given to the system?

      A. the relief valves should be readjusted

      B. the filters and strainers should be checked frequently

      C. system pressures should be readjusted

      D. the fluid should be drained and renewed

24. Electric and electrohydraulic steering gear motors are required to be:

      A. protected by a circuit breaker and a thermal overload device

      B. served by two electric power feeder circuits

      C. provided with a motor overcurrent protection device

      D. served by a single, two conductor cable

25. Auxiliary steering gear for a 20 knot vessel must meet rudder movement requirements at what minimum speed?

      A. 7 knots   C. 15 knots

      B. 10 knots   D. 20 knots

26. In an electrohydraulic steering gear, when will the variable displacement pump be on stroke?

      A. when the helm is at any angle other than amidships

      B. when the six-way valve is opened

      C. when the ram relief valves lift

      D. when the rudder angle is different from the position of the helm

27. Under normal operating conditions, the rudder is hydraulically locked unless:

      A. the manual trick wheel is engaged for steering

      B. the pump is off stroke

      C. a normal rudder order is given by the control system

      D. an electric power failure occurs at the steering gear

28. Some steam winches are fitted with neck bushings in the stuffing boxes to:

      A. lubricate the packing   C. relieve cylinder pressure

      B. eliminate pounding   D. help seal the stuffing box

29. Coast Guard regulations require an indicating light at the propulsion control station illuminate if overloading or overheating occurs in the:

      A. forced draft blower motor   C. steering gear motor

      B. fuel pump motor   D. condensate pump motor

30. What equipment must be tested not more that 12 hours prior to getting underway from a U.S. port?

      A. steering gear

B. emergency generator

C. all internal control communications and alarms

D. all of the above

31. Steering gear circuits shall only be protected by:

A. a circuit breaker with instantaneous trip

B. motor overcurrent protection

C. a non-renewable link cartridge fuse

D. a renewable link cartridge fuse

32. The clutch band of a constant tension mooring winch should slip only when:

A. excessive loads are placed on the winch

B. minimum pull is being exerted by the winch

C. automatic operation of the winch is desired

D. wire is being retrieved at the maximum rate

33. When the hydraulic control lever for a deck winch is placed in neutral or off position the spring set brake is:

A. hydraulically released and engaged by spring action

B. released by spring action and hydraulically locks the winch

C. engaged by spring action and locked by hydraulic pressure

D. opened hydraulically and held open by spring action

34. Hydraulic cranes must be properly warmed up before they are used because:

A. the hydraulic fluid will leak out otherwise

B. the hydraulic fluid must be at the proper temperature

C. the fluid strainers operate only during warm up

D. the relief valves must be tested

35. An oil hydraulic system can be safely cleaned using:

A. alcohol

B. water based detergent

C. carbon tetrachloride

D. special petroleum solvent

36. In a telemotor steering system, the function of the transmitting unit is to:

A. transmit the rudder angle to the bridge indicator

B. prevent the linkage from striking the stops when hard over

C. automatically purge the system

D. send hydraulic signals to the receiving unit

37. When the steering wheel is turned, oil is directed to the rams by:

A. modulating the oil flow with the six-way valve

B. moving the automatic pressure differential valve

C. moving the receiving telemotor which regulates the two-way valve

D. varying the position of a floating ring or tilting box

38. What would result if the solenoid burned out on a cargo winch equipped with an electrically released brake?
    A. the brake would be set by spring tension
    B. the motor would overspeed and burn up
    C. the load on the cargo boom would fail
    D. the winch would operate normally

39. The oil in a cargo winch gear box should be sampled periodically to:
    A. check that the gear box is not leaking
    B. prevent the oil from becoming flammable
    C. make sure it has not become contaminated
    D. make sure the motor bearings are lubricated

40. Winch gears must be kept in proper alignment to prevent:
    A. overheating the lube oil
    B. overspeeding of the motor
    C. wear on the bearing system
    D. damage to the gear teeth

41. If an anchor windlass motor smokes and the motor circuit has been disconnected, the cause can be:
    A. a fire in the heater circuit
    B. fire caused by the capacitive discharge leaking off the motor windlass
    C. a melted fuse in the disconnect device
    D. any of the above

42. Condensate moisture damage inside cargo winch master switches can be reduced by:
    A. installing a light bulb in the pedestal stand
    B. coating the switch box with an epoxy sealer
    C. venting the switch box regularly·
    D. using strip heaters inside the switch box

43. Proper internal lubrication of a hydraulic anchor windlass that is left idle for extended periods can be accomplished by:
    A. performing check runs at regular intervals
    B. testing the hydraulic fluid for proper ph
    C. checking the reservoir for proper level
    D. cleaning the strainers at regular intervals

44. You should check-run a hydraulic anchor windlass during long periods of inactivity to:
    A. prevent chemical breakdown of hydraulic fluid
    B. remove condensation from the fluid reservoir
    C. prevent the anchor from seizing in the hawsepipe
    D. renew the internal coating of lubrication

45. Prior to starting a steam winch, you should be certain that the:
    A. steam lines are thoroughly drained

B. clutch is engaged

C. warping head is balanced

D. exhaust valve is closed

46. Why must a hydraulic windlass be run occasionally?

    A. to test operation

    B. to free up the clutch

    C. to relieve pressures in the line

    D. to maintain hydraulic pressure

47. Purging air from an electrohydraulic steering gear would be necessary when:

    A. changing over to hand pump operation

    B. engaging the trick wheel

    C. the system has been filled with new fluid

    D. the rudder angle indicator does not match the helm position

48. When the hydraulic steering gear is working, you should:

    A. purge air from the rams every hour

    B. check the rams for overheating

    C. check the ram cylinders for leaks

    D. drain water from the ram cylinders every hour

49. If the relief valve is set lower than the system operating pressure, the result would be:

    A. accelerated action of the system components

    B. overheating of the system

    C. overspeeding of the pump

    D. extended system life

50. Prolonged cavitation in a hydraulic pump can cause:

    A. hydraulic fluid overheating

    B. fluid motor overload

    C. relief valve chatter

    D. fluid pressure surges

51. Cavitation in an anchor windlass could be caused by a/an:

    A. overload on the pump motor

    B. low fluid level in the reservoir

    C. low fluid viscosity around the shaft seal

    D. high oil level in the sump

52. When the helm is turned on the bridge, what is the *first* thing that happens with an electrohydraulic steering gear?

    A. The pumps go to full stroke

    B. the six-way valve aligns up with the running pump

    C. both port and starboard cables are energized

    D. the synchronous receiver turns, duplicating the helm motion

53. In an electrohydraulic steering gear, any change between the synchronous receiver and the follow-up results in:
   A. the pumps going to full stroke
   B. closing of the six-way valve
   C. driving the rams against the stops
   D. a slowing down or speeding up of the pumping
54. While inspecting the steering engines at sea, you should check for:
   A. leaks in the system
   B. accuracy of the rudder angle indicator
   C. movement of the trick wheel
   D. position of the six-way valve
55. When fire resistant fluid is used in a hydraulic system, it is important that:
   A. the increase in viscosity is not excessive
   B. the fluid does not dissipate too much heat
   C. the fluid be compatible with all seals
   D. a separate oil supply be furnished for the pump
56. Rudder movement is maintained in close synchronization with the steering wheel position by means of the:
   A. trickwheel   C. six-way valve
   B. follow-up control   D. rapson slide
57. Before working on a hydraulic machine with an accumulator, you should:
   A. pressurize the system
   B. draw the energy from the accumulator
   C. operate the machine until it reaches normal temperature
   D. disconnect the pump pressure control switch
58. When the desired rudder angel is attained in a typical hydraulic steering system the:
   A. ram relief valves bypass oil to stop movement
   B. the six-way valve shifts to neutral
   C. steering pump motor is de-energized
   D. follow-up takes the pump off stroke
59. A flexible hose under pressure in a hydraulic system will:
   A. tend to twist about its long axis
   B. expand in length and diameter
   C. contract in length and expand in diameter
   D. flex at right angles to the pressure
60. Which device keeps the rudder from overtraveling the bridge signal?
   A. the follow-up gear
   B. the ruler angle indicator
   C. the synchronous transmitter
   D. a rudder angle limit switch

61. Hydraulic tubing should be anchored every three or four feet to prevent:
   A. excessive vibration and pressure surges
   B. expansion and contraction of the tubing
   C. tube fitting leaks due to vibration and pressure surges
   D. the tubing from flexing

62. If you were replacing a gasket in a pipeline and were unsure as to what kind of gasket material to use, you would:
   A. turn the old gasket around and put it back in
   B. consult ship's or manufacturer's manual
   C. replace the old gasket and coat entirely with permatex
   D. make up the joint until you can ask the chief what kind to use

63. If a hydraulic pump is noisy when operating, the cause my be:
   A. an air leak in the pump suction line
   B. low fluid viscosity
   C. an oil leak through the shaft packing
   D. wrong shaft rotation

64. Noisy operation of a hydraulic pump can be caused by:
   A. high pump operating pressure
   B. a clogged strainer
   C. excessive pump speed
   D. any of the above

65. If a hydraulic pump and motor lose pressure with a loss of hydraulic control, the probable cause is:
   A. external leakage from the high pressure relief valve
   B. an internal failure in the hydraulic motor
   C. an internal failure in the hydraulic pump
   D. internal leakage through the low pressure relief valve

66. A decrease in pressure in a ship's hydraulic pump can be caused by:
   A. the four-way control valve failing to shift
   B. the pilot operated pressure valve sticking closed
   C. cold hydraulic fluid
   D. a clogged air vent filter on the oil reservoir

67. If dirt is allowed to contaminate the sump of a hydraulic deck crane, what will result?
   A. all the seals will blow out
   B. the lifting capacity of the crane will be reduced
   C. the hydraulic lines will fracture
   D. the internal parts of the pump and motor will wear excessively

68. If the hydraulic pump discharge relief valve lifts, the cause could be:
   A. a low load on the unit
   B. a clogged pump suction strainer

      C. a blockage in the line between the pump and motor

      D. the motor turning too fast

69. Which of the following is true concerning the use of fire resistant fluids in a hydraulic system?

      A. deterioration of paints, seals, and electrical insulation can occur

      B. fluid viscosity always increases

      C. components wear less

      D. only chemically active filters may be used

70. When there is no movement of the rams on hydraulic steering gear, the tilting box of the running pump is:

      A. set for maximum torque

      B. on the purge and vent stroke

      C. in the neutral position

      D. rotating backwards

71. When the steering wheel is turned, oil pressure is applied to the rams by:

      A. regulating the flow with the six-way valve

      B. moving the differential valve

      C. moving the receiving telemotor which regulates the two-way valve

      D. varying the angle of a tilting box or floating ring

72. If one hydraulic pump fails, the ship's steering can be maintained by the:

      A. trick wheel   C. standby pump

      B. accumulator   D. telemotor

73. In an emergency, electrohydraulic steering engines can be controlled by the:

      A. trick wheel   C. follow-up gear

      B. rapson slide   D. receiver unit

74. When repairing the steam valves on a reciprocating pump, the first thing that must be done is:

      A. move the piston to the lower ⅓ of the cylinder

      B. measure the steam parts

      C. disconnect the valve linkage

      D. bar the piston to the bottom of the cylinder

75. What happens to the condensate after it leaves the tank heating coils?

      A. it goes to the atmospheric drain tank

      B. it goes to the contaminated drain tank

      C. it goes to the D.C. heater

      D. it goes to the condenser

Answers to Multiple-Choice Questions
for the Deck Engineer

Equipment operations

1. B	20. A	39. A	58. C
2. A	21. C	40. B	59. C
3. D	22. D	41. C	60. B
4. C	23. C	42. C	61. D
5. A	24. B	43. C	62. B
6. A	25. C	44. B	63. B
7. A	26. C	45. A	64. D
8. C	27. B	46. B	65. C
9. C	28. B	47. D	66. D
10. C	29. C	48. D	67. B
11. C	30. B	49. C	68. D
12. A	31. C	50. C	69. C
13. C	32. A	51. C	70. B
14. A	33. B	52. C	71. B
15. D	34. B	53. C	72. A
16. C	35. D	54. D	73. D
17. B	36. D	55. A	74. A
18. C	37. C	56. D	75. B
19. A	38. C	57. A	

Deck machinery

1. D	10. B	19. B	28. D
2. C	11. B	20. C	29. B
3. A	12. B	21. B	30. B
4. C	13. C	22. B	31. C
5. C	14. B	23. C	32. C
6. C	15. D	24. D	33. B
7. A	16. B	25. D	34. A
8. D	17. B	26. B	35. C
9. A	18. B	27. A	

Electrical procedures

1. D	9. C	17. C	25. A/D
2. C	10. A	18. C	26. A
3. B	11. A	19. D	27. A
4. D	12. A	20. D	28. A
5. B	13. C	21. C	29. D
6. C	14. D	22. C	30. D
7. B	15. D	23. B	31. D
8. B	16. A	24. A	32. D

33. A	40. D	47. B	54. D
34. C	41. A	48. A	55. C
35. B	42. B	49. D	56. C
36. A	43. C	50. A	57. D
37. C	44. C	51. C	58. D
38. B	45. B	52. B	59. D
39. A	46. D	53. C	60. B

Machinery troubleshooting and procedures

1. B	20. B	39. C	58. D
2. B	21. C	40. D	59. C
3. D	22. C	41. A	60. A
4. B	23. B	42. D	61. C
5. C	24. B	43. A	62. B
6. B	25. B	44. D	63. A
7. B	26. D	45. A	64. D
8. C	27. C	46. A	65. C
9. D	28. D	47. C	66. D
10. C	29. C	48. C	67. D
11. A	30. D	49. B	68. C
12. B	31. A	50. A	69. A
13. D	32. A	51. B	70. C
14. A	33. A	52. D	71. D
15. D	34. B	53. D	72. C
16. A	35. D	54. A	73. A
17. A	36. D	55. C	74. D
18. D	37. D	56. B	75. B
19. B	38. A	57. B	

CHAPTER FOURTEEN

Multiple-Choice Questions for the Refrigeration Engineer

The refrigeration engineer works an 8-hour day and assists the electrician in the shipboard electrical maintenance and the bulk cargo refrigeration system maintenance. Duties of the refrigeration engineer include the following:

*1. Assist the electrician in his duties.

*2. Monitor and operate the brine (glycol) refrigeration system including the brine solution, recirculating pumps, temperature controllers, and diffuser fans and louvers.

3. Monitor and operate the ship's air conditioning/heating system.

4. Perform a daily round of passenger staterooms inspecting for proper electrical, heating, and air conditioning service.

*5. Maintain an accurate log of refrigerated cargo hold temperatures, and open and sign temperature recorders each watch.

*6. Perform electrical and refrigeration troubleshooting and maintenance as instructed by the chief engineer.

The topics covered by the multiple-choice questions include: Refrigeration Theory; Compressors, Condensors, and Evaporators; Accessories and Air Conditioning; and System Operations and Troubleshooting. The subjects which are covered by these topics include the following:

1. Principles of refrigeration
2. Refrigeration cycle components
3. Refrigerants
4. Refrigeration accessories
5. Refrigeration maintenance and troubleshooting
6. Air conditioning systems
7. Centrifugal refrigeration systems

Refrigeration Theory

1. The latent heat of evaporation is dissipated in the:

A. evaporator   C. condenser

B. expansion valve   D. compressor

---

* Routine off watch duties.

2. In a refrigeration system, a fluid that serves only as a heat carrier is called a:
   A. secondary refrigerant
   B. condensing refrigerant
   C. vaporizing refrigerant
   D. primary refrigerant

3. A refrigerant boils and vaporizes in the:
   A. receiver
   B. condenser
   C. compressor
   D. cooling coil

4. The "heat of compression" is:
   A. utilized in the evaporator
   B. often wasted
   C. less on water-cooled systems
   D. carried away in the water leaving the condenser

5. A good refrigerant should possess: I. low freezing point; II. low boiling point.
   A. I only
   B. II only
   C. both I and II
   D. neither I nor II

6. Which of the following refrigerants is used in a centrifugal compression system?
   A. R-5
   B. R-11
   C. R-12
   D. R-14

7. Another name for discharge pressure is:
   A. suction pressure
   B. absolute pressure
   C. head pressure
   D. condenser pressure

8. The low side of a refrigeration system is from the:
   A. expansion valve to the compressor
   B. compressor to the expansion valve
   C. expansion valve to the evaporator
   D. condenser to the expansion valve

9. The amount of CO_2 or Freon in a cylinder is measured by:
   A. pressure
   B. volume
   C. weight
   D. PSI

10. In addition to pressure, Freon gauges are calibrated in:
    A. saturated gas temperature
    B. superheated gas temperature
    C. absolute temperature
    D. absolute pressure

11. Five pounds of water heated to raise the temperature (sea level) 2° requires:
    A. 25 BTUs
    B. 10 BTUs
    C. 5 BTUs
    D. 15 minutes

12. A refrigerating unit of one (1) ton capacity can remove:
    A. 500 BTUs per minute
    B. 288 BTUs per minute
    C. 200 BTUs per minute
    D. 100 BTUs per minute

13. Absolute zero on the fahrenheit scale equals:

    A. −459°   C. −100°

    B. −273°   D. 0°

14. One pound of water at 32° F at atmospheric pressure in changing to ice at 32° F must lose:

    A. 144 BTUs   C. 970 BTUs

    B. 180 BTUs   D. 32 BTUs

15. When a pressure gauge reads zero, the absolute pressure is:

    A. 30 PSI   C. 0 PSI

    B. 14.7 PSI   D. 17.4 PSI

16. Flash gas in liquid lines:

    A. assists in keeping liquid lines cool

    B. indicates too much refrigerant in system

    C. assists in accelerating refrigerant through the system

    D. reduces system capacity

17. The heat absorbed in the evaporating coils must equal the:

    A. heat of compression

    B. heat given up by the condenser

    C. heat lost by medium being cooled

    D. heat gained by the condenser

18. Refrigeration spaces that can be locked from the outside, but cannot be opened from the inside, must have an audible alarm in which of the following locations? I. in the normal working area; II. at the exit of the refrigerated compartment.

    A. I   C. either I or II

    B. II   D. neither I nor II

19. The type of refrigerant used in centrifugal compressors is:

    A. F 5   C. F 12

    B. F 11   D. F 14

20. What separates the high pressure side from the low pressure side in a refrigeration system?

    A. condenser and thermal expansion valve

    B. king and solenoid valves

    C. compressor and thermal expansion valve

    D. condenser and solenoid

21. Sensible heat:

    A. can be measured with a thermometer

    B. cannot be measured with a thermometer

    C. changes in the receiver tank

    D. increases with the cold

22. A ton of refrigeration is equal to the removal of:

    A. 288,000 BTUs per 24 hours

    B. 28,000 BTUs per 24 hours

      C. 28,800 BTUs per 24 hours

      D. 280,000 BTUs per 24 hours

23. The boiling point of water in an open container at sea level is 212° F. If the pressure on the open container is decreased, such as going up to the top of a mountain, the boiling point will be:

      A. increased   C. the same

      B. decreased   D. none of the above

24. Absolute zero is:

      A. 970° below zero on the Fahrenheit scale

      B. 460° below zero on the Fahrenheit scale

      C. 144° below zero on the Centigrade scale

      D. the same as zero on the Centigrade scale

25. The heat used to change a liquid to a vapor is called:

      A. latent heat of fusion

      B. latent heat of vaporization

      C. specific heat of vaporization

      D. latent heat of the gas

26. If brine has a high specific gravity:

      A. brine will freeze   C. nothing will happen

      B. brine will crystallize   D. all of the above

27. Which of the following metals *cannot* be used with ammonia?

      A. steel   C. wrought iron

      B. brass   D. cast iron

28. What is Carrene No. 2?

      A. a refrigerant

      B. solvent used to clean system

      C. the capsule in a dehydrator

      D. a lubricant

29. The Fahrenheit scale is based on boiling water having a sea level temperature of:

      A. 459°   C. 180°

      B. 212°   D. 100°

30. A ton of refrigeration is equal to the cooling effect of:

      A. 2,000 pounds of ice melting in 24 hours

      B. 2,000 pounds of ice melting in 12 hours

      C. 2,000 pounds of water being converted to ice

      D. 2,240 pounds of ice melting in 24 hours

31. What is the temperature at which brine density is taken?

      A. 40° Fahrenheit   C. 20° Fahrenheit

      B. 60° Fahrenheit   D. 80° Fahrenheit

32. When the evaporator coils are located in a brine solution and the brine is pumped through the ice box, the system is known as:

      A. a direct system

      B. an indirect system

C. a low-pressure system

D. a double-evaporator system

33. The latent heat of evaporation of a refrigerant should be:

    A. low   C. of no importance

    B. high   D. nonexistent

34. A good refrigerant should:

    A. have a low boiling point

    B. have a high latent heat

    C. be able to be liquefied at normal seawater temperatures

    D. all of the above

35. Which of the following is *not* a property of Freon-12?

    A. odorless   C. flammable

    B. colorless   D. non-toxic

36. Which of the following refrigerants has the lowest boiling point?

    A. CO_2 C. F-12

    B. ammonia   D. F-22

37. The density of a brine solution in a refrigeration plant is measured by:

    A. litmus paper   C. hydrometer

    B. chemical test   D. either A or B

38. R-12 at ambient temperature is a:

    A. superheated liquid   C. odorless gas

    B. superheated gas   D. corrosive liquid

39. Zero gauge pressure corresponds on the absolute scale to:

    A. 144 PSI   C. 14.7 PSI

    B. 27.4 PSI   D. 0 PSI

40. Many pressure gauges on a Freon system have two dials or graduations on one gauge. The two dials represent:

    A. pressure and temperature

    B. liquid pressure and gas pressure

    C. suction and discharge pressure

    D. cooling water inlet and outlet temperatures

41. A good refrigerant should be:

    A. nonpoisonous   C. noninflammable

    B. nonexplosive   D. all of the above

42. Freon is:

    A. noncorrosive   C. nontoxic

    B. flammable   D. A and C

43. All of the following are desirable properties of Freon-12 *except:*

    A. odorless   C. corrodes brass or copper

    B. colorless   D. none of the above

44. The boiling point of Freon-12 is:

    A. 26° Fahrenheit   C. 32° Fahrenheit

    B. 21.6° Fahrenheit   D. 60° Fahrenheit

45. A system described as a two-ton unit could:
    A. make two tons of ice every hour
    B. make two tons of ice every 24 hours
    C. remove 288,000 BTUs in 24 hours
    D. do none of the above
46. A refrigerant gives up heat when it:
    A. condenses   C. regurgitates
    B. evaporates   D. vaporizes
47. Latent heat:
    A. can be measured with a thermometer
    B. can be measured with a pyrometer
    C. cannot be measured with a thermometer
    D. changes as the refrigerant cools
48. How many BTUs per minute are removed in a one-ton refrigeration unit?
    A. 144   C. 300
    B. 200   D. 500
49. The heat used to change a solid to a liquid is called:
    A. latent heat of fusion   C. latent heat of the liquid
    B. sensible heat of fusion   D. specific heat of fusion
50. The latent heat of vaporization of water is:
    A. 144 BTUs   C. 970 BTUs
    B. 940 BTUs   D. 288 BTUs

Compressors, Condensors, and Evaporators

1. In terms of pressure and temperature, what happens to the primary refrigerant in the compressor?
    A. its pressure and temperature are both lowered
    B. its pressure and temperature are both raised
    C. its pressure is lowered and its temperature is raised
    D. its pressure is raised and its temperature is lowered
2. What is the purpose of subcooling R-12 in the condenser?
    A. to increase the system efficiency by sensible heat transfer
    B. to stop the liquid from flashing
    C. to reduce the load on the compressor
    D. to remove latent heat of vaporization and the suction piping
3. The purpose of the purge valve at the top of the condenser in a refrigerating system is to:
    A. remove any air that may accumulate in the system
    B. take out unpleasant fumes from the refrigerant

C. vent off excess refrigerant in an emergency

D. permit opening the refrigerating system for cleaning and inspecting

4. The capacity of a reciprocating compressor can be regulated by which of the following? I. a hot-gas bypass; I. an unloader.

 A. I   C. either I or II

 B. II   D. neither I nor II

5. A leaky compressor suction valve can usually be detected by:

 A. a fluctuating suction-pressure gauge

 B. a higher suction pressure

 C. closing in on the suction valve having no effect on the suction pressure

 D. any of the above

6. Some causes of a noisy compressor are:

 A. worn bearings, pins, etc.

 B. too much oil in crankcase

 C. slugging due to flooding back of refrigerant

 D. any of the above

7. A double-trunk piston is used to:

 A. prevent gas from getting to crankcase

 B. absorb some of the side thrust

 C. prevent oil from mixing with the refrigerant

 D. all of the above

8. The refrigerant gas returning to the compressor would be:

 A. superheated   C. dense

 B. saturated   D. flooded

9. The device used for low-pressure control and high-pressure cutout on a compressor is called a:

 A. cutout   C. controller switch

 B. pressure controller   D. cutout switch

10. Both the temperature and the pressure of the refrigerant are increased in the:

 A. compressor   C. condenser

 B. evaporator   D. expansion valve

11. Where are the zinc plates located?

 A. saltwater side of the condenser

 B. refrigerant side of the condenser

 C. in the evaporator coils

 D. in the suction strainer

12. Air or noncondensable gas is removed from a refrigeration system by a:

 A. separating chamber   C. purge valve

 B. system of baffles   D. vacuum reducing valve

13. The compressor suction line conveys the refrigerant vapor from:
   A. condenser to evaporator C. evaporator to compressor
   B. compressor to condenser D. receiver to compressor
14. The discharge pressure of the compressor would be:
   A. the pressure which corresponds to a temperature from 5° to 15° below that of the condenser discharge
   B. the pressure which corresponds to a temperature from 5° to 15° F higher than the condenser discharge
   C. the pressure which corresponds to a temperature equal to that of the condenser discharge
   D. none of the above
15. A compressor capacity reduction device always:
   A. reduces compressor capacity by reducing compressor horsepower proportionately
   B. reduces compressor capacity by reducing compressor speed
   C. reduces compressor capacity by by-passing hot gas
   D. reduces compressor capacity as the refrigeration load dictates
16. What is the high side of the refrigeration system?
   A. compressor to condenser
   B. evaporator to compressor
   C. expansion valve to evaporator
   D. compressor to expansion valve
17. You would purge a Freon-12 system when the temperature of the liquid in the receiver is more than _____ than the saturated gas temperature corresponding to the discharge pressure:
   A. 10° higher C. 5° higher
   B. 10° lower D. 5° lower
18. Belt drive is preferred over direct drive for the low speed compressor because it:
   A. permits the use of a smaller high speed motor
   B. absorbs torsional vibration
   C. maintains the leak proof seal ring
   D. eliminates the use of mineral lubricating oil
19. Short-cycling means that the compressor:
   A. grounds out frequently C. runs too fast
   B. stops and starts frequently D. runs too slow
20. Slugging is usually caused by:
   A. too much oil in the system
   B. too much refrigerant in the system
   C. expansion valve not operating properly
   D. too much cooling water to condenser
21. A hermetically sealed unit is a:
   A. belt driven unit
   B. motor and compressor in one unit

    C. moisture proof unit

    D. water sealed unit

22. Two compressors should not be operated in parallel on an R-12 system because:

    A. they are difficult to parallel and operate

    B. of control difficulties

    C. oil will accumulate in one compressor crankcase

    D. one compressor will do all the work

23. In a refrigeration system, a compressor is desired over a pump to circulate refrigerant because:

    A. a pump has no valves

    B. a refrigerant has to be compressed to be liquefied

    C. a pump is too costly

    D. none of the above

24. What is the purpose of automatic unloaders used on some refrigeration compressors?

    A. better capacity control and more flexibility

    B. less starting torque

    C. to unload pressure when compressor stops

    D. A and B of above

25. Refrigeration compressor valves are opened and closed by:

    A. external springs   C. pressure difference

    B. inherent spring tension   D. a camshaft

26. What would cause a Freon compressor to start?

    A. solenoid opened   C. solenoid closed

    B. expansion valve opened   D. expansion valve closed

27. Liquid slugging is:

    A. the pounding of liquid refrigerant in the suction line at a point of restriction

    B. a presence of liquid in the condenser causing excessive noise

    C. liquid in compressor clearance space

    D. excessive liquid refrigerant in the receiver

28. The following shaft seal is *not* used on a Freon-12 compressor:

    A. packing   C. bellows

    B. metallic   D. diaphragm

29. How do you tell the oil level in a compressor?

    A. sight glass   C. drain oil from compressor

    B. remove dipstick   D. there is no way

30. The coolant used for a finned condenser is:

    A. oil   C. water

    B. Freon   D. air

31. A hermetically sealed refrigeration unit should have:

    A. condenser cleaned annually

    B. oil changed monthly

C. refrigeration recharged annually or when necessary

D. compressor replaced as a unit

32. Oil foaming causing carry over is dangerous because it:

    A. robs crankcase of lube oil

    B. affects refrigerant's boiling point

    C. thins the oil

    D. does none of the above

33. Compressor relief valves discharge:

    A. into receiver

    B. into evaporator

    C. overboard or into compartment

    D. back to compressor suction side

34. How would you make the rise in the temperature of the condenser water decrease from 10° to 7°?

    A. decrease water supply

    B. increase water supply

    C. speed up compressor

    D. increase the suction pressure

35. The system should be purged:

    A. while the system is operating

    B. while starting up the system

    C. after the system has been shut down for a few hours

    D. once a week

36. The amount of liquid refrigerant that is allowed to flow through the expansion valve is:

    A. the same as the amount boiled off in the coil

    B. entirely independent of the amount boiled off in the coil

    C. greater than the amount boiled off in the coil

    D. less than the amount boiled off in the coil

37. The thermostatic expansion valve controls the amount of refrigerant that is allowed to flow to the:

    A. compressor   C. cooling coils

    B. condenser   D. receiver

38. How does the temperature at the outlet side of the valve compare with the temperature at the inlet side when the thermostatic valve is operating properly?

    A. temperature is much lower at the outlet side

    B. temperature is lower at the inlet side

    C. temperature is approximately the same at the outlet and the inlet sides

    D. temperatures at both outlet and inlet can vary, making any of the above statements true at different times

39. The "hot gas" used in hot-gas defrosting is taken from the:

A. compressor discharge line   C. condenser discharge line
B. compressor suction line   D. receiver

40. The refrigerant temperature in the evaporator is controlled by:
I. pressure in the evaporator; II. temperature of the cooling water to condenser.
A. I   C. both I and II
B. II   D. neither I nor II

41. A ruptured diaphragm in a thermostatic expansion valve will cause the valve to:
A. open
B. close
C. remain in its position
D. flood the evaporator with Freon

42. Frost on the evaporator coils:
A. keeps the refrigerated space cooler
B. reduces the efficiency of the system
C. reduces the compressor load
D. does not affect the system

43. How is the solenoid valve mounted?
A. solenoid and valve horizontal
B. solenoid coil horizontal to the valve
C. solenoid vertical below the valve
D. solenoid vertical above the valve

44. What would cause the expansion valve to open?
A. rise in temperature of the cooling coils
B. compressor cutting out
C. compressor cutting in
D. none of the above

45. To inspect an expansion valve when *not* functioning properly:
A. remove inspection plate
B. remove entire unit
C. remove power assembly and inspect cage
D. remove bonnet

46. The thermal expansion valve is located between the:
A. receiver and the king valve
B. king valve and the solenoid valve
C. solenoid valve and the evaporator coils
D. charging valve and the solenoid valve

47. The greatest decrease in refrigerant temperature occurs in the:
A. expansion valve   C. compressor
B. evaporator   D. condenser

48. Air circulation in the icebox is accomplished by the use of:
A. louver doors   C. diffuser fans
B. hollow sidewalls   D. air vents to deck

49. To increase heat transfer in the evaporator:
   A. increase suction pressure   C. defrost coils
   B. increase air circulation   D. B and C
50. When refrigerant leaves the condenser, it next goes to the:
   A. evaporator coils   C. compressor
   B. expansion valve   D. condenser
51. Thermostatic expansion valves are:
   A. either all the way open or all the way closed
   B. normally open
   C. throttled depending on load
   D. controlled by suction pressure
52. If the thermostatic expansion valve in a refrigeration system did not
   appear to function properly, you would suspect the cause to be:
   A. foreign matter in the valve
   B. ruptured control bulb tubing
   C. moisture in the system
   D. all of the above
53. When the thermostatic expansion bulb of an expansion valve is
   placed at the center of the coil instead of the end, it will:
   A. increase the capacity   C. increase the superheat
   B. decrease the capacity   D. deliver more refrigerant
54. The solenoid valve is located:
   A. between strainer and expansion valve
   B. before strainer and expansion valve
   C. after expansion valve
   D. at none of the above
55. As Freon leaves the expansion valve:
   A. pressure decreases, volume increases
   B. volume decreases, pressure increases
   C. volume increases, pressure increases
   D. pressure increases, volume decreases
56. What is the function of the adjustment on a thermostatic expansion
   valve?
   A. nonexistent
   B. for controlling pressure
   C. for controlling superheat
   D. for controlling the solenoid valve
57. When a solenoid valve closes, it:
   A. prevents any flow through the valve
   B. permits a small flow through a bypass
   C. tends to freeze tight
   D. must be manually opened
58. Which of the following will cause an automatically controlled Fre-
   on-12 compressor to start?

A. opening of solenoid valve

B. opening of expansion valve

C. closing of solenoid valve

D. closing of expansion valve

59. If the solenoid valve closed by accident, the compressor would be stopped by the:

A. low-pressure cutout switch

B. high-pressure cutout switch

C. low-water cutout switch

D. automatic trip

60. The thermostatic expansion valve is designed to maintain:

A. constant flow   C. constant superheat

B. constant temperature   D. constant pressure

61. The expansion valve on a Freon system controls the:

A. superheat of the gas leaving the compressor

B. back pressure in the evaporator

C. temperature of the icebox

D. superheat of the gas leaving the evaporator

62. In a forced convection evaporator if the fan were to stop, the thermostatic expansion valve would:

A. gradually close down

B. gradually open up

C. automatically close and stay closed tight

D. cause the safety valve to blow

63. The solenoid valve used in refrigeration systems operates with a (an):

A. pressure sensitive bellows

B. internal spring operated return valve

C. electromagnet and movable core

D. small electric servomotor

64. If the solenoid valve was de-energized, the valve would be:

A. closed by a falling plunger

B. closed by refrigerant pressure

C. opened by spring pressure

D. opened by refrigerant pressure

65. The purpose of the expansion valve bypass is to:

A. get extra refrigeration capacity

B. regulate system if expansion valve fails

C. A or B

D. A and B

66. A feeler or thermal bulb is used with what type of expansion valve?

A. thermal   C. hand operated

B. automatic   D. pressure operated

67. An evaporator pressure regulator is designed to maintain a constant pressure or temperature in the evaporator:
 A. regardless of how high the compressor suction pressure may go
 B. regardless of how high the condenser pressure may go
 C. regardless of how low the compressor suction pressure may go
 D. regardless of how low the condenser pressure may go

68. The temperature of the meat and fish box is:
 A. 5° to 10° F above zero   C. 12° to 18° F above zero
 B. 5° to 10° below zero   D. 35° to 45° F above zero

69. What controls individual box temperature?
 A. expansion valve
 B. solenoid valve
 C. back pressure valve
 D. regulation of cooling water

70. An automatic refrigeration system will start when a (an):
 A. solenoid opens   C. solenoid closes
 B. expansion valve opens   D. diaphragm closes

71. The solenoid valve on an R-12 system is controlled by the:
 A. expansion valve
 B. suction pressure regulations valve
 C. water-regulating valve
 D. temperature in the box that is being cooled

72. Frost which appears on the evaporator coils of a direct expansion system:
 A. is best removed by means of an axe
 B. will increase the refrigeration effect
 C. can be removed by passing hot vapors through the coils
 D. can be removed the fastest by simply shutting down the coils

73. Excess frost on the evaporator coils:
 A. keeps the icebox cooler
 B. reduces the efficiency of the plant
 C. takes the load off the compressor
 D. does not affect the system

74. What is the temperature range on the vegetable box?
 A. 20° to 30°   C. 35° to 45°
 B. 30° to 40°   D. 40° to 50°

75. On a Freon-12 refrigerating system you would find a solenoid valve:
 A. on the condenser   C. before the condenser
 B. after the receiver   D. on the compressor

76. The solenoid valve controls the:
 A. amount of refrigerant entering the evaporator coils
 B. amount of refrigerant going to the expansion valve

C. amount of refrigerant going to the compressor

D. pressure of the refrigerant going to the evaporator coils

77. The solenoid valve can be typed as a:

    A. thermal valve   C. bellows valve

    B. magnetic stop valve   D. bimetallic valve

78. Obstruction of the expansion valve is *usually* caused by:

    A. congealed oil in the system

    B. scale

    C. water in the system

    D. all of the above

79. If the thermal expansion valve becomes inoperative, the iceboxes will have to be controlled by the:

    A. solenoid valve   C. king valve

    B. manual expansion valve   D. manual solenoid valve

80. Dairy products should be kept at a temperature of:

    A. 10° to 20°   C. 35° to 45°

    B. 20° to 30°   D. 15° to 25°

Accessories and Air Conditioning

1. The storage tank for liquid refrigerant in a refrigeration cycle is called a:

    A. dehydrator   C. charging tank

    B. purge tank   D. receiver

2. A dehydrator is sometimes installed in a bypass line between the:

    A. receiver and the thermostatic expansion valve

    B. thermostatic expansion valve and the compressor

    C. compressor and the condenser

    D. condenser and the receiver

3. A sight glass in a full liquid line will be:

    A. full of bubbles   C. light green

    B. cloudy   D. clear

4. The liquid line strainer is located between the:

    A. king valve and expansion valve

    B. solenoid valve and expansion valve

    C. evaporator and receiver

    D. compressor and evaporator

5. Where is the low-pressure cutout switch located?

    A. discharge side of compressor

    B. suction side of compressor

    C. before the receiver

    D. in the chill box

6. The purpose of the oil trap is:
    A. to remove oil from the charging tank
    B. to add oil to the compressor
    C. to remove oil from the refrigerating gas
    D. none of the above
7. The suction pressure switch is operated by:
    A. electric current   C. pressure on a bellow
    B. thermocouple   D. a relay cutout
8. The charging connection in a refrigerating system is located:
    A. before the receiver
    B. between the condenser and the receiver
    C. between the receiver and the king valve
    D. between the king valve and the solenoid valve
9. From what side of the system is refrigerant removed?
    A. bypass   C. charging
    B. suction   D. discharge
10. The following is found on a Freon-12 liquid branch line before the
    expansion valve:
    A. king valve   C. strainer
    B. regulating valve   D. relief valve
11. The storage tank for liquid refrigerant in a refrigeration cycle is
    called a:
    A. dehydrator   C. charging tank
    B. purge tank   D. receiver
12. The purpose of the low-pressure cutout switch is to:
    A. maintain liquid refrigerant at the suction of the compressor
    B. maintain a preset suction pressure to the compressor
    C. cut out the compressor at a set pressure
    D. cut compressor in and out at a preset pressure
13. Where is the scale trap located?
    A. discharge side of the compressor
    B. suction side of the compressor
    C. between the condenser and receiver
    D. between the solenoid valve and expansion valve
14. The dehydrator on the Freon-12 system is cut in:
    A. when charging the system   C. during normal operation
    B. to remove moisture   D. both A and B
15. In a single compressor refrigeration system, compartment tempera-
    ture is controlled by:
    A. a king valve
    B. a back-pressure regulating valve
    C. a low-pressure cutout switch
    D. a solenoid valve

16. Which of the following is *not* necessary on a refrigeration compressor system?
    A. condenser   C. evaporator coils
    B. receiver   D. compressor

17. The elements of a thermostat switch are usually of the:
    A. diaphragm type   C. valve type
    B. bimetal type   D. pilot-valve type

18. The oil separator is located between the:
    A. evaporator and the compressor
    B. compressor and the condenser
    C. condenser and the dehydrator
    D. solenoid valve and the thermal expansion valve

19. What is the receiver on a refrigeration plant used for?
    A. showing where the refrigerant is
    B. storing the refrigerant
    C. condensing the refrigerant
    D. charging the unit

20. What would you find before the solenoid valve?
    A. liquid line strainer or trap   C. compressor
    B. expansion valve   D. evaporator coils

21. The dehydrating agent in a Freon system is usually:
    A. slaked lime   C. activated alumina
    B. sodium chloride   D. calcium chloride

22. The king valve is the main shutoff valve:
    A. between receiver and liquid line
    B. of the compressor
    C. of the condenser
    D. of the water supply

23. Another name for the liquid valve is the:
    A. master valve   C. Freon valve
    B. king valve   D. shutoff valve

24. The ratio of the weight of water vapor in a sample of air to the weight of water vapor that the same sample of air would contain if saturated, at the existing temperatures, is the definition of:
    A. relative humidity   C. specific humidity
    B. absolute humidity   D. total humidity

25. The type of refrigerant used in centrifugal compressors is:
    A. F-5   C. F-12
    B. F-11   D. F-14

26. Flash gas in liquid lines:
    A. assists in keeping liquid lines cool
    B. indicates too much refrigerant in system
    C. assists in accelerating refrigerant through the system
    D. reduces system capacity

27. What is done with the cooling water and reheater when you wish to reduce humidity?
    A. increase both temperatures
    B. decrease both temperatures
    C. decrease cooling water temperature and increase reheater temperature
    D. increase cooling water temperature and decrease reheater temperature

28. In a room with the relative humidity 65 percent and a dry bulb temperature of 60° F, what would take place if the temperature is raised to 70° F?
    A. wet bulb temperature would lower
    B. reduced relative humidity
    C. higher dew point temperature
    D. lower dew point temperature

29. What type of compressor is designed for use in a shipboard air conditioning plant rated at 150 tons?
    A. gas-pumping reciprocating
    B. gas-pumping centrifugal
    C. liquid-pumping reciprocating
    D. liquid-pumping centrifugal

30. Which condition will occur when the relative humidity is 100 percent?
    A. the wet-bulb temperature will be below the dew-point temperature
    B. the dry-bulb temperature will be below the dew-point temperature
    C. the wet-bulb depression will be 0°
    D. the wet-bulb depression will be greater than 0°

31. What is the year-round range of relative humidity for the best condition of health and comfort?
    A. 15 to 50 percent   C. 40 to 60 percent
    B. 30 to 50 percent   D. 15 to 70 percent

32. In a centrifugal refrigeration system an economizer would be installed between which two components?
    A. condenser and receiver
    B. condenser and cooler
    C. condenser and second stage
    D. cooler and first stage

33. Moisture is removed from the air in an air conditioning system by:
    I. preheater; II. reheater.
    A. I   C. either I or II
    B. II   D. neither I nor II

34. The process of adding moisture to air to increase the relative humidity is known as:
    A. sublimation   C. humidification
    B. desiccation   D. moisturization

35. The main distribution duct in an air conditioning system which contains the cooling coils and filters is called the:
    A. manifold   C. chamber
    B. condenser   D. plenum

36. Proper air ventilation is important for the ship's cargo holds in order to prevent:
    A. heat loss   C. mold and slime
    B. solidification   D. slugging back

37. What determines the capacity of a refrigerating unit?
    A. speed of the compressor
    B. supply of cooling water to the condenser
    C. none of the above
    D. A and B of the above

38. In a centrifugal Freon refrigeration system, the overall capacity of the system is increased by:
    A. opening more bypass lines
    B. opening additional expansion valves
    C. adding refrigerant
    D. speeding up the machine

39. The humidity of the atmosphere can be determined by the use of the:
    A. anemometer   C. manometer
    B. potentiometer   D. psychrometer

40. Hunting of a T.E.V. can be caused by excessive:
    A. flash gas   C. frost
    B. capacity   D. ventilation

41. Most T.E.V. and thermostat power assemblies are filled with the same refrigerant as used in the system. When a different refrigerant is used, this is known as what type of bulb?
    A. compound   C. multiuse
    B. cross-charged   D. mixed

42. The device, which is installed in the compressor suction line to prevent liquid from entering the compressor when hot gas defrosting, is called a:
    A. re-vaporator   C. receiver
    B. dehydrator   D. solenoid

43. A centrifugal compressor's purge recovery unit:
    A. reclaims water
    B. purges air without losing refrigerant
    C. purges air with some loss of refrigerant
    D. purges lube oil from the refrigerant

44. The purpose of a kathabar or cargocaire system is to:
    A. keep dew point from going too high
    B. keep dew point from going to low
    C. keep temperature from going too high
    D. keep temperature from going too low

45. Flash gas which enters the evaporator of a refrigeration system produces:
    A. overloading   C. sweating
    B. slugging   D. inefficiency

46. The instrument used to measure air flow in an air conditioning system is called a (an):
    A. anemometer   C. hygrometer
    B. psychrometer   D. pneumercator

47. The process which is used to enlarge the ends of copper tubing for joining operations is called:
    A. swaging   C. knurling
    B. sweating   D. crimping

48. Which of the following controls the capacity of a centrifugal system?
    A. suction dampers   C. thermal expansion valve
    B. discharge valves   D. unloader

49. The liquid refrigerant flow to the water chiller in a centrifugal compressor system is controlled by:
    A. back pressure regulator   C. solenoid valve
    B. thermal expansion valve   D. float valve

50. The dew point is reached when the wet bulb temperature is:
    A. equal to the dry bulb temperature
    B. twice the dry bulb temperature
    C. 10° below dry bulb temperature
    D. 5° above the dry bulb temperature

51. If people in an air conditioned room complain of being too cool, the trouble might be the:
    A. heater has failed to cut-out at the proper temperature
    B. air velocity is too low
    C. relative humidity is too high
    D. relative humidity is too low

52. A lower thermostatic temperature setting will provide a desired degree of comfort in a room where:
    A. low relative humidity is maintained
    B. triple banded squirrel cage fans are used
    C. air circulation is at maximum
    D. high relative humidity is maintained

53. What instrument measures the rate of air flow?
    A. thermometer   C. psychrometer
    B. anemometer   D. potentiometer

54. Which fluid normally cools the primary refrigerant in a central air conditioning system?

    A. air

    B. seawater

    C. fresh water

    D. calcium sulphate brine

55. Which process lowers the humidity of the air supplied in an air conditioning system?

    A. cooling the air to a temperature just above the dew point

    B. heating the air to a point at which moisture will boil off, then recooling it

    C. cooling the air to a point below dew point, then reheating it

    D. heating the air and then cooling it to a point below dew point

56. The surging that occurs in a centrifugal air conditioning compressor is a result of:

    A. low pressure in the condenser

    B. pressure build-up in the condenser

    C. low pressure in the condenser at low load

    D. high pressure in the evaporator at high load

57. A reheater in an air conditioning system is designed to control the _____ temperature.

    A. chilled water

    B. dew point

    C. primary air

    D. dry bulb

58. When air contains some moisture, but is not saturated, the dew point temperature is:

    A. between the wet and dry bulb temperatures

    B. equal to the total heat of air

    C. higher than the wet bulb temperature

    D. lower than the dry bulb temperature

59. In a two stage centrifugal air conditioning system, the liquid refrigerant passes through the condenser directly to the:

    A. evaporator

    B. chiller

    C. economizer

    D. expansion valve

60. The latent heat of water vapor in air depends on:

    A. dry bulb temperature

    B. wet bulb temperature

    C. dew point

    D. dry point

61. When air is at its dew point and no change in temperature or pressure occurs it:

    A. has a low absolute humidity

    B. has the lowest relative humidity

    C. cannot give up its moisture

    D. will gain no additional moisture

62. In a chilled water air conditioning unit using a reciprocating compressor, the refrigerating effect of the primary refrigerant can be increased by:

A. increasing refrigerant pressure in the coil
B. increasing chilled water flow through the cooler
C. sub-cooling the refrigerant in the condenser
D. superheating the refrigerant in the compressor

63. A room humidistat lowers the humidity of air by _____ the re-heater temperature.
   A. raising the cooling coil temperature and lowering
   B. raising both the cooling coil temperature and
   C. lowering both the cooling coil temperature and
   D. lowering the cooling coil temperature and raising

64. To reduce the refrigerating load while maintaining the designed dry bulb temperature and relative humidity in an air conditioning system, you should:
   A. admit only enough warm outside air to provide proper ventilation
   B. raise the offset reheating temperature
   C. lower the compressor head pressure
   D. operate the purge recovery unit continuously

65. Any air mixture whose dew point remains constant will also have an unchanging:
   A. dry bulb temperature   C. specific humidity
   B. wet bulb temperature   D. specific volume

66. As the amount of moisture in the air increases, the difference between the dry bulb and wet bulb temperature will:
   A. increase
   B. decrease
   C. remain unchanged
   D. be at a maximum at the dew point temperature

67. Which method is most frequently used to control refrigerant flow in a shipboard system?
   A. direct expansion with constant superheat
   B. indirect expansion with constant superheat
   C. low-side float control
   D. high-side float control

68. Rather than design an infinite variety of valve sizes for thermostatic expansion valves, some manufacturers use:
   A. an adjusting cap to meet the various size differences
   B. a flexible diaphragm
   C. internal restrictors of different sizes
   D. a feeler bulb with an adjustable pressure line

69. Coast Guard regulations (46 CFR; part 113) require that each walk-in refrigerated space have a/an:
   A. alarm system (audible) operated from within the refrigerated space

B. alarm system (audible) operated from outside the refrigerated space

C. warning light visible from outside the refrigerated space

D. warning light visible from within the refrigerated space

70. One benefit of proper air circulation in a cargo refrigeration compartment is:

A. more temperature differential

B. increased moisture content

C. reduced slime and mold

D. increased density of the air

71. Forced circulation evaporators have a tendency to cause rapid de-
hydration of foods unless:

A. a complete change of air takes place every 30 seconds

B. foods are packaged in corrugated boxes

C. the air is circulated slowly with minimum temperature
change

D. a humidifier is installed

72. Vapor seals used in the insulation of refrigerated spaces serve to:

A. prevent freon vapor from saturating the insulation

B. hold water vapor on the cold side of the insulation

C. reduce the possibility of moisture laden warm air entering
the insulation

D. reduce the possibility of moisture laden cold air entering
the insulation

73. To add refrigerant to the low side of an R-12 air-conditioning system, the refrigerant should be introduced through the:

A. suction service valve as a vapor

B. suction service valve as a liquid

C. discharge service valve as a vapor

D. charging valve as a liquid

74. Routine maintenance on hermetically sealed air-conditioning units
should include:

A. changing the air filter

B. recharging the system

C. changing the compressor

D. reviewing container volume

75. When pumping down an automatically controlled R-12 air conditioning compressor to test the low pressure cutout, you should:

A. stop the compressor

B. secure the condenser

C. close the main liquid line valve

D. stop the circulation pump

System Operations and Troubleshooting

1. During plant operation, which of the following symptoms will indicate a clogged R-12 liquid line strainer?
     A. temperature of the tubing on the outlet side of the strainer will be much warmer than the tubing on the inlet side
     B. temperature of the tubing on the inlet side of the strainer will be much warmer than the tubing on the outlet side
     C. pressure on the outlet side of the strainer tubing will be much higher than on the inlet side
     D. pressure on both the inlet and outlet sides of the strainer tubing will be the same
2. What should you do to correct low condensing pressure in an operating refrigeration system?
     A. clean the valves and valve nests
     B. adjust the high-pressure cutout switch
     C. reduce the water supply
     D. increase the water pressure
3. Slugging of the refrigerant in an R-12 refrigeration plant may be indicated by:
     A. high condensing pressure
     B. low condensing pressure
     C. sudden loss of oil from crankcase
     D. leaking discharge valves
4. If the compressor short cycles on the high pressure cutout, which of the following would you check?
     A. to be sure system is getting cooling water
     B. if plenty of cooling water is running through but it is not picking up heat, the condenser tubes need cleaning
     C. for too much refrigerant in the system
     D. all of the above
5. If the high-pressure switch on the compressor opens and stops the compressor, a possible cause could be:
     A. too much cooling water going through the condenser
     B. not enough refrigerant in the system
     C. a leak in the evaporator coils
     D. not enough cooling water going through the condenser
6. Which of the following conditions will *not* cause the compressor to short cycle on the low pressure control switch when the system contains a sufficient charge of R-12 refrigerant?
     A. excessive oil circulating in the system
     B. insufficient water flow through the condenser
     C. moisture frozen in expansion valve orifice
     D. thermal expansion valve leaking

7. If a compartment suddenly stops cooling, this would usually be caused by:

    A. king valve   C. expansion valve

    B. solenoid valve   D. A and B above

8. An over charge of refrigerant would result in:

    A. high suction pressure   C. high head pressure

    B. low suction pressure   D. low head pressure

9. Whenever you suspect that the lubricating oil charge in the crankcase contains moisture, you should:

    A. drain and clean the crankcase

    B. cut in the stand-by compressor

    C. renew the oil

    D. use a dryer when the compressor is operating

10. Short cycling means that the compressor:

    A. grounds out frequently

    B. stops and starts frequently

    C. runs too fast

    D. runs too slow

11. What would happen if there were a sudden drop in the suction pressure?

    A. the oil level in the crankcase would decrease

    B. the crankcase would fill up

    C. there would be no change

    D. the oil in the crankcase would foam up

12. Increasing head pressure with no change in inlet cooling water temperature would probably be caused by:

    A. restriction in refrigerant piping

    B. air and noncondensable gases in the receiver

    C. air and noncondensable gases in the condenser

    D. flooding back of liquid refrigerant from the evaporator

13. The major difficulties encountered with the thermal expansion valve can usually be traced to:

    A. lube oil in the system

    B. moisture or foreign matter at the valve/seat or orifice

    C. change in spring tension caused by changing temperatures

    D. solvent action of the refrigerant

14. A Freon unit will tend to short-cycle when operating under:

    A. heavy loads   C. light loads

    B. normal conditions   D. all of the above

15. When the cut-in point is set too high on the low-pressure control switch to an R-12 refrigeration system, the compressor will:

    A. operate continuously   C. operate unloaded

    B. not operate   D. short-cycle

16. A refrigeration system has high head pressure as a result of an over charge of refrigerant (R-12). You should:

    A. increase the amount of cooling water

    B. decrease the amount of cooling water

    C. remove some refrigerant from the system

    D. add refrigerant to the receiver

17. If a compressor runs continuously, the cause might be a:

    A. defective thermal bulb

    B. clogged scale trap

    C. stuck high-pressure switch

    D. stuck low-pressure switch

18. If in an R-12 system the cooling space is cold, suction pressure is high, discharge pressure is low, and the compressor runs continuously, the probable cause is:

    A. air in system or compressor

    B. condenser clogged

    C. high head pressure

    D. low head pressure

19. If the head pressure is too high:

    A. the relief valve should open before the high pressure cutout

    B. the relief valve should open and let excess refrigerant go to the receiver

    C. the high pressure cutout switch should operate before the relief valve opens

    D. you should close in on the suction valve

20. What would *not* cause the compressor to run continuously?

    A. over charge of Freon   C. door to the box ajar

    B. not enough Freon   D. diffuser fans not working

21. Which of the following conditions is an early indication of crankshaft seal failure?

    A. large amounts of oil leaking at the shaft

    B. presence of foreign matter in the system piping

    C. formation of moisture at the pulley wheel mount

    D. overflow of refrigerant into compressor line

22. If the cooling water to the condenser should suddenly fail:

    A. the solenoid valve will close

    B. the expansion valve will close

    C. the compressor will shut down

    D. an alarm will ring to notify the engineer

23. Two symptoms that indicate an inadequate supply of water passing through the condenser of a refrigeration plant are:

    A. excessively low temperature of the overboard water and low discharge pressure

    B. high suction pressure and high temperature of the suction line

    C. high condensing pressure and compressor short cycling on high pressure switch

    D. high suction line temperature and high discharge pressure

24. Liquid reaching the compressor through the suction line is called:
    A. flooding back   C. overflowing
    B. superheating   D. recycling
25. If the compressor were to run continuously without lowering the temperature, the trouble would probably be:
    A. insufficient refrigerant in the system
    B. leaks
    C. leaky discharge valves
    D. any of the above
26. Moisture should be kept out of an R-12 system because it tends to cause:
    A. icing of the automatic controls
    B. embrittlement of some parts of the automatic controls
    C. sludge in the lubricating oil
    D. all of the above conditions
27. After detecting and repairing a leak in the Freon-12 system:
    A. continue checking for more leaks
    B. recharge with Freon
    C. test run the unit and purge
    D. all of the above
28. The danger with a new Freon system is:
    A. metal or dirt particles
    B. phosgene formation
    C. Freon combines with metal to form an explosive
    D. all of the above
29. When using a halide torch for testing for leaks which is *not* important?
    A. adjust to a clear white flame
    B. adjust and clean reactor plate
    C. hold exploring tube close to joint
    D. move exploring tube slowly around joint
30. A reactor plate is essential to the operation of:
    A. soldering torch   C. halide torch
    B. relief valve   D. none of the above
31. The best way to check a Freon system when charging is:
    A. weigh the cylinder
    B. look at the bull's eye
    C. feel the suction line and run machine intermittently
    D. open purge valve
32. When securing a Freon-12 system for repairs:
    A. leave Freon-12 in system
    B. pump down to a slight vacuum
    C. pump down to 1 to 2 PSI
    D. pump down to 10 to 15 PSI
33. Air that may enter a refrigeration plant tends to collect in the:

    A. upper part of the receiver

    B. upper part of the condenser

    C. downstream end of the cooling coil

    D. inlet end of the condenser

34. To check for a suspected large leak in an R-12 system located in an enclosed space, you should use:

    A. a halide torch

    B. a hydrostatic test with water

    C. an ammonia and water solution brushed on the suspected area

    D. a soap suds solution brushed on the suspected area

35. Under normal operating conditions how full should the receiver of a properly charged refrigeration system be when the compressor stops?

    A. 25 percent   C. 85 percent

    B. 50 percent   D. 100 percent

36. What takes place when the solenoid valve closes?

    A. expansion valve opens

    B. expansion valve closes

    C. high pressure cuts out compressor

    D. low pressure cuts out compressor

37. When there is a Freon leak, the halide torch will burn:

    A. orange   C. white

    B. blue   D. green

38. Oil used in a refrigerating system is:

    A. lube oil SAE 20   C. lube oil SAE 10

    B. straight mineral oil   D. vegetable oil

39. A quick method to test a condenser for a Freon-12 leak is:

    A. test water chemically

    B. air test

    C. test air pocket in condenser heads with halide torch

    D. hydrostatic test

40. The purpose of running a refrigerating unit in short spurts when the system is being started after a shutdown is to:

    A. let a compartment cool gradually

    B. eliminate damage to the compressor by overload

    C. determine actual compressor oil level

    D. allow refrigerant vapor cycling time

41. When adding refrigerant to the high pressure side of an R-12 system, the refrigerant should be admitted through the:

    A. charging service valve as a liquid

    B. suction service valve as a liquid

    C. suction service valve as a vapor

    D. discharge service valve as a vapor

42. To prevent a refrigerating unit from accidentally starting while undergoing repairs, you should:
    A. secure and tag all electrical switches in the circuit
    B. place a crowbar in the flywheel of the unit
    C. inform all persons in the area not to start the unit
    D. take the fuse and put it in your pocket

43. To remove refrigerant when repairing the refrigeration evaporator section, you should:
    A. connect the empty drum to the evaporator outlet
    B. connect the empty drum to the expansion valve outlet
    C. use the purge valve connection
    D. pump all the refrigerant into the receiver

44. How are small leaks detected in a Freon system?
    A. soap suds   C. adding ammonia
    B. smoke test   D. smell

45. When new piping has been installed in a Freon-12 system, the system should be pressure tested with:
    A. CO_2 C. compressed air
    B. nitrogen   D. A and B of the above

46. When dealing with contaminated oil from a hermetic compressor that has had a burnout, you should:
    A. store the oil in a clean refrigerant drum
    B. use rubber gloves
    C. circulate the oil through a filter drier
    D. remove the oil with a portable charging cylinder

47. When the refrigerant leaves the condenser it will flow towards the:
    A. diffuser   C. evaporator
    B. expansion valve   D. suction of compressor

48. Purging is the process used to:
    A. eliminate moisture from the system
    B. separate refrigerant from the oil
    C. eliminate non-condensable gases from the system
    D. decrease the total amount of refrigerant in the system

49. What color is the flame on a halide torch, without the presence of Freon?
    A. blue   C. green
    B. orange   D. purple

50. When charging a Freon system, all the valves should be in their normal position except the:
    A. expansion valve   C. king valve (liquid)
    B. purge valve   D. solenoid valve

Answers to Multiple-Choice Questions
for the Refrigeration Engineer

Refrigeration Theory

1. C	14. A	27. B	40. A
2. A	15. B	28. A	41. D
3. D	16. D	29. B	42. D
4. D	17. C	30. A	43. C
5. C	18. A	31. B	44. B
6. B	19. B	32. B	45. B
7. C	20. C	33. B	46. A
8. A	21. A	34. D	47. C
9. C	22. A	35. C	48. B
10. A	23. B	36. A	49. A
11. B	24. B	37. C	50. C
12. C	25. B	38. B	
13. A	26. B	39. C	

Compressors, condensers, and evaporators

1. B	21. B	41. B	61. D
2. B	22. C	42. B	62. A
3. A	23. B	43. D	63. C
4. C	24. A	44. A	64. A
5. D	25. C	45. C	65. B
6. D	26. A	46. C	66. A
7. D	27. C	47. A	67. D
8. A	28. A	48. C	68. B
9. B	29. A	49. D	69. B
10. A	30. D	50. B	70. A
11. A	31. D	51. C	71. D
12. C	32. A	52. D	72. C
13. C	33. D	53. B	73. B
14. B	34. B	54. A	74. C
15. D	35. C	55. A	75. B
16. D	36. A	56. C	76. B
17. D	37. C	57. A	77. B
18. A	38. A	58. A	78. C
19. B	39. A	59. A	79. B
20. C	40. A	60. C	80. C

Accessories and air conditioning

1. D	3. D	5. B	7. C
2. A	4. A	6. C	8. D

9. D	26. D	43. B	60. C
10. C	27. C	44. A	61. D
11. D	28. B	45. D	62. C
12. D	29. B	46. A	63. D
13. B	30. C	47. A	64. A
14. D	31. C	48. A	65. C
15. D	32. C	49. D	66. B
16. B	33. D	50. A	67. A
17. B	34. C	51. D	68. C
18. B	35. D	52. D	69. A
19. B	36. C	53. B	70. C
20. A	37. D	54. B	71. C
21. C	38. D	55. C	72. C
22. A	39. D	56. B	73. A
23. B	40. A	57. D	74. A
24. A	41. B	58. D	75. C
25. B	42. A	59. C	

System operations and troubleshooting

1. B	14. C	27. D	40. B
2. C	15. B	28. A	41. A
3. C	16. C	29. A	42. A
4. D	17. D	30. C	43. D
5. D	18. D	31. A	44. A
6. A	19. C	32. C	45. D
7. D	20. A	33. B	46. B
8. C	21. A	34. D	47. B
9. D	22. C	35. C	48. C
10. B	23. C	36. D	49. A
11. D	24. A	37. D	50. C
12. C	25. D	38. B	
13. B	26. D	39. C	

CHAPTER FIFTEEN

Multiple-Choice Questions for the Junior Engineer

The topics covered by the multiple-choice questions include: Electrical Review; Engine Room Procedures; Steam Review; and Refrigeration Review. The subjects which are covered by these topics include the following:

1. Direct and alternating current equipment
2. Electrical maintenance and troubleshooting
3. Hand tools
4. Valves, piping, and fittings
5. Pumps
6. Water tube boilers
7. Steam and water cycles
8. Steam turbines
9. Gravity lube oil systems
10. Fuel oil service systems
11. Diesels
12. Evaporators
13. Lube oil purifiers
14. Refrigeration systems
15. Refrigeration maintenance and troubleshooting

Electrical Review

1. The electrolyte in a lead-acid storage battery is:
   - A. hydrogen chloride
   - B. sulfuric acid
   - C. calcium chloride
   - D. magnesium chloride
2. On an electric (portable) drill the ground wire is connected to the hull and:
   - A. armature
   - B. coils
   - C. main switch
   - D. body
3. In a faceplate motor starter, the starting arm is held in the OFF position by a (an):
   - A. strong spring
   - B. cotter pin
   - C. electrical circuit
   - D. magnet
4. You can test a motor field for an open condition with a (an):
   - A. ammeter
   - B. megger
   - C. voltmeter
   - D. wattmeter

5. What is another name for a motor generator set?
    A. rotary converter   C. relay
    B. transformer   D. exciter

6. A megohmmeter is used to measure:
    A. voltage   C. resistance
    B. current   D. power

7. In a compound-wound motor, part of the line current flows through the:
    A. frame   C. interpoles
    B. stator   D. shunt field coils

8. Ambient temperature means:
    A. the amount of temperature rise with no load
    B. normal operating temperature, less the room temperature
    C. the amount of temperature developed by an operating motor
    D. the temperature of the compartment where the motor is located

9. A noisy magnet or chatter in an A.C. controller is probably caused by:
    A. poor contact with the overload relay
    B. abnormal starting current
    C. a broken shading coil
    D. an incorrect installation

10. What happens in a series circuit when the voltage remains constant and the resistance increases?
    A. current increases
    B. current decreases
    C. current remains the same
    D. current increases by the square

11. If the load on a D.C. motor is increased, and speed remains constant, what type of motor is it?
    A. compound wound   C. universal
    B. series   D. shunt

12. What would you do if you got acid (battery acid) in your eyes?
    A. wash out with a soda and water solution
    B. wash out with mineral oil
    C. wash out with a boric acid solution
    D. wash out with fresh water

13. What would you use to wash off a battery?
    A. baking soda   C. hydrochloric acid
    B. salt water   D. none of the above

14. If you had two 6-volt batteries in parallel, what would happen to the voltage?
    A. double   C. none of these apply
    B. stay the same   D. both A and B

15. After a motor has been overhauled, what should you *not* do?
    A. check oil   C. turn it by hand
    B. remove all tools   D. turn it by electricity
16. Too high of a charge on a battery would cause what?
    A. increased battery life   C. buckled plates
    B. decreased battery life   D. none of the above
17. What damage can result to the components of a winch master control switch if the gasket in the cover deteriorates?
    A. overheating of the winch motor
    B. contamination of lube oil
    C. sparking at the winch motor brushes
    D. rapid corrosion of switch components
18. A circuit that has one wire in contact with the hull of a ship is called a:
    A. short circuit   C. series circuit
    B. closed circuit   D. grounded circuit
19. A commutator can be safely cleaned using:
    A. oil stones   C. crocus cloth
    B. sandpaper   D. leather
20. A commutator that is operating properly appears:
    A. a shiny copper color
    B. a glazed chocolate color
    C. dark brown and shiny
    D. brass red and glazed
21. If you do not know the manufacturer's recommended spring pressure for the brushes in a motor, you could safely use a pressure of:
    A. 1 to 1½ PSI   C. 8 to 10 PSI
    B. 4 to 6 PSI   D. 12 to 14 PSI
22. Two types of instrument transformers are:
    A. auto and power   C. step up and step down
    B. potential and current   D. potential and high voltage
23. Which are correct for the groups of a D.C. motor?
    A. series, synchro, compound   C. synchronous only
    B. series, compound, shunt   D. series, compound, induced
24. Which type of motor will slow down as the load increases?
    A. squirrel cage (low slip)   C. wound rotor
    B. squirrel cage (high slip)   D. synchronous
25. To keep the current through a D.C. voltmeter as low as possible, the moving coil circuit is provided with a (an):
    A. series inductor   C. high series resistance
    B. external shunt   D. high parallel resistance
26. The direction of rotation of a D.C. motor can be reversed by reversing the:

A. brush-staggered order

B. brush holder positions

C. motor interpole connections

D. motor armature leads

27. Ohm's law can be correctly stated as:

A. amperage equals voltage plus resistance

B. resistance equals amperage divided by voltage

C. amperage plus voltage plus resistance equals current

D. voltage equals amperage times circuit resistance

28. If a motor had to operate on an overload, what would you do?

A. use smaller fuses

B. use larger fuses

C. use higher voltage

D. frequent watching of motor and bearings

29. Moisture in a D.C. motor would cause:

A. short circuit   C. speed up

B. slow down   D. none of the above

30. The purpose for squirrel cage windings in a synchronous motor is to:

A. provide a means for starting

B. make balancing more precise

C. produce a higher power factor

D. eliminate arcing between the stator and the rate

31. What would the amps be at 240 volts with an 8 ohm resistance?

A. 32.5 amps   C. 25 amps

B. 1.5 amps   D. 30 amps

32. High mica would cause:

A. arcing   C. poor brush contact

B. brush vibration   D. all of the above

33. In a three-phase circuit, the phases are:

A. 120° apart   C. 180° apart

B. 160° apart   D. 360° apart

34. If two A.C. generators are operated in parallel, the load is distributed evenly by:

A. a rheostat

B. a balance coil

C. changing field excitation

D. adjusting the governor settings

35. An across the line starter gives:

A. high speed   C. slow starting power

B. poor voltage control   D. maximum torque

36. The voltage output of an A.C. generator is controlled by:

A. varying the D.C. exciter voltage

B. varying the reluctance of the air gap

      C. regulating the speed of the prime mover

      D. shorting out part of the armature windings

37. If you were operating an electric machine and the temperature was excessive for a prolonged period of time, what would happen?

      A. good brake service

      B. it's good wear for motor bearings

      C. it would ruin the insulation

      D. none of the above

38. How would you reverse the direction of a D.C. shunt wound motor?

      A. change armature leads

      B. change any two leads

      C. change any two of the three leads

      D. none of these apply

39. What is "pressure" in electricity?

      A. volts   C. kilowatts

      B. amps   D. none of these

40. One horse power is equal to:

      A. 33,000 foot-pounds per second

      B. 33,000 foot-pounds per hour

      C. 33,000 foot-pounds per minute

      D. 500 KW per hour

41. A shunt-wound generator is one in which the field windings are in parallel with the:

      A. armature   C. commutator

      B. brushes   D. field poles

42. The standard American frequency is:

      A. 120 Hz   C. 60 Hz

      B. 180 Hz   D. 50 Hz

43. In a three-wire, 115 to 230 volt distribution system, the voltage between the two hot legs is:

      A. 0 volts   C. 230 volts

      B. 115 volts   D. 440 volts

44. Which protective device prevents generator overload?

      A. the field rheostat   C. the circuit breaker

      B. the equalizing bus   D. the generator governor

45. A ring of sparks around the commutator indicates:

      A. a reversed magnetic field

      B. an open armature coil

      C. too much residual magnetism

      D. poor commutating brush contact

46. When shore power supplies a battery-charging panel, the batteries will discharge if:

      A. the polarity is reversed

      B. D.C. voltage is supplied

C. the voltage fluctuates

D. too little current is supplied

47. How would you accurately check the operating speed of a turbo-generator?

    A. with a hand held speedometer

    B. with the switchboard frequency meter

    C. using the switchboard RPM indicator

    D. using a hand held tachometer

48. Generator brushes are staggered to:

    A. reduce current pulsations

    B. reduce brush chatter

    C. prevent uneven commutator wear

    D. allow greater power generation

49. Which is an acceptable means of correcting high mica between commutator bars?

    A. undercutting   C. burnishing

    B. sanding   D. filing

50. When current and voltage reach maximum values at the same time, the power factor is:

    A. minimum   C. leading

    B. maximum   D. lagging

Engine Room Procedures

1. Water in the lube oil system may be detected by: I. sounding lube oil tanks with water sensitive paste; II. observing the purifier discharge.

    A. I   C. I and II

    B. II   D. neither I nor II

2. By definition a separator: I. removes solids from the lube oil; II. removes water from the lube oil.

    A. I   C. I and II

    B. II   D. neither I nor II

3. In a disc type centrifugal purifier the particles don't have far to travel to become separated from the oil because of the: I. ring dam; II. three wing device.

    A. I   C. I and II

    B. II   D. neither I nor II

4. Sediment collects in a tubular purifier:

    A. on top cover   C. on sides of bowl

    B. in drain line   D. on the discs

5. Electrohydraulic steering units are protected from pounding forces (rudder shock) by:

A. buffer springs   C. relief valves
B. follow up mechanism   D. relieving gear

6. External and internal leakage in hydraulic systems may be caused by:
   A. unusual vibration   C. excessively worn parts
   B. abnormal pressures   D. any of the above

7. The second effect on a two pass evaporator receives its steam from:
   A. desuperheated steam   C. auxiliary back pressure
   B. vapors from first effect   D. none of the above

8. The drain from both effects in a low pressure evaporator have their pressures equalized in the:
   A. equalizer tank   C. flash chamber
   B. drain tank   D. air ejector condenser

9. A solo shell, double-effect evaporator has:
   A. two cylindrical shells
   B. two separate tube bundles
   C. one tube bundle
   D. a four stage flash attachment

10. "Water hammer" is caused by:
    A. hitting water pipe with hammer
    B. too much water in pipe system
    C. water in steam lines
    D. steam in water lines

11. It is possible to operate the warping heads alone on a steam anchor windlass if you:
    A. open the engine throttle only a small amount
    B. release the brake on the wildcat
    C. disengage the windlass from the engine
    D. engage the devil's claw with the windlass

12. The dead center of a lathe can be properly used only after the end of the workpiece has been:
    A. bored   C. center drilled
    B. countersunk   D. tapered

13. If the point angle on a drill is less than 59°, the:
    A. hole will be drilled larger
    B. hole will take longer to drill
    C. drill will not center properly
    D. drill will cut undersized

14. Which will cause a twist drill to drill oversized?
    A. a lip clearance angle greater than 20°
    B. a cutting edge angle less than 59°
    C. the cutting edges being ground at different angles
    D. the drill being used without a pilot hole

15. Blue smoke coming from the diesel exhaust would indicate:
    A. excessive fuel consumption/unburned fuel
    B. burning of lube oil due to possible blow-by
    C. lean fuel/air mixture, too much air
    D. none of the above

16. Fuel is ignited in the cylinder of an operating diesel engine by:
    A. a spark plug in the precombustion chamber
    B. an electrical discharge from the distributor
    C. the heat of compression within the cylinder
    D. heat from the fuel injection nozzle

17. If a 1- to 2-inch micrometer reads .250, what is the correct reading?
    A. ½ inch   C. 1¼ inch
    B. 1 inch   D. 2¼ inch

18. A taper shank drill is removed from the drill press spindle with a:
    A. drill drift   C. taper punch
    B. vise grip   D. leather mallet

19. The valve which is always partially open when the evaporator is in operation is the:
    A. vapor valve
    B. continuous blowdown valve
    C. bottom blowdown valve
    D. surface blowdown valve

20. What kind of bolts would you use on a saltwater line?
    A. cold rolled   C. cast iron
    B. brass   D. all of the above

21. Studs and nuts intended for use in main steam line flanges and fittings are marked with an "H" or a "T" to show they are:
    A. heat resistant   C. half threaded
    B. hard finished   D. corrosion resistant

22. Before installing a new flange gasket be sure that the:
    A. flange faces are painted
    B. isolating valves are open
    C. flange faces are absolutely clean
    D. old gasket is in place

23. When distilling salt water the cooling-water discharge from the distiller is fed back to the evaporator as feedwater:
    A. to cut down on the amount of cooling water needed
    B. to prevent an excess amount of cooling water from being discharged to the bilges
    C. to supply hot water to the evaporator for more economical operation
    D. none of the above

24. The second effect on a two pass evaporator receives its steam from:

A. auxiliary back pressure   C. vapors from first effect
B. desuperheated steam   D. none of the above

25. What precaution should you take when lagging a pipeline with asbestos material?
   A. be sure there is no condensate in the lines
   B. wear a dust mask and avoid breathing the asbestos dust
   C. be aware of the flammable properties of asbestos
   D. always wear an oxygen breathing apparatus

26. An instrument used to indicate the level of a fluid in a tank is called a:
   A. pneumercator   C. levelometer
   B. viscosimeter   D. calorimeter

27. When a piece of work is being face machined in the lathe chuck, the tool bit should be set:
   A. above center   C. at 29°
   B. below center   D. at dead center

28. A roughened checkered surface is put on round stock in a lathe with a:
   A. knurling tool   C. checkering tool
   B. threading tool   D. chamfering tool

29. Why do you add cornstarch to an evaporator?
   A. increase the rate of vaporization
   B. make the water taste better
   C. prevent high temperatures
   D. cut down on priming and scale

30. What would you *not* do if you found fuel oil returning to the contaminated drain tank?
   A. check condensate returns from steam heating line in fuel oil tanks
   B. isolate leaky coils and repair
   C. drain contaminated tank so as to prevent oil from entering condensate system
   D. put pressure on fuel tank to find leak

31. The oil in a cargo winch gear box should be sampled periodically to:
   A. prevent the gear box from leaking
   B. prevent the oil from becoming inflammable
   C. make sure it has not become contaminated
   D. make sure the motor bearings are lubricated

32. On a steam driven anchor windlass, the clutch is used to:
   A. regulate the speed at which the anchor chain pays out
   B. hold the anchor securely in the hawsepipe
   C. engage and disengage the wildcat from the engine
   D. regulate the speed of the warping heads

33. To make sure stock is running true in a lathe, you should use a:
    A. center gauge   C. dial indicator
    B. micrometer   D. gauge block

34. Pipe thread taps are:
    A. straight   C. tapered
    B. not fluted   D. not hardened

35. Before starting an auxiliary diesel engine, you should:
    A. change fuel oil strainers
    B. clean the air filter
    C. check the crankcase oil level
    D. vent the cooling system

36. Proper filtering and straining of diesel fuel is important because:
    A. fuel injectors may be damaged by foreign particles in fuel oil
    B. fuel oil transfer pumps cannot tolerate small amounts of grit in the oil
    C. dirty fuel will clog the intake air filter
    D. the fuel oil pump will overspeed if dirt is not removed

37. What types of lubricating oil systems are used on diesel engines?
    A. forced feed and gravity   C. gravity and wick
    B. forced feed and splash   D. wet sump and dry sump

38. What would cause white smoke after you just started the diesel?
    A. too weak battery power   C. water in the gas
    B. water in the fuel   D. water in the oil

39. The rotating part of a micrometer is the:
    A. anvil   C. frame
    B. barrel   D. thimble

40. A grinding wheel is "trued" with a:
    A. lathe tool   C. garnet stone
    B. dressing tool   D. round file

41. Lint from cleaning rags can be harmful to a hydraulic machine because lint:
    A. can cause rusting of internal parts
    B. causes the hydraulic fluid to break down
    C. clogs filters and promotes leakage
    D. solidifies and causes cracked lines

42. When checking rudder angle indicator from bridge to steering gear, you turn the wheel hard left and right, back and forth, and the rudder moves sluggishly. What might be the cause?
    A. wrong telemotor   C. too high a voltage
    B. using wrong power cable   D. air in the system

43. Which process is used to bring a hole to finished size with accuracy?
    A. coring   C. broaching
    B. boring   D. reaming

44. When drilling a hole in a piece of work held in a lathe chuck, you mount a drill chuck in the:
    A. compound rest   C. tailstock
    B. cross feed   D. head stock

45. How often should the emergency diesel be run under load?
    A. once a year   C. once a week
    B. once a month   D. at inspection time only

46. If black smoke is coming from the exhaust stack of a diesel engine, what could be the trouble?
    A. bad exhaust valves   C. leaky fuel injectors
    B. not enough air   D. all of the above

47. When using a micrometer to measure a drill for size, you should measure across the drill:
    A. margins   C. shank
    B. flutes   D. web

48. The proper tool to use for cutting new external threads is called a thread:
    A. tap   C. broach
    B. die   D. chaser

49. What would cause a diesel to have black smoke?
    A. leaky injector   C. water in the gas
    B. too heavy oil   D. water in the oil

50. Dirt in the fuel oil system of a diesel engine can cause:
    A. clogged filters   C. poor combustion
    B. overloading of the diesel   D. erosion of fuel lines

51. The liner which has no direct contact with the cooling water is what kind of a liner?
    A. wet   C. integral
    B. dry   D. none of the above

52. All of the following are used for low temperature diesel starting except:
    A. ether
    B. jacket water heaters
    C. cylinder compression ratio reduced
    D. air intake heaters

53. Overgreasing of ball bearing installed on pumps will result in:
    A. smoother pump operation
    B. overheating of the bearing
    C. reduced corrosion in the bearing
    D. increased pump capacity

54. A pounding noise in a steam cylinder of a mooring winch could be caused by:
    A. a loose piston rod   C. leaky packing
    B. low steam pressure   D. low winch load

55. Which of the following types of valves is used in the bilge manifold?
    A. swing check   C. angle
    B. nonreturn   D. globe
56. If a cargo winch were running hot, what would you do?
    A. speed it up so that a great amount of air will circulate through it
    B. slow it down, stop it, and take the load off
    C. nothing as this is normal condition for cargo winches
    D. remove the load and run it top speed
57. Before you start a steam-driven winch that has been idle for a long time, you should:
    A. repack all valve stems
    B. grease all bearings
    C. replace the foundation bolts
    D. balance the warping heads
58. At dock side or in a lock the ship's position may be maintained automatically by the use of a:
    A. gypsy winch   C. vertical capstan
    B. constant tension winch   D. A and C above
59. In a low pressure evaporator, double effect, what is the steam pressure carried on the first stage?
    A. 10 to 25 PSI   C. 5 to 10 PSI
    B. 15 to 30 PSI   D. 1 to 5 PSI
60. Emulsification of oil will occur when mixed with:
    A. air   C. black oil
    B. water   D. ice cream
61. Any abnormal condition or emergency that occurs in the engine room must be reported immediately to the:
    A. engineer on watch   C. fireman on watch
    B. oiler on watch   D. first assistant engineer
62. The purpose of the jaw clutch installed on a steam anchor windlass is to:
    A. stop the engine when raising the anchor
    B. engage and disengage the engine
    C. control the flow of steam to the engine
    D. hold the anchor with the devil's claw
63. The greatest cause of fuel injection equipment malfunction can be attributed to:
    A. backlash   C. dirt
    B. distortion   D. timing
64. To reduce pulsations in pipelines, the discharge side of a steam reciprocating feed pump is equipped with a (an):
    A. reed valve   C. relief valve
    B. air chamber   D. feedwater regulator

65. The instrument always used in conjunction with the salinity indicator is the:

    A. pyrometer   C. hydrometer
    B. manometer   D. thermometer

66. When distilling salt water the evaporator, should be blown down when the salinity reaches:

    A. 3/32   C. 2/32
    B. 1/32   D. 5/32

67. Rotating flyweights acting against spring pressure make a simple type of:

    A. governor   C. safety valve
    B. reducing valve   D. feedwater regulator

68. A spring bearing on the line shaft is lubricated by:

    A. the lube oil gravity tank
    B. water leak-off from the stern tube
    C. an oil ring and scraper
    D. the main lube oil pump

69. An overspeeding diesel engine could best be stopped by:

    A. disconnecting the battery cables from the starting motor
    B. blocking the air intake and securing the fuel supply
    C. draining the hydraulic fluid from the governor sump
    D. blocking the flow of cooling air to the radiator

70. The ratio of the volume of air at B. D. C. (bottom dead center) as compared to the volume of air at T. D. C. (top dead center) is known as:

    A. ignition ratio   C. power ratio
    B. compression ratio   D. injection ratio

71. The coils in the evaporator are attached to the headers by:

    A. pipe nipples   C. welding
    B. union-type fittings   D. bolted flanges

72. The system used for breaking scale from the evaporator coils while the evaporator is in operation is called:

    A. recirculating   C. cracking-off
    B. blowing-down   D. dumping

73. The most efficient diesel cooling water temperature is:

    A. 120° F   C. 170° F
    B. 145° F   D. 195° F

74. The process used to retard corrosion on iron pipe is called:

    A. soldering   C. tempering
    B. annealing   D. galvanizing

75. What type of gasket is used on a steam joint?

    A. rubber   C. wire inserted rubber
    B. asbestos   D. none of these apply

76. An electrohydraulic windlass is controlled by the operation of a handwheel which:
    A. controls the speed of the electric motor
    B. controls the output of the electrohydraulic unit
    C. operates the devil's claw
    D. disconnects the warping heads

77. Which type of file will produce a fine finish when draw filing?
    A. a double-cut file   C. a single cut file
    B. a bastard file   D. a second cut file

78. Before the longitudinal carriage feed of a lathe is engaged, you must be sure the:
    A. spindle clutch is disengaged
    B. carriage clamp screw is loosened
    C. carriage stop screw is loosened
    D. thread dial indicator is zeroed

79. The purpose of annealing any metal is to make the metal:
    A. harder   C. softer
    B. tougher   D. smoother

80. Copper ring gaskets are usually annealed by heating:
    A. cherry red and slowly air cooling
    B. straw yellow and oil quenching
    C. sparkling white and water tempering
    D. brick red and air tempering

81. When installing packing in a packing box:
    A. leave one old turn at the bottom of the packing box
    B. remove one turn and install one new turn of packing
    C. leave sufficient end clearance on each turn to allow for expansion
    D. place end cuts directly in line with each other

82. The twist drill gauge can be used to measure the drill:
    A. length   C. clearance angle
    B. diameter   D. web thickness

83. If the lube oil in a diesel engine is too cold, the result would be:
    A. lube oil pump would lose suction
    B. diesel would not start
    C. diesel would be hard starting
    D. overheating of the cooling system due to excess friction

84. If the relief valve on a diesel engine cylinder lifts, the cause could be:
    A. too much fuel injected into cylinder
    B. high head pressure
    C. water in the cylinder
    D. exhaust valve stuck closed

85. Moisture damage inside cargo winch master switches can be prevented by:
    A. installing a light bulb in the pedestal stand
    B. putting a drain line on the switch box
    C. venting the switch box regularly
    D. installing heating elements inside the switch box

86. How can you decrease the chance of contaminating the hydraulic fluid when you are working on machinery?
    A. clean fittings before you disconnect them
    B. place drip pans under leaky fittings
    C. seal any cracks in lines with Permatex
    D. coat all threads with graphite and oil

87. What kind of tap should be used to finish the threading operation in a blind hole?
    A. a short tap   C. a plug tap
    B. a taper tap   D. a bottoming tap

88. Each graduation on a micrometer barrel represents:
    A. 0.0025 inch   C. 0.025 inch
    B. 0.0050 inch   D. 0.250 inch

89. On a diesel engine, a freshwater heat exchanger is used rather than a saltwater one to:
    A. maintain fuel oil temperature
    B. maintain lube oil temperature
    C. cut down on rust and corrosion
    D. keep the engine block from freezing in cold weather

90. What attention should be given to the lube oil system of a diesel engine before starting?
    A. oil should be cooled   C. oil level should be checked
    B. oil should be filtered   D. oil should be heated

91. What could result if you repacked a valve having a badly scored stem?
    A. jamming of the valve in the open position
    B. leaking and premature failure of the packing
    C. corrosion of the valve disc
    D. deterioration of the valve seat

92. If one fuel oil strainer of a duplex unit becomes clogged while you vessel is steaming at sea, you should *first*:
    A. clean the dirty strainer as quickly as possible
    B. change the strainer over to the clean side
    C. stop the fuel oil service pump
    D. open the strainer bypass valve

93. What system is most likely to be at fault if a diesel engine runs rough?

A. lubrication   C. fuel

B. cooling   D. ignition

94. With the diesel running, white smoke starts coming out of the stack and the diesel stops. What would be the cause?

    A. low lube oil pressure

    B. fuel oil filters full of water

    C. super charger running too fast

    D. leaky injector

95. What is the flexible coupling used for?

    A. take up for vibration in the shaft

    B. small amount of misalignment

    C. to allow for expansion

    D. connects between the bull gear and the tail shaft

96. The designation "schedule 80 extra strong" refers to the:

    A. weight of steel plate   C. piping wall thickness

    B. tensile strength of bolts   D. tubing bursting strength

97. Low diesel lubricating oil temperature at reduced loads can be avoided by regulating the:

    A. pressure relief valve

    B. cooler bypass valve

    C. lubricating oil pump governor

    D. priming pump control

98. If a diesel engine starts, then quits, the problem may be:

    A. ignition system   C. lube oil system

    B. fuel oil system   D. air system

99. If a bilge pump failed to build up discharge pressure, you should check for:

    A. excessive water in the bilges

    B. a clogged suction strainer

    C. oil in the bilges

    D. a closed skin valve

100. In order to convert taper per foot to taper per inch, you should:

    A. subtract 12 inches   C. add 12 inches

    B. divide by 12 inches   D. multiply by 12 inches

Steam Review

1. Shrink when applied to boilers is caused by:

    A. formation of steam bubbles

    B. collapse of steam bubbles

    C. contraction of boiler drum while cooling down

    D. contraction of boiler casing

2. Superheaters are designed to:
    A. raise the sensible heat of the steam
    B. raise the mechanical efficiency of the plant
    C. provide a continuous flow through the desuperheater
    D. reduce foaming and carryover

3. After the initial lifting of the valve disc on a huddling chamber safety valve has occurred, the valve is opened all the way by:
    A. steam pressure acting on an increased area
    B. reactive force of steam expanding through an orifice
    C. high velocity of steam
    D. steam pressure acting on the blow-down ring

4. The main reason for keeping a burner register fully open when steaming is to prevent:
    A. boiler explosions   C. register from warping
    B. the fires being blown out   D. improper fuel-air mixture

5. Fuel viscosity at the atomizer can be reduced by:
    A. increasing the fuel oil heater steam supply
    B. mixing heavier oil with the fuel
    C. changing the atomizer orifice size
    D. increasing fuel oil pressure

6. Downcomers are placed outside of the inner casing rather than inside to obtain:
    A. preheating of the air supply
    B. minimum boiler rating
    C. desired circulation characteristics
    D. increased generating area

7. The air from the after-condenser of the air ejector is led to the:
    A. intercondenser   C. deaerator
    B. feed water   D. atmosphere

8. In a turbine installation the condensate pump discharges to:
    A. the air ejector condenser
    B. the hot well or feed and filter tank
    C. overboard
    D. the feedwater heater

9. The internal feed line is located:
    A. in the bottom of the steam and water drum
    B. between the feed pump and the boiler
    C. in the superheater
    D. in the upper part of the furnace

10. The feed-stop valve is located:
    A. on the feed pump
    B. on the main steam line
    C. nearest the steam and water drum on the feed line
    D. on the superheater

11. The deaerating (D.C.) heater is used in:
    A. the open type feedwater system
    B. the low pressure type steam plant
    C. all steam plants
    D. the closed type feedwater system

12. The cooling water supplied to the vent condenser in a D.C. heater is:
    A. sea water   C. portable water
    B. fresh water   D. condensate

13. If the salinity indicator registers high salinity in the main condenser hot well, you would suspect the cause to be:
    A. saturated steam coming from the boiler
    B. leaking tubes in the third stage heater
    C. high water pressure in the lube oil cooler
    D. leaking tubes in the main condenser

14. A sudden loss of vacuum in the main condenser can be caused by:
    A. damaged carbon packing rings
    B. a flooded condensate pump suction
    C. a sudden decrease in sea temperature
    D. excessive condenser cooling water

15. Water level in the boiler would rise most frequently as a result of:
    A. the feedwater regulator being stuck open
    B. closing of the turbine throttle
    C. opening of the turbine throttle
    D. leaving the feed stop valve open

16. The main feed pump will lose suction if the:
    A. D.C. heater goes dry
    B. vent condenser becomes air bound
    C. condensate pump suction is flooded
    D. main condenser loses vacuum

17. What would the *first* indication of a broken coil in the feedwater heater?
    A. the boiler water level would go up
    B. the boiler water level would go down
    C. the relief valve on the shell would open
    D. the feed pump would slow down

18. When a ship is underway, how is make up feed water added to the boilers?
    A. standby pump   C. condensate pump
    B. feed pump   D. vacuum drag

19. In a manually controlled feedwater system the proper water level is maintained by:
    A. operating the recirculating valve
    B. opening the feed pump steam valve

C. operating the feed stop valve

D. operating the feed check valve

20. Oxygen is removed from the feed water by the:

A. main air ejectors jet action

B. scrubbing action in the D.C. heater

C. auxiliary air ejectors

D. vent condenser fan

21. Air in the main condenser is harmful because it will:

A. cause heat to be transferred too rapidly

B. decrease the vacuum in the main condenser

C. cause the turbine casing to warp and bow

D. decrease the turbine exhaust steam pressure

22. The boiler feed water in the feedwater heater is heated by:

A. superheated steam   C. desuperheated steam

B. auxiliary exhaust steam   D. steam from the boiler

23. What is the "bilge injection," or emergency bilge suction connected to?

A. the general service pump   C. the bilge pump

B. the fire pump   D. the main circulator

24. Air leakage into the packing gland of a condensate pump is prevented by:

A. special packing in the stuffing box

B. the vacuum in the pump suction

C. a water seal line to the packing gland

D. an air seal line from the compressed air line

25. An oil leak into the feedwater system could be detected by:

A. examining the leak off from the main feed pump

B. checking the surface of the condensate in the D.C. heater

C. examining the water in the drain inspection tank

D. blowing down the contaminated evaporator and sampling the water

26. When the temperature of the feed water leaving the feedwater heater is low, it is an indication that the:

A. reducing valve is not functioning properly

B. back pressure is too low

C. back pressure is too high

D. atmospheric exhaust valve is open

27. An economizer is used to:

A. heat the fuel oil

B. heat air before it enters the furnace

C. desuperheat the steam

D. heat the feed water before it enters the boiler

28. The burner assembly is frequently referred to as a/the:

A. burner   C. barrel
B. register   D. air foils

29. To properly clean a burner tip, you should use:
    A. light sand blast grit   C. a jackknife
    B. a soft metal tool   D. a wire brush

30. If a steaming boiler does not have enough air for proper combustion, the:
    A. fires will be too hot   C. boiler will pant or rumble
    B. boiler will smoke grey   D. fires will hiss and sputter

31. Condensate from fuel oil bunker heaters returns to:
    A. reserve feed system
    B. main feed system
    C. contaminated (observation) tank
    D. bilges

32. To give the boiler a bottom blow:
    A. raise water level
    B. fires must be out, raise water level
    C. fires only need to be out
    D. just insure water level is above 2 inches

33. If the boiler water level drops out of sight while your vessel is steaming, you should:
    A. blow down the gauge glass
    B. start the standby feed pump
    C. close the main steam stop
    D. cut out the boiler fires

34. Giving the boiler a surface blow would be the best action to take when:
    A. removing scale and sludge
    B. lowering boiler water level
    C. preparing to blow tubes
    D. releasing the watch

35. When the condenser vacuum drag line to the reserve feed tank is open in rough weather, careful attention must be given to prevent losing the:
    A. condensate pressure   C. loop seal
    B. condenser vacuum   D. gland seal

36. The point of highest pressure in the steam and water cycle is found between the:
    A. boiler and the feed pump
    B. feed pump and the boiler
    C. boiler and main engine
    D. steam and water drum and superheater

37. When securing a steam atomization fuel oil burner:

     A. close steam valve first
     B. close oil valve first
     C. close valves at the same time
     D. close either first

38. Boiler water hardness is increased by:
     A. dissolved gases in the water
     B. zero alkalinity in the water
     C. improper operation of the D.C. heater
     D. scale forming salts in the water

39. The valve in the fuel oil manifold between the master valve and manifold is the:
     A. quick closing valve   C. burner valve
     B. root valve   D. recirculating valve

40. The root valve is located between:
     A. master valve and manifold
     B. burner valve and manifold
     C. quick closing valve and master valve
     D. pneumatic valve and manifold

41. Proper combustion is indicated by:
     A. yellowish flame   C. golden yellow flame
     B. white flame   D. brilliant white flame

42. Too much air would be indicated by:
     A. yellowish flame   C. golden yellow flame
     B. white flame   D. brilliant white flame

43. If the fires in a boiler furnace begin sputtering or hissing, you should suspect:
     A. excessive fuel pressure at the burners
     B. loss of fuel pump suction
     C. low fuel oil temperature
     D. water contamination of the fuel oil

44. In case of carry-over, the best corrective action is to:
     A. blow down the boiler with the surface blow
     B. trip the turbine and open the turbine casing drains
     C. close the steam line drains and run the turbine astern
     D. put the turbine throttle full astern

45. The most important valve on the boiler is the:
     A. main steam stop   C. superheater safety valve
     B. safety valve   D. feed check valve

46. All boilers must have how many feed lines?
     A. 1   C. 3
     B. 2   D. 4

47. The boiler may be given a bottom blow:
     A. to lower water level   C. only while making steam
     B. to remove scum   D. when fires are secured

48. You should blow down a gauge glass periodically to:
   A. remove any sediment from the glass
   B. maintain the proper water level in the steam drum
   C. provide water samples for the Second Assistant
   D. test the feedwater stop check valve

49. The function of swash plates:
   A. is to separate steam and water
   B. is to direct feed water into the drum
   C. is to direct chemical feeds into the drum
   D. minimizes water from splashing around as the ship rolls

50. If one fuel oil strainer of a duplex unit becomes clogged while your vessel is steaming at sea, you should *first*:
   A. clean the dirty strainer as quickly as possible
   B. change the strainer over to the clean side
   C. stop the fuel oil service pump
   D. open the strainer bypass valve

51. The flame scanner in a boiler burner management system will shut off the fuel to the burners if the:
   A. fires are too hot   C. fires go out
   B. steam pressure is too high   D. fuel is hot

52. If you notice that the boiler burner cones have carbon building on them the cause would be:
   A. water in the fuel oil
   B. fuel oil temperature too high
   C. burner is not set right in relation to the cones
   D. too much air

53. The purpose of maintaining a chemical reserve in feedwater treatment is to:
   A. decrease effect of impurities
   B. neutralize impurities as they enter the boiler
   C. combine with impurities to make sludge
   D. provide coating on interior of boiler tubes

54. To safely lower the firing rate of a boiler you should *always* decrease the fuel oil pressure:
   A. by opening the oil recirculating valve
   B. by opening the fuel pump bypass
   C. before decreasing the forced draft pressure
   D. after decreasing the forced draft pressure

55. To properly remove the burner tip nut from the burner barrel, the barrel should be:
   A. clamped in a machinist's vice on the workbench
   B. fixed in the burner stowage rack
   C. held by the fixture on the burner cleaning bench
   D. removed from the gooseneck before removing the tip nut

56. It is good engineering practice to shift and clean the fuel oil strainers when the:
    A. burners show excessive carbon buildup
    B. fuel oil transfer pump loses suction
    C. pressure drops excessively across the strainers
    D. fires being to hiss and sputter

57. Safety valves vent to the:
    A. high pressure drains   C. bilge
    B. atmosphere   D. auxiliary exhaust line

58. To safely increase the firing rate of a boiler, you should *always* increase the forced draft pressure:
    A. after increasing the fuel pressure
    B. by opening the burner register wider
    C. by opening additional burner registers
    D. before increasing the fuel pressure

59. The feed pump discharge pressure is higher than the steam drum pressure to:
    A. ensure feedwater flow into the boiler
    B. keep the steam drum pressure high
    C. prevent water hammer in the feed line
    D. help the feedwater flash to steam

60. What valve should you leave closed when you are starting a turbine-driven boiler feed pump?
    A. pump discharge valve
    B. pump suction valve
    C. turbine steam supply valve
    D. turbine exhaust valve

61. Which should be checked *first* when you are taking over the fireroom watch?
    A. the fuel pressure to the burners
    B. the condition of the furnace fires
    C. the boiler water level
    D. the boiler steam pressure

62. The following valve on the boiler is never completely closed:
    A. feed check valve   C. upper gauge glass valve
    B. feed stop valve   D. air cock

63. Dead burners must be kept in the register:
    A. when at sea   C. only during warm-up
    B. while maneuvering   D. never

64. The boiler fuel oil system discharge strainers are also known as the:
    A. cold strainers   C. coarse strainers
    B. hot strainers   D. magnetic strainers

65. The boiler fuel oil service pump takes suction from the:

A. fuel oil heater discharge

B. contaminated drain inspection tank

C. fuel oil settling tank

D. double bottom fuel tanks

66. Black smoke coming from a boiler can be caused by low fuel temperature and by:

A. excessively high fuel pressure

B. an improper air/fuel ratio

C. low fuel pressure

D. high fuel temperature

67. Foaming in the steam drum is caused by:

A. oxygen in the water   C. poor boiler design

B. density too high   D. excessive steam demands

68. A function of the desuperheater installed in a boiler steam drum is to:

A. add moisture to superheated steam

B. provide steam for auxiliary machinery

C. distribute feedwater within the boiler

D. raise the temperature of the steam in the dry pipe

69. If the water level in a boiler water gauge glass has remained stationary while answering bells, the:

A. gauge glass is not working

B. feedwater regulator is working properly

C. feedwater regulator is broken

D. water level is too high

70. Which is opened prior to lighting fires and closed when blowing steam?

A. superheater vent   C. soot blower drains

B. air cock   D. none of the above

71. The fuel oil solenoid valve may be closed by:

A. the forced draft fan in stopping

B. the scanner failing to see a flame in furnace

C. the fuel oil pressure dropping to 100 PSI

D. A and B above

72. If the fires in a steaming boiler have been extinguished accidentally, you should *not* relight any burner until:

A. the boiler furnace has been thoroughly purged

B. the furnace refractory has cooled below ignition temperature

C. all burning embers in the furnace are extinguished

D. all the fuel has been recirculated from the burners

73. Vibration in a propulsion turbine is:

A. normal when first starting up

B. abnormal and should be investigated

C. caused by high condenser vacuum

D. prevented by flexible shaft couplings

74. Loss of lube oil pressure requires:

    A. securing the turbine   C. shifting strainers

    B. stopping the turbine   D. shifting lube oil pumps

75. A spring bearing on the line shaft is lubricated by:

    A. the lube oil gravity tank

    B. water leak off from the stern tube

    C. an oil ring and scraper

    D. the main lube oil pump

76. In case of carry-over, the *best* corrective action is to:

    A. blow down the boiler with the surface blow

    B. trip the turbine and open the turbine casing drains

    C. close the steam line drains and run the turbine astern

    D. put the turbine throttle full astern

77. When vacuum is lost on a turbo generator the trip is actuated by:

    A. sentinel valve   C. slugs of water

    B. back pressure   D. overspeed trip

78. Excessive steam leaks from high pressure turbine gland would most likely be due to:

    A. excessive gland seal steam pressure

    B. worn carbon rings

    C. loose casing bolts

    D. packing improperly seated

79. Air in the main condenser is harmful because it will:

    A. cause heat to be transferred too rapidly

    B. decrease the vacuum in the main condenser

    C. cause the turbine casing to warp and bow

    D. decrease the turbine exhaust steam pressure

80. If the salinity alarm went off and no make up feed is being added what could be the cause?

    A. leak in the lube oil cooler

    B. leak in the main condenser

    C. leak in the generating tubes

    D. leak in the fuel oil heater

81. Rotating flyweights acting against spring pressure make a simple type of:

    A. governor   C. safety valve

    B. reducing valve   D. feedwater regulator

82. While warming up the turbine or cooling it:

    A. the lube oil system must be operating

    B. the jacking gear must be engaged

    C. the main condenser must be operating

    D. all of the above

83. To assure that a bearing is receiving proper oil supply, you should check the:
    - A. bull's eye in the gravity tank overflow
    - B. lube oil temperature at the cooler outlet
    - C. lube oil strainer magnets
    - D. sight flow glass in the bearing oil supply line

84. The jacking gear on main propulsion turbines is used to:
    - A. cool the rotor evenly
    - B. provide emergency propulsion
    - C. lift the reduction gear casing
    - D. reduce the turbine speed during maneuvering

85. The normal pressure to the bearings in a turbine lube oil system will range between:
    - A. 3 to 4 PSI
    - B. 5 to 6 PSI
    - C. 8 to 10 PSI
    - D. 18 to 20 PSI

86. When making an inspection of the steering gear, the most important item to check for is:
    - A. which machinery is operating
    - B. saltwater leaks around rudder post
    - C. hydraulic leaks
    - D. electrical overloads

87. The guarding valve prevents steam from entering the:
    - A. ahead turbine while maneuvering
    - B. astern turbine
    - C. ahead turbine at all times
    - D. none of the above

88. The guarding valve remains open:
    - A. never
    - B. during maneuvering
    - C. at all times
    - D. only during turbine warm-up

89. Oil flowing through the sight glass in the line between the lube oil gravity tank and sump indicates that the:
    - A. gravity tank is overflowing
    - B. lube oil pump is stopped
    - C. lube oil suction strainer is clogged
    - D. lube oil sump is full

90. If a bilge pump failed to build up discharge pressure, you should check for:
    - A. excessive water in the bilges
    - B. a clogged suction strainer
    - C. oil in the bilges
    - D. a closed skin valve

91. Magnets are installed in the propulsion turbine lube oil strainers to attract metal particles from the:
    A. turbine bearings   C. turbine blading
    B. bearing journals   D. reduction gears

92. Of what type are strainers used in the lube oil system?
    A. simplex   C. bucket
    B. duplex   D. quick change

93. If the D.C. heater were to run out of water, what would happen?
    A. the feed pump would become air bound
    B. the condensate pump would become air bound
    C. water would back up into the condenser
    D. the main circulating pump would not operate properly

94. Reduction gears on main propulsion units are lubricated by:
    A. grease cups and gravity feed lines
    B. oil flinger rings mounted on the shaft
    C. leak-off lines from the lube oil cooler
    D. spray nozzles at the gear-meshing points

95. How would you accurately check the operating speed of a turbogenerator?
    A. with a hand held speedometer
    B. with the switchboard frequency meter
    C. using the switchboard RPM indicator
    D. using a hand held tachometer

96. The boiler superheater vents should *always* be open when you are:
    A. using the steam sootblowers
    B. blowing down the boiler
    C. lighting off or securing the boiler
    D. raising the water level above normal

97. Babbit is a metal alloy commonly used for lining:
    A. bearings   C. bearing journals
    B. shim stock   D. saltwater piping

98. The valve closest to the boiler in the feed line is the:
    A. feed pump discharge valve
    B. feed check valve
    C. feed stop valve
    D. feedwater heater bypass valve

99. If the lube oil pressure for the main turbine *suddenly* increased the cause may be:
    A. a leaking lube oil cooler   C. dirt clogging the system
    B. the oil is too cold   D. a leak in the gravity tank

100. The feed pump discharge pressure is higher than the steam drum pressure to:
    A. ensure feedwater flow into the boiler
    B. keep the steam drum pressure high

C. prevent water hammer in the feed line

D. help the feedwater flash to steam

Refrigeration Review

1. Insufficient refrigerant in a refrigeration plant may result in:
    A. high discharge pressure
    B. frosting of the crankcase
    C. high temperature of the overboard water
    D. low suction pressure
2. What is the probable cause if the compressor runs continuously in an R-12 refrigeration plant?
    A. an open solenoid valve switch
    B. an inadequate supply of refrigerant
    C. clogged condenser tubes
    D. excess of liquid refrigerant
3. Which of the following actions should you take to correct a low condensing pressure in a refrigeration system?
    A. purge the condenser
    B. add refrigerant
    C. adjust the thermostatic expansion valve
    D. increase the compressor speed
4. The "hot gas" used in hot-gas defrosting is taken from the:
    A. compressor discharge line   C. condenser discharge line
    B. compressor suction line   D. receiver
5. After hot-gas defrosting has been accomplished the condensed refrigerant in the coil is:
    A. drained from the system
    B. left in the coil
    C. expanded into another coil
    D. sent in liquid form to the compressor
6. A solenoid valve serves to control the:
    A. pressure in the evaporator coils
    B. amount of R-12 entering the evaporator
    C. flow of R-12 toward the expansion valve
    D. amount of circulating water to the cooling coils
7. Air that may enter a refrigeration plant tends to collect in the:
    A. upper part of the receiver
    B. upper part of the condenser
    C. downstream end of the cooling coil
    D. inlet end of the condenser
8. If there is a kink in the line between the thermal bulb and expansion valve, what would you replace?

      A. thermal bulb and tube   C. the bulb
      B. top of expansion valve   D. none of these

9. Which could cause abnormally high temperature in one refrigerated space?
      A. not enough condenser cooling water
      B. the automatic controls are not working properly
      C. the scale trap is clogged
      D. there is air in the system

10. Atmospheric pressure at sea level is:
      A. 15.7 PSI   C. 14.0 PSI
      B. 14.7 PSI   D. 0 PSI

11. How would you remove the frost on evaporator coils?
      A. hammer   C. halide torch
      B. hot gas line   D. blow torch

12. Low head pressure from the compressor of an R-12 system can be caused by:
      A. too much condenser cooling water
      B. not enough condenser cooling water
      C. excessive refrigerant in the system
      D. air in the refrigeration system

13. In an R-12 refrigeration system, the thermal expansion valve sensing bulb is located:
      A. near the evaporator coil outlet
      B. near the evaporator coil inlet
      C. on the liquid line strainer
      D. at the solenoid valve outlet

14. The thermostatic expansion valve of an R-12 refrigeration system controls the:
      A. back pressure in the evaporator coils
      B. temperature in the refrigerated space
      C. superheat in the refrigerant leaving the evaporator
      D. refrigerant pressure in the high side

15. Which could cause the high pressure cutout to stop the compressor in an R-12 system?
      A. too much condenser cooling water
      B. a shortage of liquid refrigerant
      C. excessive frost on the evaporator
      D. not enough condenser cooling water

16. High suction pressure in an R-12 refrigeration system can be caused by:
      A. a dirty dehydrator
      B. a clogged liquid strainer
      C. the king valve being open too wide
      D. the expansion valve being open too wide

17. Too much refrigerant in an R-12 system can cause:
    A. oil foaming in the compressor crankcase
    B. the compressor to short-cycle
    C. the compressor to run continuously
    D. low pressure in the compressor crankcase

18. Which valve is normally closed when charging an R-12 refrigeration system through the high side?
    A. the thermal expansion valve
    B. the dehydrator inlet valve
    C. the suction line valve
    D. the liquid line king valve

19. When adding oil to an R-12 system, precautions must be taken to ensure that:
    A. the compressor suction pressure is not too high
    B. all air is purged from the pump and charging fittings
    C. a clean funnel is used to pour the oil through
    D. the condenser is completely shut down first

20. A low refrigeration compressor discharge pressure can be caused by:
    A. warm food in the refrigerator
    B. leaking compressor discharge valves
    C. faulty door gaskets on the refrigerator
    D. wasted zinc plates in the condenser

21. A dehydrator is normally used in an R-12 system when it is necessary to:
    A. purge noncondensable gases and vapors
    B. add refrigerant to the system
    C. remove oil from the refrigerant
    D. remove refrigerant from the oil

22. The freezing point on the Fahrenheit thermometer is:
    A. 0°   C. 32°
    B. 30°   D. 34°

23. The freezing point on the Celsius thermometer is:
    A. 32°   C. 15°
    B. 0°   D. 30°

24. What would cause a refer compressor to knock and heavy frost to form on the compressor head?
    A. solenoid valve stuck open
    B. expansion valve stuck closed
    C. flooding back to the compressor
    D. both A and C

25. When multiple refrigerated boxes having individual temperatures are supplied by a single refrigeration compress, the individual box temperature is controlled by the:

    A. compressor speed   C. suction valves

    B. expansion valves   D. solenoid valves

26. If a refrigeration compressor is running continuously without lowering the temperature in the refrigerator, the trouble may be:

    A. excessive condenser cooling water

    B. warm food in the refrigerator

    C. a shortage of refrigerant

    D. a shortage of compressor oil

27. If the suction pressure for an operating refrigeration compressor is below normal, the cause may be:

    A. too much liquid refrigerant

    B. the expansion valve overfeeding

    C. a clogged suction strainer

    D. the compressor short cycling

28. Low refrigeration suction pressure is caused by:

    A. air in the system

    B. leaky compressor suction valves

    C. a malfunctioning solenoid valve

    D. flooding back

29. What color is the flame on a halide torch without any refrigerant present?

    A. blue   C. green

    B. orange   D. purple

30. The amount of heat released by steam when it changes to water at the same temperature is called:

    A. latent heat of condensation

    B. latent heat of vaporization

    C. latent heat of saturation

    D. sensible heat of condensation

31. To correct compressor slugging and flooding back, you should:

    A. change discharge pressure

    B. remove some refrigerant

    C. clean the expansion valve screen

    D. adjust the expansion valve

32. Sensible heat changes:

    A. the temperature of a substance without changing its form

    B. the shape of a substance

    C. a solid to a liquid

    D. a liquid to a gas

33. The thermostatic expansion valve on an R-12 refrigeration system controls the:

    A. back pressure in the evaporator coils

    B. temperature in the refrigerated space

    C. superheat in the refrigerant leaving the evaporator

    D. refrigerant pressure in the high side

34. A ruptured diaphragm in a thermostatic expansion valve will cause the valve to:

    A. open

    B. close

    C. remain in its position

    D. flood the evaporator with refrigerant

35. When a refrigeration plant is to be shut down for an extended period, most of the refrigerant should be:

    A. distributed equally throughout the system

    B. drained from the system

    C. pumped down to the condenser

    D. returned to the receiver

36. As a rule, the degree of superheat picked up by the refrigerant vapor before it leaves the cooling coil is about:

    A. 45° to 50° F   C. 15° to 20° F

    B. 30° to 38° F   D. 4° to 12° F

37. If the compressor runs continuously, the cause might be a:

    A. defective thermal bulb

    B. clogged scale trap

    C. stuck high-pressure switch

    D. stuck low-pressure switch

38. Which could cause a refrigeration compressor to run continuously?

    A. a clogged scale trap

    B. a clogged refrigerant dehydrator

    C. the low pressure cut-out is stuck closed

    D. the high pressure cut-out is stuck open

39. When working on a Freon-12 system you should use:

    A. gloves   C. glasses or safety goggles

    B. sandpaper   D. rubber boots

40. The thermostatic expansion valve is designed to maintain constant:

    A. flow   C. superheat

    B. temperature   D. pressure

41. The single-trunk, piston-type compressor is undesirable for an R-12 unit because the:

    A. lubricant temperatures become excessive

    B. refrigerant is superheated by the oil

    C. lubricant mixes with the refrigerant

    D. refrigerant reduces crankcase pressure

42. How many BTUs in a ton of refrigeration?

    A. 12,000   C. 120,000

    B. 2,000   D. 1,200

43. Latent heat changes the:
    A. physical state of a substance
    B. temperature of a substance
    C. atmospheric pressure
    D. sensible pressure
44. In a refrigeration system, a fluid that serves only as a heat carrier is called a:
    A. secondary refrigerant   C. vaporizing refrigerant
    B. condensing refrigerant   D. primary refrigerant
45. A refrigerant boils and vaporizes in the:
    A. receiver   C. compressor
    B. condenser   D. cooling coil
46. In terms of pressure and temperature, what happens to the primary refrigerant in the compressor?
    A. its pressure and temperature are both lowered
    B. its pressure and temperature are both raised
    C. its pressure is lowered and its temperature is raised
    D. its pressure is raised and its temperature is lowered
47. The amount of liquid refrigerant that is allowed to flow through the expansion valve is:
    A. the same as the amount boiled off in the coil
    B. entirely independent of the amount boiled off in the coil
    C. greater than the amount boiled off in the coil
    D. less than the amount boiled off in the coil
48. The thermostatic expansion valve controls the amount of refrigerant that allowed to flow to the:
    A. compressor   C. cooling coils
    B. condenser   D. receiver
49. What action should be taken prior to tightening the cap on a liquid line strainer that has been cleaned?
    A. purge the air out of the strainer
    B. test the strainer for leaks
    C. replace the strainer screen spring
    D. open the strainer outlet valve
50. An excessive amount of cold water flowing through the condenser is indicated by unusually:
    A. low temperature in the cooling coil
    B. low compressor discharge pressure
    C. high pressure on the suction side of the thermostatic expansion valve
    D. high refrigerant vapor pressure in the condenser

Bearings and Lubrication

1. A common cause of cracking of the babbit lining in a turbine journal bearing is:
     A. prolonged operation at low speed
     B. prolonged operation at high speed
     C. vibration generated by the rotor
     D. excessive thrust bearing wear

2. A dented race in an antifriction bearing could be caused by:
     A. water in the bearing
     B. abrasives in the lubricant
     C. dirt in the bearing
     D. vibration while the bearing is inoperative

3. Hot running bearings can be caused by:
     A. inadequate lube oil supply   C. excessive loading
     B. contaminated lube oil   D. any of the above

4. An overheated bearing in the main propulsion unit is indicated by:
     A. bubbles in the sight glass
     B. sludge in the strainers
     C. a high oil level in the sump
     D. high temperature of the lube oil leaving the bearing

5. As found in a reduction gear drive system, thrust bearings serve to:
     A. transmit the force produced by the propeller to the structure of the ship
     B. limit the radial movement of the shaft
     C. increase the shaft speed
     D. hold the main engine in place

6. Why is a high lube oil level in the main engine reduction gear sump undesirable?
     A. oil churning may result   C. oil temperature may rise
     B. the oil may become aerated   D. all of the above

7. Which is an example of a half bearing?
     A. a piston pin bushing   C. a spring bearing
     B. a crankshaft main bearing D. a thrust bearing

8. Journal bearings used in modern turbine rotors are manufactured in two halves in order to:
     A. permit removal of the bearing without removing the rotor from the turbine
     B. facilitate interchanging with other bearing halves
     C. maintain axial alignment and reduce thrust
     D. provide for positive oil flow at all loads

9. Most main propulsion unit reduction gear bearings are:
     A. self-lubricating   C. spherical-seated
     B. rigidly mounted   D. self-aligning

10. A ball bearing will overheat if:
    A. completely full of grease   C. in use for a long time
    B. half full of grease   D. operated at high speed

11. Overgreasing of ball bearings installed on pumps will result in:
    A. smoother pump operation
    B. overheating of bearings
    C. reduced corrosion of bearings
    D. increased pump capacity

12. Filters are installed ahead of air line lubricators for the primary purpose of removing:
    A. heat of compression
    B. air supply pressure pulses
    C. moisture in the air supply
    D. turbulence in the air supply

13. The amount of wear on a split-type bearing is accurately determined by using a:
    A. dial-indicating outside caliper
    B. spider gage
    C. screw thread outside micrometer
    D. ball-anvil outside micrometer

14. Antifriction bearings should not be excessively lubricated because:
    A. the bearings will require immediate flushing
    B. dirt will accumulate inside the bearings
    C. excess lubrication will result in slippage
    D. the bearing will overheat

15. What process consumes the greatest amount of power and produces the greatest amount of heat?
    A. overcoming sliding friction
    B. overcoming rolling friction
    C. overcoming fluid friction
    D. overcoming oil wedge friction

16. While making your rounds, you notice the main lube oil temperature is higher than normal. To remedy this situation, you should:
    A. speed up the main lube oil pump
    B. open the lube oil cooler seawater inlet valve wider
    C. throttle in on the lube oil cooler seawater discharge valve
    D. open the lube oil cooler seawater discharge valve wider

17. In a segmental, pivoted-shoe thrust bearing, the thrust load among the shoes is equalized by the:
    A. base ring   C. leveling plates
    B. oil wedge   D. thrust collar

18. The most practical method of determining the condition of a shaft bearing while the shaft is turning is to:
    A. visually inspect the bearing

    B. check the lube oil temperature

    C. check the lube oil viscosity

    D. perform a carbon blot on an oil sample from the bearing

19. Which construction method would apply to babbitt lined split-type reduction gearing bearings?

    A. they are always mounted with the split in a horizontal plane

    B. they are secured in their housings so pressure points will occur at the joint faces

    C. they are split into four equal-sized segments

    D. they are rigidly mounted and doweled in their housings

20. The element of a Kingsbury thrust bearing which transmits the thrust from the shaft to the oil film and shoes is the:

    A. collar   C. upper leveling plate

    B. lower leveling plate   D. base ring

21. The maximum temperature rise of oil passing through any reduction gear or bearing should not exceed:

    A. 30°F   C. 70°F

    B. 50°F   D. 90°F

22. The best indication that a bearing is being properly lubricated is the:

    A. oil pressure at the lube oil pump discharge

    B. lube oil strainer condition during cleaning and inspection

    C. oil temperature shown by the bearing thermometer

    D. oil temperature leaving the lube oil cooler

23. In a disk type purifier, which method is used to separate lube oil into thin layers and create shallow settling distances?

    A. a discharge ring

    B. a three wing device

    C. a tubular bowl

    D. a series of cone shaped plates

24. How are line shaft bearings usually lubricated?

    A. gravity-feed   C. oil lubricating disks

    B. pressure-feed   D. oil lubricating rings

25. The presence of scale and dirt on the saltwater side of a lube oil cooler element is usually indicated by:

    A. clogged lube oil strainers

    B. seawater leaking into the lube oil system

    C. decreasing lube oil pressure

    D. gradually increasing lube oil temperature

26. If a line shaft bearing commences to overheat, you should slow down the shaft. If overheating persists, you should next:

    A. increase lube oil pressure to the bearing

    B. decrease lube oil pressure to the bearing

    C. apply emergency cooling water externally to the bearing

D. flood the bearing with a higher viscosity oil to provide emergency lubrication and cooling

27. Which of the following types of bearings is designed to limit end movement and to carry loads applied in the same direction as the shaft axis?

    A. rigidly mounted reduction gear bearing
    B. segmental pivoted-shoe thrust bearing
    C. self-aligning radial bearing
    D. spherically-seated radial bearing

28. Which frictional component is lubricated by a hydrodynamic film of lubricant?

    A. crossheads   C. guide bearings
    B. guides   D. Kingsbury thrust bearings

29. Which type of bearing lubrication scheme can carry the highest unit loading?

    A. ring lubricated bearings
    B. disk lubricated bearings
    C. pressure lubricated bearings
    D. oil whip lubricated bearings

30. An oil fog lubrication system is recommended for:

    A. gear shaft bearings
    B. high speed continuous operation of roller bearings
    C. low and moderate speed ball bearings
    D. heavily loaded and high speed ball bearings

31. Which journal bearing most easily accommodates the minor turbine shaft misalignment?

    A. ball bearings
    B. roller bearings
    C. spring bearings
    D. spherical-seated bearings

32. The oil film pressure produced by a rotating journal is:

    A. the same as the pressure in the lubricating system
    B. less than the pressure in the lubricating system
    C. greater than the pressure in the lubricating system
    D. highest at the oil groove location

33. In a gravity feed lube oil system, supply pressure to the main lube oil header is:

    A. the result of the height of the gravity tank above the manifold
    B. the sum of the lube oil static head pressure and service pump discharge pressure
    C. the difference between the lube oil static head pressure and service pump discharge pressure
    D. merely the service pump discharge pressure, since the

static heads of the lines to and from the gravity tank cancel out one another

34. A grease gun is used to lubricate a _____ bearing.
    A. condensate pump ball   C. main turbine
    B. main shaft   D. diesel engine wrist pin

35. A good quality lubricating oil for use in any machinery should have the characteristic of being:
    A. acid free   C. rapid oxidizer
    B. capable of emulsifying   D. additive free

36. The grade of grease to use with Zerk pressure fittings is:
    A. soft   C. hard
    B. medium   D. extra hard

37. At what point in a condition monitoring lubricating system is the pressure switch for the low oil pressure warning signal usually installed?
    A. at a point on the inlet side of the main bearings as close to the bearings as possible
    B. at a point on the outlet side of the main bearings as close to the bearings as possible
    C. at the point of highest pressure in the supply line to the bearings
    D. at the point of lowest pressure in the supply line to the bearings

38. A poorly cleaned bowl in a lube oil purifier may result in:
    A. insufficient oil supply to the gravity tank
    B. improper separation
    C. excessive lube oil consumption
    D. excessive water discharge rate

39. What part of a Kingsbury thrust bearing tilts to permit the formation of a wedge-shaped film of oil?
    A. tilting plates   C. dowel disk
    B. lower leveling plate   D. shoe

40. In compression type grease cups, the lubricant is forced into the bearing by:
    A. gravity flow   C. a pressure gun
    B. spring pressure   D. a Zerk fitting

41. In which lube oil line would you expect to find an illuminated sight glass (bull's-eye)?
    A. lube oil pump suction   C. gravity tank discharge
    B. lube oil pump discharge D. gravity tank overflow

42. What is meant by the term "base" when referring to grease?
    A. texture of the grease under load
    B. temperature at which the grease softens or melts
    C. type of soap used in its manufacture

    D. temperature below which the grease will be ineffective as a lubricant

43. The source of metal particles adhering to the magnets in a lube oil strainer is probably the:

    A. shaft journal   C. reduction gears

    B. bearing shell   D. babbit material

44. Coast Guard Regulations (46 CFR 56.5080) concerning lubricating oil systems for main propulsion turbines require that:

    A. the lube oil system must function satisfactorily when the vessel has a permanent list of 25 degrees

    B. oil coolers shall have three separate means of circulating water

    C. lube oil piping shall be independent of other piping systems

    D. two auxiliary lube oil pumps must be provided

45. The viscosity of an oil is a measure of its:

    A. weight   C. demulsibility

    B. internal friction   D. S.E. number

46. Journal bearing wear in a main propulsion turbine can be measured by using:

    A. calibrated wedges

    B. a micrometer depth gauge

    C. a rotor position micrometer

    D. an axial clearance indicator

47. The lignum vitae in a stern tube bearing is normally lubricated with:

    A. grease   C. water

    B. oil   D. tallow

48. Demulsibility of lube oil is defined as:

    A. the ability of oil to separate from water

    B. the temperature at which oil flows rapidly

    C. a measure of the water in a lube oil system

    D. an emulsion of different grades of oil

49. The entrance of water into the main propulsion lube oil system is undesirable because:

    A. the flash point of the lube oil is raised to a dangerously high level

    B. water causes oil to clog in journal bearings

    C. emulsification occurs with resultant loss of lubricating qualities

    D. all oil additives break down into acids when in contact with water

50. Excessive water in a lube oil system can be detected by:

    A. oil forming large bubbles

    B. the lube oil purifier water discharge rate

    C. condensate accumulating on the lube oil cooler discharge line

D. sweating on the reduction gear casing

Miscellaneous Review

1. When the pressure is reduced, which steam trap operates on the principle that hot water under pressure tends to flash into steam?
   A. ball float
   B. thermostatic
   C. bimetallic
   D. impulse
2. Incomplete combustion due to insufficient air yields an excess amount of:
   A. carbon dioxide
   B. carbon monoxide
   C. nitrogen oxide
   D. sulfur dioxide
3. To minimize metal corrosion, boiler water is best kept:
   A. fairly acidic
   B. slightly acidic
   C. neutral
   D. alkaline
4. The two most common gasses used in pneumatic systems are:
   A. compressed air and nitrogen
   B. helium and nitrogen
   C. oxygen and hydrogen
   D. oxygen and acetylene
5. A sprayer plate marked 32Y20 in a return flow atomizer system should be used only with a/an:
   A. burner tip marked 20
   B. burner tip marked 32
   C. orifice plate marked 20
   D. orifice plate marked 32
6. What is the purpose of boiler sliding feet?
   A. to ensure an airtight seal between the boiler inner and outer casings
   B. to accommodate the changing length of the water drum as it expands or contracts with temperature changes.
   C. to compensate for deflection of the hull in way of the boiler supports
   D. to allow for unequal expansion between the wrapper and tube sheets
7. In a cross-compound turbine, steam enters at the:
   A. high pressure, intermediate, and low pressure units simultaneously
   B. high pressure unit and then flows to the low pressure unit
   C. high pressure unit and then flows to another high pressure unit
8. A fluctuating and unsteady vacuum in an evaporator is probably caused by:
   A. wet steam entering the air ejector nozzle
   B. pinhole leaks in the evaporator tube nests
   C. rapid scaling on the evaporator tube nests

       D. high water level in the last effect

9. Where is the dry pipe located in a boiler?
       A. at the superheater outlet
       B. behind the superheater screen tubes
       C. in the top of the steam drum
       D. below the generation tube bank

10. Downcomers installed on auxiliary package boilers are protected from direct contact with hot gasses by:
       A. refractory and insulation   C. steel baffles
       B. several rows of screen tubes   D. water wall tubes

11. Sacrificial zinc anodes are used on the saltwater side of heat exchangers to:
       A. keep heat transfer surfaces shiny and clean
       B. prevent rapid accumulation of marine growth
       C. provide a protective coating on heat exchanger surfaces
       D. reduce electrolytic action on heat exchanger metals

12. Expansion due to temperature differentials in a steam turbine is provided for by the use of:
       A. casing flexible joints
       B. rotor position indicators
       C. a deep flexible I beam
       D. pivoted shoe type thrust bearings

13. If you screw down on the hand wheel of a spring loaded reducing valve, you will:
       A. compress the adjusting spring against the diaphragm
       B. release spring tension from the diaphragm
       C. increase steam pressure
       D. decrease spring tension

14. The quantity of steam in a two stage, flash type distilling plant is held constant by a/an:
       A. orifice plate
       B. attemporator
       C. back pressure regulator
       D. first stage bypass valve

15. A pointer on a pressure gauge which responds sluggishly should be repaired by:
       A. tapping the gauge housing lightly
       B. bending the needle to free the linkage
       C. cleaning the residue from gear teeth
       D. greasing the hair spring

16. The type of gauge most commonly used to measure pressure is the:
       A. bimetallic type   C. bourdon tube type
       B. diaphragm type   D. resistance temperature

17. A compound gauge will most likely be found installed on the:

A. suction side of a bilge pump
B. exhaust manifold of an auxiliary diesel
C. discharge line from an air compressor
D. chemical feed tank of an evaporator

18. A compound bourdon tube gauge will measure pressure and:
    A. humidity   C. temperature
    B. vacuum   D. density

19. To accurately measure very low pressures, use a:
    A. compound gauge   C. manometer
    B. bourdon   D. dead weight gauge

20. The firing range of a variable capacity return flow fuel atomizer is regulated to meet steam demand by varying the:
    A. fuel oil damper setting   C. burner register opening
    B. fuel oil return pressure   D. atomizer orifice setting

21. What is the effect on velocity and pressure when steam passes through a nozzle?
    A. velocity increases and pressure increases
    B. velocity increases and pressure decreases
    C. velocity decreases and pressure increases
    D. velocity decreases and pressure decreases

22. An explosion or flareback could occur in a boiler if:
    A. too much excess air were supplied for combustion
    B. the boiler firing rate exceeded the end point of circulation
    C. the fuel being burned had been heated to the flash point
    D. a fire box is not purged before attempting to light a fire

23. Under proper boiler operating condition, what is the color of the flame farthest from an atomizer?
    A. bright yellow or orange   C. light brown haze
    B. dark brown   D. dazzling white

24. What pumps are normally used for fuel oil service?
    A. two-stage centrifugal
    B. positive displacement rotary
    C. explosion proof gear
    D. nonvented plunger

25. Boiler water which is highly alkaline leads to the possible problem of:
    A. caustic embrittlement
    B. scale formation
    C. calcium carbonate precipitation
    D. sodium sulphite reacting with dissolved oxygen

26. The final check of reduction gear tooth contact is usually made by:
    A. alignment gauges   C. bluing the teeth
    B. dial indicators   D. bridge gauges

27. Pigtail siphons protect bourdon tube gauges from direct exposure to steam by:

    A. changing the steam's direction

    B. reducing the steam's velocity

    C. creating a water loopseal

    D. bleeding off a portion of the steam

28. When the pressure on a compound gauge is released, the gauge pointer is returned to zero psig by action of:

    A. bourdon tube   C. compound diaphragm

    B. spring return arm   D. compensating spring

29. An auxiliary boiler equipped with a return flow fuel atomization system has a:

    A. constant fuel combustion rate

    B. constant fuel return pressure

    C. variable fuel supply temperature

    D. variable fuel return pressure

30. The first step in breaking the vacuum on a main turbine unit should be to:

    A. secure the steam to the main air ejector

    B. secure the steam to the gland seal system

    C. stop the main circulating pump

    D. stop the main condensate pump

31. A vacuum differential is maintained between any two stages of a multiple effect distilling plant by a/an:

    A. steam trap   C. loop seal

    B. butterfly valve   D. adjustable controller

32. The glass in a flat type water gauge on a boiler is protected from the hot steam and water by a/an:

    A. asbestos gasket   C. felt cushion

    B. mica shield   D. copper insulator

33. On an automated boiler, loss of forced draft air will result in which of the following?

    A. stopping of the feed pump

    B. stopping of the fuel oil service pump

    C. closing of the master fuel oil cutoff

    D. all of the above

34. The purpose of the sentinel valve installed in a turbine casing is to:

    A. warn the engineer of back flow of steam from the exhaust trunk

    B. warn the engineer of excessive pressure in the low pressure turbine casing

    C. relieve excess pressure at turbine extraction points

    D. vent excess steam to the main condenser

35. A salinity indicator cell is located in the:

    A. seawater side of the main condenser

    B. main condenser hot well

      C. evaporator brine suction line

      D. low pressure turbine casing drain

36. The lube oil heater for the main propulsion unit is normally used:

      A. when the vessel is operating at full speed

      B. if the oil temperature is 120°F

      C. when warming up a cold plant

      D. when the gravity tank overflows

37. The function of a safety valve on a marine boiler is to prevent the pressure in the boiler from rising above:

      A. design test pressure

      B. maximum allowable working pressure

      C. the pressure used in the accumulation test

      D. the hydrostatic test pressure

38. The outlet temperature differential between two fluid mediums in a shell and tube heat exchanger is greatest in:

      A. cross type   C. counter type

      B. parallel type   D. circular type

39. The operation of a thermostatic steam trap depends upon the:

      A. thermal expansion of a fluid

      B. position of a float

      C. tendency of hot water to flash into steam

      D. flow characteristics of a liquid through an orifice

40. Helical gears are preferred over spur gears because helical gears:

      A. prevent torsional vibrations

      B. reduce gear noise

      C. ensure positive lube oil flow at all loads

      D. tolerate misalignment well

41. When you are raising steam on a cold boiler, the air cock is closed when:

      A. the boiler is cut in on the line

      B. steam has formed and all air is vented

      C. the economizer drain is closed

      D. all burners are lighted and firing normally

42. What conditions would cause "panting" in a steaming auxiliary boiler?

      A. insufficient combustion air   C. flame failure

      B. low water level   D. faulty flame scanner

43. A two-element boiler feedwater regulator is controlled by:

      A. steam flow and feedwater flow

      B. steam flow and drum water

      C. drum water level and feedwater flow

      D. drum water level and drum pressure

44. Magnets located in lube oil strainers serve to:

      A. remove all metallic particles from the lube oil

    B. remove ferrous metallic particles from the lube oil

    C. remove nonferrous metallic particles from the lube oil

    D. hold the strainer cover in place when removing or installing the cover bolts

45. A smoking burner with a pulsating flame in an auxiliary boiler is an indication that the:

    A. fuel oil supply temperature is normal

    B. burner electrode is incorrectly positioned

    C. air fuel ratio is incorrect

    D. ignition current is too low

46. How does an electrical salinity indicator work?

    A. measures the hydrogen ion concentration

    B. measures the electrical resistance of the water

    C. determines the conductivity of the dissolved oxygen

    D. measures the voltage of the chlorine ions

47. Which atomizing sprayer plate has the largest capacity?

    A. 4309   C. 2 PCRS 3509

    B. 2909   D. 3009

48. The correct procedure for bottom blowing an auxiliary boiler is to bottom blow:

    A. when the boiler has been secured long enough for most solids to settle

    B. When the boiler has been cooled to ambient temperature

    C. only after raising the water level to within ½ inch of the high water cutout

    D. only after bypassing the low pressure pressuretrol

49. The jacking gear is used in preparation for starting a marine turbine and reduction gear unit to:

    A. allow the rotor to cool evenly

    B. allow a film of oil to form on the spring bearings

    C. prevent the gland seal steam from distorting the rotor

    D. listen for rubbing noises from the gland seal condenser

50. Severe priming in a boiler could cause damage to the:

    A. superheater

    B. steam drum internals

    C. feedwater regulating valve

    D. control desuperheater

Diesel Review

1. The function of the aftercooler installed between the turbocharger and intake manifold on some diesel engines is to:

    A. increase the density of the intake air

    B. decrease turbocharger power usage

      C. reduce exhaust gas temperature

      D. compensate for turbocharger RPM fluctuations

2. Aftercooling of a turbocharged diesel engine will result in _____ brake horsepower.

      A. higher torque but lower   C. higher torque but higher

      B. lower torque but higher   D. lower torque and lower

3. Performance of a turbocharged engine can be improved by:

      A. decreasing valve over lap   C. aftercooling intake air

      B. preheating   D. preheating light fuels

4. Getting fresh air into the cylinder of a diesel engine and the exhaust gases out requires power. The consumption of this power is referred to as:

      A. compression delay   C. ignition delay

      B. sealing loss   D. pumping loss

5. In accordance with Coast Guard Regulations, which of the following starting aids is/are acceptable for use with the emergency diesel generator?

      A. injection of ether into the air intake

      B. thermostatically controlled electric water jacket heater

      C. thermostatically controlled electric oil sump heater

      D. heating the starting battery

6. The service life of a worn aluminum piston for an auxiliary diesel for which no spares are readily available can be extended by:

      A. turning down the piston skirt to concentratic values in a lathe

      B. knurling the piston skirt surface

      C. building up the piston skirt with a liquid epoxy material and then remachining

      D. increasing the dimension of the ring land grooves

7. Which is the only method allowed by Coast Guard regulations to ease the starting of emergency diesel generator engines?

      A. bayonet type electrical oil heaters

      B. steam or hot water lube oil heating

      C. thermostatically controlled electric water jacket heating

      D. electric resistance heaters in the air intake manifold

8. Cold weather starting of a diesel engine may be made easier by:

      A. decreasing the compression ratio

      B. using a special fuel having a high ignition temperature

      C. increasing the starting air supply

      D. heating the jacket water

9. Improper cooling of a cylinder liner due to scale deposits may cause:

      A. low compression pressure

      B. piston seizure

      C. increased lube oil consumption

      D. poor contact between compression rings and liner

10. The lower section of a piston is called the:

      A. land   C. crown

      B. skirt   D. plate

11. Cavitation erosion in the cooling water system of a diesel engine usually occurs at the pump impeller and on the waterside of the:

      A. fuel nozzle holders   C. engine cylinder liners

      B. exhaust valve guides   D. engine exhaust manifold

12. An electric heater built into the cylinder water jacket would be used to:

      A. raise lube oil viscosity for easier starting in cold weather

      B. increase air inlet temperature

      C. increase compression ratio

      D. increase jacketwater temperature for easier starting in cold weather

13. The upper section of a piston is called the:

      A. land   C. crown

      B. skirt   D. plate

14. An advantage of aluminum pistons compared to cast iron pistons is:

      A. greater high temperature strength

      B. better heat conductivity

      C. greater weight per cubic inch

      D. increased resistance to wear

15. Air scavenging of a diesel engine cylinder:

      A. blows out the exhaust gases

      B. supplies oxygen for combustion

      C. cools the valves and cylinder walls

      D. all of the above

16. In an operating diesel engine, pre-ignition can be caused by:

      A. excessively late fuel injection

      B. oil in the air charge

      C. water in the fuel

      D. injection continuing after the fuel charge is ignited

17. Which engine component increases air density and helps improve engine operating efficiency?

      A. impeller   C. aftercooler

      B. compressor   D. exhaust diffuser

18. What harmful consequence can result from sludge in the lube oil system of a trunk piston diesel engine?

      A. clogged oil pump suction screens

      B. increased oil temperature

      C. stuck piston rings

      D. any of the above

19. Prolonged operation of a diesel engine closed cooling system with temperatures lower than designed normal could:
    A. increase power output
    B. decrease lube oil viscosity
    C. eliminate fuel knock
    D. cause sulphuric acid formation

20. To determine the main bearing clearances in a propulsion diesel engine, you should us a/an:
    A. depth micrometer   C. plastigauge
    B. anvil faced micrometer   D. vernier caliper

21. A cracked cylinder head on a diesel engine could be indicated by:
    A. excessive lube oil consumption
    B. water draining from the fuel leakoff valves
    C. combustion gases venting at the expansion tank
    D. excessive fuel oil consumption

22. A cracked cylinder head in an operating engine would be indicated by:
    A. a steady flow of water from the expansion tank vent
    B. combustion gases venting at the expansion tank
    C. lower temperature at the cylinder head water discharge
    D. water draining from the fuel leakoff lines

23. A crack in a cylinder liner can be caused by:
    A. worn piston rings
    B. installation of undersized sealing rings
    C. operating the engine at low loads
    D. restricted cooling water passages

24. In the simple mechanical governor, the:
    A. centrifugal force rotates the ball head
    B. flyweight centrifugal force is balanced by spring pressure
    C. flyweight centrifugal force is balanced by hydraulic pressure
    D. speeder spring actuates the fuel control rod

25. The governor on a diesel engine controls crankshaft RPM by adjusting the:
    A. intake air supply   C. fuel injection pumps
    B. turbocharger speed   D. engine speed droop

26. On most diesel engines, the governor controls the speed by:
    A. controlling the amount of fuel injected into the cylinders
    B. varying the speed of the turbocharger
    C. adjusting the compression ratio
    D. changing the timing of the fuel injection camshaft

27. Which is a characteristic of a governor operating isochronously?
    A. zero speed droop   C. negative speed droop
    B. positive speed droop   D. varying speed droop

28. A diesel generator engine operates at 1800 RPM. The overspeed governor will normally be set between:
    A. 1980 and 2070   C. 2200 and 2300
    B. 2100 and 2200   D. 2300 and 2400
29. The process of supplying the intake of a diesel engine with air at a pressure greater than atmospheric is called:
    A. engine displacement   C. air injection
    B. scavenging   D. supercharging
30. The exhaust system for a turbocharged diesel engine functions to:
    A. power the aftercoolers
    B. power the turbocharger
    C. reduce the cylinder scavenge effect
    D. cool the turbocharger
31. Compared to a naturally aspirated engine, a supercharged diesel has:
    A. a cylinder air charge of higher pressure
    B. increased pumping losses
    C. less valve overlap
    D. reduced blow by
32. A supercharged diesel engine will cause an increase in:
    A. ignition lag   C. lube oil consumption
    B. engine horsepower   D. specific fuel consumption
33. A device which will function to bring an engine to a full stop in order to protect it from damage due to excessively high speed is known as a/an:
    A. torque limiter   C. overspeed governor
    B. overspeed trip   D. load limit governor
34. The overspeed trip device installed in some diesel engines is automatically actuated by:
    A. spring force   C. centrifugal force
    B. hydraulic pressure   D. mechanical linkage
35. The principal characteristic of an isochronous governor is that it will:
    A. slow the machine down as the load is increased
    B. shut down the engine if it overspeeds
    C. have excessive speed droop
    D. maintain a constant speed with variations of load
36. What does every mechanical governor have as its basic element?
    A. power piston
    B. control rack
    C. weights acted on by centrifugal force
    D. isochronous droop spring
37. Which is found with both mechanical and hydraulic governors?
    A. direct linkage between the ball head and fuel rack
    B. a servomotor

C. a compensating device

D. flyweights

38. The direct acting mechanical governor used with some small diesel engines controls fuel flow to the engine by:

    A. governor flyweight action on a pilot valve which controls fuel injection

    B. governor flyweight motion acting on fuel controls through suitable linkage

    C. positioning a butterfly valve in the fuel delivery system

    D. positioning a servomotor piston attached to the fuel controls

39. What is the best method for stopping an overspeeding diesel engine?

    A. disconnect the battery cables from the starting motor

    B. drain the hydraulic fluid from the governor sump

    C. block the flow of cooling air to the radiator

    D. block the air intake and secure the fuel supply

40. The overspeed trip installed on a diesel engine will stop the engine by shutting off the:

    A. water supply   C. lube oil supply

    B. fuel oil supply   D. exhaust damper

41. Besides piston cooling fins assisting in cooling, they also provide extra strength for the piston:

    A. skirt   C. wrist pin

    B. head   D. oil rings

42. Trunk type diesel engine pistons are most effectively cooled when heat is:

    A. radiated through the engine block

    B. transferred to water cooled cylinder walls

    C. conducted through the piston crown

    D. transferred to escaping exhaust gases

43. The air supplied to the cylinders by a turbocharger is often reduced in volume by a/an:

    A. air compressor   C. aftercooler

    B. diffuser   D. venturi

44. If a diesel engine runs out of fuel, you can expect trouble from:

    A. overheated injector pumps

    B. water condensed in the cylinders

    C. fuel dilution of the lube oil

    D. air in the fuel system

45. Some diesel engines are equipped with a Roots-type blower so that they will have:

    A. more air to combine with the fuel

    B. more amps per kilowatt hour

    C. high no-load RPMs

    D. higher voltage output

46. The principle hazard to personnel when a diesel nozzle tester is in use is:
     A. electrical shock   C. explosion
     B. toxic fumes   D. blood poisoning

47. When maneuvering, you discover heavy smoke coming from the turbocharger casing. You should:
     A. check the air filter for dirt
     B. check for an exhaust leak
     C. check the cooling water temperature
     D. notify the bridge and ask to shut the engine down

48. An automated diesel engine should normally shut down due to:
     A. low lube oil temperature
     B. high ambient air temperature
     C. low lube oil pressure
     D. high exhaust system back pressure

49. A propulsion diesel engine is normally shut down by:
     A. shutting off the air supply
     B. overspeeding the engine
     C. securing the fuel supply
     D. securing the ignition system

50. Air compression in a positive displacement rotary supercharging blower occurs only:
     A. between the rotating blower lobes
     B. between the casing and blower lobes
     C. after the engine reaches operating speed
     D. as air moves into the discharge passage

Answers to Multiple-Choice Questions for the Junior Engineer

Electrical review

1. B	14. B	27. D	40. C
2. D	15. D	28. D	41. A
3. A	16. C	29. A	42. C
4. B	17. D	30. A	43. C
5. A	18. D	31. D	44. C
6. C	19. B	32. D	45. B
7. D	20. B	33. A	46. A
8. D	21. A	34. D	47. D
9. C	22. B	35. D	48. C
10. B	23. B	36. A	49. A
11. D	24. B	37. C	50. B
12. D	25. C	38. A	
13. A	26. D	39. A	

Engine room procedures

1. C	26. A	51. B	76. B
2. B	27. D	52. C	77. C
3. D	28. A	53. B	78. B
4. C	29. D	54. A	79. C
5. C	30. D	55. B	80. A
6. D	31. C	56. B	81. C
7. B	32. C	57. B	82. B
8. C	33. C	58. B	83. C
9. B	34. C	59. D	84. C
10. C	35. C	60. B	85. D
11. C	36. A	61. A	86. A
12. C	37. D	62. B	87. D
13. B	38. B	63. C	88. C
14. C	39. D	64. B	89. C
15. B	40. B	65. D	90. C
16. C	41. C	66. A	91. B
17. C	42. D	67. A	92. B
18. A	43. D	68. C	93. C
19. B	44. C	69. B	94. B
20. B	45. B	70. B	95. B
21. A	46. D	71. B	96. C
22. C	47. A	72. C	97. B
23. C	48. B	73. C	98. B
24. C	49. A	74. D	99. B
25. B	50. A	75. B	100. B

Steam review

1. B	17. C	33. D	49. D
2. A	18. D	34. B	50. B
3. A	19. D	35. B	51. C
4. D	20. B	36. B	52. C
5. A	21. B	37. B	53. B
6. C	22. B	38. D	54. C
7. D	23. D	39. A	55. C
8. A	24. C	40. B	56. C
9. A	25. C	41. C	57. B
10. C	26. B	42. D	58. D
11. D	27. D	43. D	59. A
12. D	28. B	44. B	60. A
13. D	29. B	45. B	61. C
14. A	30. C	46. B	62. B
15. C	31. C	47. D	63. B
16. A	32. B	48. A	64. B

65. C	74. B	83. D	92. B
66. B	75. C	84. A	93. A
67. B	76. B	85. C	94. D
68. B	77. B	86. C	95. D
69. A	78. A	87. B	96. C
70. B	79. B	88. B	97. A
71. D	80. B	89. A	98. C
72. A	81. A	90. B	99. C
73. B	82. D	91. D	100. A

Refrigeration review

1. D	14. C	27. C	40. C
2. B	15. D	28. C	41. C
3. B	16. D	29. A	42. A
4. A	17. B	30. A	43. A
5. C	18. D	31. D	44. A
6. C	19. B	32. A	45. D
7. B	20. B	33. C	46. B
8. B	21. B	34. B	47. A
9. B	22. C	35. D	48. C
10. B	23. B	36. D	49. A
11. B	24. C	37. D	50. B
12. A	25. D	38. C	
13. A	26. C	39. C	

Bearings and lubrication

1. C	14. D	27. B	40. B
2. D	15. A	28. D	41. D
3. D	16. D	29. C	42. C
4. D	17. C	30. B	43. C
5. A	18. B	31. D	44. C
6. D	19. D	32. C	45. B
7. C	20. A	33. A	46. B
8. A	21. B	34. A	47. C
9. B	22. C	35. A	48. A
10. A	23. D	36. B	49. C
11. B	24. D	37. D	50. B
12. C	25. D	38. B	
13. D	26. C	39. D	

Miscellaneous review

1. D	5. D	9. C	13. A
2. B	6. B	10. A	14. A
3. D	7. B	11. D	15. C
4. A	8. A	12. C	16. C

17. A	26. C	35. B	44. B
18. B	27. C	36. C	45. C
19. C	28. A	37. B	46. B
20. B	29. D	38. B	47. B
21. B	30. A	39. A	48. A
22. D	31. C	40. B	49. C
23. A	32. B	41. B	50. A
24. B	33. C	42. A	
25. A	34. B	43. B	

Diesel review

1. A	14. B	27. A	40. B
2. C	15. D	28. A	41. B
3. C	16. B	29. D	42. B
4. D	17. C	30. B	43. C
5. B	18. D	31. A	44. D
6. B	19. D	32. B	45. A
7. C	20. C	33. B	46. D
8. D	21. C	34. C	47. D
9. B	22. B	35. D	48. C
10. B	23. D	36. C	49. C
11. C	24. B	37. D	50. D
12. D	25. C	38. B	
13. C	26. A	39. D	

Suggested Readings

The following books are suggested for the student to use before attempting any of the examinations for the qualified member of the engine department. It is advisable to use these texts in conjunction with the sample multiple-choice questions and answers given in this text. By following this procedure the student will find his knowledge expanding and will gain confidence about the subject matter in any of the given topics. Note that after each reference there is an indication of the QMED examination, or examinations, for which the reference is applicable.

Bureau of Naval Personnel. *Principles of Naval Engineering.* Washington, D. C.: Government Printing Office, 1970. (Fireman/Watertender, Oiler, Pumpman, Machinist, Refrigeration Engineer, Deck Engineer, Junior Engineer)

Firefighting Manual for Tank Vessels, C.G. 329. Washington, D. C.: United States Coast Guard, 1974. (General Safety, Pumpman)

How to Run a Lathe. South Bend, Ind.: South Bend Lathe, 1966. (Machinist)

Hubert, Charles I. *Preventive Maintenance of Electrical Equipment.* New York: McGraw Hill, 1969. (Deck Engineer, Electrician)

Kates, Edgar J. *Diesels and High Compression Gas Engines.* Alsip, Ill.: American Technical Publishers, 1974. (Oiler, Junior Engineer)

A Manual for the Safe Handling of Flammable and Combustible Liquids and Other Hazardous Products, C. G. 174. Washington, D. C.: United States Coast Guard, 1976. (General Safety, Pumpman)

Marsh, Warren R. *Principles of Refrigeration.* Albany, N. Y.: Delmar Publishers, 1979. (Refrigeration Engineer, Junior Engineer)

National Maritime Research Center, Maritime Administration. *Marine Fire Prevention, Firefighting and Fire Safety.* Washington, D. C.: United States Department of Commerce. (General Safety)

Naval Education and Training Support Command. *Machinist's Mate 1 & C.* Washington, D. C.: Government Printing Office, 1972. (Fireman/Watertender, Oiler, Pumpman, Refrigeration Engineer, Deck Engineer, Junior Engineer)

———. *Machinist's Mate 3 & 2.* Washington, D. C.: Government Printing Office, 1972. (Fireman/ Watertender, Oiler, Pumpman, Machinist, Refrigeration Engineer, Deck Engineer, Junior Engineer)

Polsen, Charles G. *Fundamentals of Steam Generators.* Brooklyn, N. Y.:

School of Marine Engineering and Navigation, District 2 MEBA, 1969. (Fireman/Watertender, Junior Engineer)

Smith, Percy de Willard. *Deck Machinery*. Cambridge, Md.: Cornell Maritime Press, 1973. (Deck Engineer, Junior Engineer)

———. *Modern Marine Electricity and Electronics*. Cambridge, Md.: Cornell Maritime Press, 1966. (Electrician, Junior Engineer)

Van Valkenburgh. *Basic Electricity*. Volumes 1 through 5. Rochelle Park, N. J.: Hayden Book Company, 1979. (Electrician, Deck Engineer, Junior Engineer)